I am delighted to have the opportunity to bring to your attention this current edition of Irish Farmhouse Holidays brochure which highlights the wealth of excellent accommodation and range of facilities which are available throughout rural Ireland.

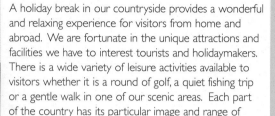

A holiday break in our countryside provides a wonderful and relaxing experience for visitors from home and abroad. We are fortunate in the unique attractions and facilities we have to interest tourists and holidaymakers. There is a wide variety of leisure activities available to visitors whether it is a round of golf, a quiet fishing trip or a gentle walk in one of our scenic areas. Each part of the country has its particular image and range of activities.

Through its members, Irish Farmhouse Holidays offers visitors an ideal opportunity to experience life in rural areas of the country. A holiday in the countryside is a totally enjoyable experience for both young and old. It provides many urban visitors with their first taste of rural farm life. Children can come into proximity with farm animals and experience at first hand how a working farm operates.

It is heartening to see that the number of visitors to our rural areas continues to grow. This is important in maintaining vibrant rural communities and generating income opportunities. I would like to congratulate Irish Farmhouse Holidays on the production of this excellent brochure which continues to play a pivotal role in marketing rural Ireland to the widest possible audience.

I would like to wish all availing of a holiday break whether from home or abroad, a happy and enjoyable stay during their time.

Joe Walsh TD
Minister for Agriculture, Food and Rural Development

HEAD OFFICE
Irish Farmhouse Holidays Association
2 Michael Street, Limerick.
Tel: 061-400700 Fax: 061-400771
Website: http://www.irishfarmholidays.com e-mail: farmhols@iol.ie

HOW TO BOOK

Reservations can be made by contacting the home directly or through a tourist information office. You should confirm your booking in writing and enclose the required deposit. In the event of an emergency contact the nearest county area representative.

Always reserve first and last nights accommodation in advance. June/July/August - 48 hours in advance. Dublin - 2 weeks, preferably more in advance. Confirm booking within 7 days with agreed deposit. Rooms may be guaranteed by credit card - check when booking. Check rate and cancellation policy when booking. Late arrivals - after 6pm by special agreement with home.

Onward reservations will be made for the cost of the phone call. To avoid disappointment, please avail of this facility.

Arrival Times

It is advisable to inform the house of your expected arrival time. A very early arrival may cause inconvenience unless pre-arranged. Rooms are normally held until 6 p.m. It is important to phone the house if you are delayed to ensure that your room will be held.

Cancellations

Should you find it necessary to cancel your reservation please contact the house as soon as possible. Rooms which are reserved and not occupied may cause loss of revenue for which you may be held legally responsible.

Meals

Dinner is available at many of our houses and these are indicated by a symbol. High Tea and/or light meals ⊠ are also available in some houses. Please check the symbols in the guide for reference. Dinner is normally booked by 12 p.m.

Heating

Most homes provide heating, usually central heating, and many have open peat or log fires.

Guide Dogs and Pets

Look for the symbol for guide dogs ⬚ and pets ⚎ throughout the brochure, and check when booking.

Reduction for children

Reductions for children normally apply when children share their parents room or when three or four children share a family room. Please check at the time of booking.

Travel Agents Vouchers

Your Travel Agent will give you a list of the premises which accept Vouchers and these are indicated in our brochure by the ⚙ symbol. Vouchers normally are valid for bed and breakfast in a standard room, but in some cases may include en suite facilities.
A supplement will be charged for private facilities if not included. A single supplement will be charged when one person occupies a room for two or more persons.

Disabled Persons

The National Rehabilitation Board produces an Accommodation Guide for disabled persons. All premises with the symbol ♿ in this brochure have been approved as suitable for disabled persons by Farm and Country Standards/NRB.

Compliments and comments

Complaints should always be brought to the attention of the proprietor before departure. Failing satisfaction and in the case of alleged overcharging your receipt should be sent with your complaint to the Irish Farmhouse Holidays Association, 2 Michael Street, Limerick.

To maintain the high standard, which the association is renowned for, all comments on the general level of service and the standard you experienced are welcome. All constructive criticisms will be taken seriously to ensure continued improvement of service.

NEAREST TOWN/VILLAGE Distance in Km		County	
Family Name	Tel:	Fax:	
NAME OF FARMHOUSE	Open:		
Address	No Rooms:	Triple:	
	Twin/Double:	Family:	
	Single:	En suite:	
B&B:	HBW ES:	S.Supp:	Dinner:
B&B ES:	3 day HB:	CSP:	High Tea:
HBW:	3 day HB ES:		

Description of Farmhouse

✗ ⬚ ☕ ♪ ⬚ ⚎ S

ABBREVIATIONS

Travel Agency Vouchers Accepted. There may be an extra charge for 'en suite' rooms. Check when booking.

Travel Agency Vouchers Not Accepted.

B&B	Standard Room. Bed and Breakfast.
B&B ES:	Room with private bath/shower and toilet.
HBW:	Standard Room, 7 B&Bs and 7 Dinners.
HBW ES:	Half Board Weekly in room with bath/shower, 7 B&Bs and 7 Dinners.
3 Day HB:	Standard Room. 3 B&Bs and 3 Dinners.
3 Day HB ES:	3 Day Half Board in room with bath/shower, 3 B&Bs and 3 Dinners.
S.Supp:	Single occupancy of double/triple room.
CSP:	Percentage deducted for children sharing parents room.
Farm Guesthouse	Farm Guesthouse (these homes usually have more guestrooms and are more commercial in operation).

Symbols: (Facilities available in, or in the vicinity of, the farmhouse)

✗	Dinner	☍	Tennis Court
☒	Light Meals	🏃	Squash Court
☌	Pets Allowed	⛳	18 Hole Golf Course
☝	Guide Dogs only Allowed	⛳	9 Hole Golf Course
S	Single Lettings	☑	Pitch and Putt
☃	Working Farm	⌯	Crazy Golf
☃	Open Working Farm	✓	Driving Range
F	Technical Working Farm	⚑	Pony for Guest Use
⚿	Guest Participation in Farm Work	⊗	No Smoking
☃	Facilities for Children	**CD**	Craft Demonstrations
⌨	Tea/coffee (facilities in bedroom)	**BD**	Breadmaking Demonstrations
⌇	Angling Facilities	TV	TV in all Bedrooms
⛵	Boats for Hire	OBA	Off Season Bookings by Arrangement
⚲	Wine Licence		
⚫	Games Room	EC	EuroCheques
✈	20 miles from Airport	AE	American Express
⛴	20 miles Ferryport	DC	Diners Club
♿	Access for Disabled Approved by NRB	V	VISA/Barclaycard
⌗	Organic Farm Produce	AM	Access/Mastercard
U	Riding Stables Approved by Aire		
⚤	Organised Walking Programmes		
⚙	Bicycles for Hire		

BUCHUNGEN

Sie Können Ihre Unterkunft buchen, indem Sie die Pension Direkt oder über ein Fremdenverkehrsbüro kontaktieren. Bitte bestätigen Sie Ihre Buchung schriltlich und fügen Sie die erforderliche Anzahlung bei.In Nottällen wenden Sie sich bitte an den naheliegendsten Gebietsvertreter.

Bitte reservieren Sie immer die erste und die letzte Übernachtung im voraus. Juni/Juli/August - 48 Stunden im voraus, für Dublin mindestens 2 Wochen im voraus.

Bestätigen Sie die Buchung vornehmen und fragen Sie danach, wenn Siedie Buchung vornehmen und fragen Sie auch nach dem Preis und dem Verfahren im Fall einer Stornierung. Späte Ankunft - nach 18.00 nach Vereinbarung mit dem Unterkunftsbesitzer.

Vorausbuchungen für die weitere Reise werden gerne gegen Erstattung der Telefonkosten vorgenommen. Bitte nutzen Sie diese Möglichkeit, um Ettäuschungen zu vermeiden.

Ankunftszeiten

Es ist ratsam, Ihre Gastgeber wissen zu lassen, wann Sie etwa ankommen werden. Eine sehr frühe Ankunftszeit verursacht möglicherweise Unannehmlichkeiten, falls nicht vorab vereinbart. Normalerweise werden die Zimmer bis 18.00 Uhr freigehalten. Sollten Sie sich verspäten, ist es wichtig, bei Ihrem Farmhaus telefonisch Bescheid zu geben, damit Ihr Zimmer für Sie freigehalten wird.

Absagen

Sollten Sie Ihre Reservierung rückgängig machen müssen, so benachrichtigen Sie bitte Ihre Gastgeber so bald wie möglich. Falls Zimmer reserviert, aber nicht belegt werden, entstehen möglicherweise finanzielle Einbußen, für die Sie gesetzlich belangt werden können.

Mahlzeiten

In vielen unserer Häuser kann man Abendmenüs bekommen; diese Häuser sind mit einem Symbol ⊠ ausgewiesen. In einigen Häusern wird ebenfalls Abendbrot und/oder eine leichte Mahlzeit serviert. Bitte entnehmen Sie entsprechende Hinweise der Legende. Abendmenüs sind normalerweise bis 12 Uhr mittags zu buchen.

Heizung

Die meisten Häuser sind geheizt, in der Regel mit Zentralheizung. Viele haben offene Torf- oder Holzfeuer.

Blindenhunde und Haustiere

Achten Sie in der Broschüre auf das Symbol für Blindenhunde ☒ und Haustiere ⚐, und fragen Sie bei der Buchung nach, ob diese mitgebracht werden können.

Kinderermäßigung

Kinderermäßigung wird normalerweise gewährt, wenn Kinder im Zimmer der Eltern schlafen oder wenn drei bis vier Kinder ein Zimmer teilen. Bitte erkundigen Sie sich im Einzelnen, wenn Sie buchen.

Gutscheine von Reisebüros

Ihr Reisebüro stellt Ihnen eine Liste der Häuser zur Verfügung, die Gutscheine annehmen. Diese sind in unserer Broschüre mit einem ⬤ gekennzeichnet. Die Gutscheine gelten für Übernachtung mit Frühstück in einem Standardzimmer, in einigen Fällen jedoch auch für ein Zimmer mit eigenem Bad. In der Regel wird hierfür jedoch ein Zuschlag erhoben. Wenn eine Einzelperson ein Mehrbettzimmer belegt, wird ein Einzelzimmerzuschlag berechnet.

Behinderte

Das National Rehabilitation Board gibt ein Unterkunftsverzeichnis für Behinderte heraus. Alle in dieser Broschüre mit einem ♿ gekennzeichneten Häuser sind vom NRB und nach den Farm and Country Anforderungen als für Behinderte geeignet eingestuft.

Beschwerden und Kommentare

Beschwerden sollten zunächst dem Hauseigentümer vorgebracht werden. Sollte Ihrer Beschwerde nicht in befriedigender Weise entsprochen werden, so wenden Sie sich bitte telefonisch an den Vorsitzenden der Irish Farm Holidays Association - sofern Ihr Urlaub noch nicht beendet ist, oder schreiben Sie nach Ihrer Heimkehr. Wenn Sie der Meinung sind, daß man Ihnen zuviel berechnet hat, behalten Sie bitte Ihre Quittung und legen Sie eine Kopie davon Ihrem Beschwerdebrief bei. Konstruktive Kritik hilft uns, unsere Dienstleistungen zu verbessern. Gerne leiten wir auch Ihr Lob an unsere Mitglieder weiter.

NÄCHSTE STADT/ORTSCHAFT Entfernung in km		GRAFSCHAFT	
Familienname	Tel:	Fax:	
NAME DES	Geöffnet:		
FARMHAUSES	Anz.der Zimmer:	Dreibett:	
Anschrift	Zweibett/Doppel:	Familienzimmer:	
	Einzelzimmer:	mit Bad:	
B&B:	**HBW ES:**	**S.Supp:**	**Dinner:**
B&B ES:	**3 day HB:**	**CSP:**	**High Tea:**
HBW:	**3 day HB ES:**		

✗ 🛏 ♨ ♪ ⛾ ⚐ S

Beschreibung des Farmhauses

Abkürzungen:

Reisebürogutscheine werden angenommen. Möglicherweise wird ein Zuschlag für Zimmer mit eigenem Bad erhoben. Bitte fragen Sie bei der Buchung.

Vouchers Not Accepted

Reisebürogutscheine werden NICHT akzeptiert.

B&B	Bed & Breakfast (Übernachtung u. Frühstück).
B&B ES:	Zimmer mit eigenem Bad/Dusche und WC.
HBW:	Standardzimmer, 7 Übern. u. Frühst., 7 Abendmahlz.
HBW ES:	Halbpension pro Woche in Zimmer mit Bad/Dusche, 7 Übern. u. Frühst., 7 Abendessen.
3 Day HB:	Standardzimmer, 3 Übern. u. Frühst., 3 Abendessen.
3 Day HB ES:	3 Tage Halbpension in Zimmer mit Bad/Dusche, 3 Übern. u. Frühst., 3 Abendessen.
S.Supp:	Einzelbelegung eines Mehrbettzimmers.
CSP:	Preisnachlaß für Kinder, die das Zimmer der Eltern teilen.
Farm Guesthouse	Bäuerliche Pension. (Diese Häuser haben mehr Zimmer als gewöhnlich und werden kommerzieller geführt.)

Symbole: (Einrichtungen, die im Farmhaus oder in der Nähe verfügbar sind)

✕ Abendessen	𝟞𝟞 Fahrradverleih
✕ Leichte Mahlzeiten	ℚ Tennisplatz
✌ Haustiere erlaubt	✗ Squash
➡ Nur Blindenhunde erlaubt	▶₁₈ 18-Loch Golfplatz
S Einzelübernachtungen	▶ 9-Loch Golfplatz
🚜 Farmbetrieb	☑ Pitch and Putt
🖼 Farmbetrieb, der besichtigt werden kann	🏌 Minigolf
F Technischer Farmbetrieb	✓ Golfübungsgelände
👬 Gäste können mitarbeiten	🐎 Ponyreiten für Gäste
🐂 Einrichtungen für Kinder	⊗ Nichtraucher
☕ Tee-/Kaffeezubereitungs-möglichkeiten im Zimmer	⊂⊃ Kunsthandwerks-demonstrationen
♪ Angelgewässer	BD Brotbacken wird gezeigt
⬜ Bootsverleih	TV Fernsehgerät im Zimmer
♀ Weinlizenz	OBA Buchungen außerhalb der Saison nach Vereinbarung
◆ Hobbyraum	
✈ 32 km vom Flughafen	EC Euroschecks
⛴ 32 km vom Fährhafen	AE American Express
♿ Behindertengerecht, vom NRB zugelassen	DC Diners Club
⚙ Biofarmprodukte	V VISA/Barclaycard
U Vom Irischen Reitverband zugelassen Reitställe	AM Access/Mastercard
♨ Organisierte Wanderprogramme	

RÉSERVATIONS

Les réservations peuvent se faire directement auprés de l'établissement ou par l'intermédiaire d'un bureau d'information touristique. Les réservations doivent être confirmées par écrit, accompagnées des arrhes requis. En cas d'urgence, contacter le représentant local le plus proche.

Il est recommandé de toujours réserver d'avance l'hébergement de la première et de la dernière nuit, 48 heures à l'avance en juin/juillet/août, 2 semaines ou plus si possible à Dublin. Confirmer la réservation sous sept jours avec les arrhes convenus. Une carte de crédit peut être demandé pour garantir la chambre - se renseigner lors de la réservation . Arrivées tardives - après 18.00 heures avec l'accord de l'établissement.

Les réservations pour les étapes suivantes seront faites pour vous moyennant le prix de la communication téléphonique. Afin d'éviter toute déception, nous vous recommandons d'utiliser ce service.

Heures d'arrivée

Nous vous demandons d'avertir la ferme de votre heure d'arrivée envisagée. Une arrivée de très bonne heure peut être gênante si elle n'a pas fait l'objet d'un accord préalable. Les chambres sont normalement gardées jusqu'à 18.00 heures. Il est donc important de prévenir la ferme de tout retard afin de faire garder votre chambre.

Annulations

En cas de nécessité d'annuler votre réservation veuillez contacter la ferme le plus tôt possible. En effet, les chambres réservées mais non occupées peuvent donner lieu à une perte de revenus dont vous pourriez être tenu responsable légalement.

Repas

Les nombreuses fermes assurant le repas du soir sont indiquées par un symbole. Une collation et/ou un repas léger ☒ sont également servis dans certaines fermes. Veuillez consulter les symboles dans notre guide. Il est nécessaire de réserver le dîner avant midi.

Chauffage

La plupart des fermes sont équipées du chauffage central ou de cheminées (bûches ou tourbe).

Chiens d'aveugle et animaux domestiques

Chercher le symbole chien d'aveugle ☐ ou animaux domestiques ☐ dans le guide et se renseigner au moment de la réservation.

Réductions pour les enfants

Des réductions sont normalement consenties lorsque les enfants partagent la chambre de leurs parents ou lorsque trois ou quatre enfants partagent une chambre familiale. Veuillez şe renseigner au moment de la réservation.

Bon d'agences de voyages

Votre agent de voyages vous remettra une liste des établissements acceptant les bons; ceux-ci sont repérés par le symbole ☐ dans notre brochure. Les bons sont valables pour une chambre à une personne avec petit déjeuner comportant dans certains cas une salle de bains avec WC privés. Un supplément pourra être demandé pour une salle de bainss si celle-ci n'est pas inclue. Un supplément sera demandé lorsqu'une personne seule occupe une chambre à deux ou plusieurs personnes.

Personnes handicapées

Le National Rehabilitation Board édite un guide de l'hébergement destiné aux handicapés. Les établissements repérés du symbole ☐ dans cette brochure sont homologués par Farm and Country Standards/NRB comme étant adaptés aux besoins des personnes handicapées.

Réclamations et commentaires

Les réclamations doivent d'abord être faites au propriétaire de la ferme. Si vous n'obtenez pas satisfaction vous devrez contacter le président de l'Irish Farmhouse Holidays Association par téléphone si vous êtes encore en vacances ou par écrit si vous êtes de retour chez vous. Si vous estimez avoir payé un prix excessif, nous vous demandons de conserver vos reçus qui devront accompagner votre réclamation. Vos critiques et observations nous aideront à améliorer notre produit. Nous serons d'autre part heureux de transmettre vos compliments à nos membres.

VILLE/VILLAGE LES PLUS PROCHES			COMTÉ	
Nom de famille **NOM DE LA FERME** **Adresse**		Tel: Ouvert: Nombre de Chambres: Deux Personnes: Individuelle:	Fax: À Trois Personnes: Familiale: SDB/WC:	
B&B: B&B ES: HBW:	HBW ES: 3 day HB: 3 day HB ES:	S.Supp: CSP:	Dinner: High Tea:	
		✕ 🐂 🖥 ♪ ▶ ☐ S		

Description de la ferme

ABBREVIATIONS

 Bons d'agences de voyages acceptés. Un supplément peut être demandé pour les chambres avec salle de bains/douche/WC. Se renseigner au moment de la réservation.

Vouchers Not Accepted **Les bons d'agences de voyages ne sont pas acceptés.**

B&B Chambre et petit déjeuner.

B&B ES: Chambre avec salle de bains/douche/WC privé.

HBW: Chambre, petit déjeuner et repas du soir sur 7 jours.

HBW ES: Demi pension par semaine comportant la chambre avec salle de bains/douche, petit déjeuner et repas du soir sur 7 jours.

3 DAY HB: Chambre, petit déjeuner et repas du soir sur 3 jours.

3 DAY HB ES: Demi pension comportant la chambre avec bain/ douche, petit déjeuner et repas du soir sur 3 jours.

S.Supp: Occupation individuelle d'une chambre double/triple.

CSP: Réduction pour enfant(s) partageant la chambre des parents.

Farm Guesthouse Guesthouse à la ferme (ces établissements offrent généralement un plus grand nombre de chambres aux visiteurs).

Symboles: (Équipements disponibles á la ferme ou á proximité)

- ✘ Dîner
- ⊠ Repas légers
- 🐾 Animaux domestiques autorisés
- → Chiens d'aveugle seulement
- S Chambres individuelles
- Ferme en activité
- Ferme ouverte en activité
- F Ferme technique en activité
- Participation du visiteur aux activités du ferme
- Aires de jeux pour enfants
- Thétière/cafetière dans les chambres
- ♪ Pêche
- Location de barques
- ⌇ Licence de vin
- ♦ Salle de jeux
- Aéroport à 32 km
- Ferryport à 32 km
- ♿ Accès pour handicapés agréé par le NRB
- Produits organiques de la ferme
- ∪ Centres équestres agréés par AIRE
- ⚲ Randonnées pédestres organisées
- ⚶ Location de bicyclettes
- ℺ Court de tennis

- 🏃 Court de squash
- ⛳18 Terrain de golf 18 trous
- ⛳9 Terrain de golf 9 trous
- ⊿ Pitch and putt
- ⚑ Golf miniature
- ⚐ Terrain d'entraînement de golf
- ⚑ Poney à la disposition des clients
- ⊗ Interdiction de fumer
- CD Démonstrations d'artisanat
- BD Démonstrations de fabrication traditionelle de pain
- TV Télévision dans les chambres
- OBA Réservations hors saison sur demande
- EC Eurochèques
- AE Carte American Express
- DC Carte Diners Club
- V Carte VISA/Barclaycard
- AM Carte Access/Mastercard

Reserveren

Reserveringen kunnen worden gemaakt door het landhuis zelf of via een toeristenbureau te benaderen. U dient uw reservering schriftelijk te bevestigen en de aanbetaling bij te sluiten.

In noodgevallen kunt u contact opnemen met de dichtstbijzijnde vertegenwoordiger voor het betreffende graafschap.

Reserveer voor de eerste en laatste nacht altijd accommodatie vooraf. Juni/juli/augustus - 48 uur vooraf. Dublin - 2 weken vooraf reserveren, bij voorkeur eerder. Bevestig de reservering binnen 7 dagen met de overeengekomen aanbetaling.

Kamers kunnen met een credit card worden gegarandeerd - controleer bij het reserveren. Controleer het tarief en de annuleringsregels bij het reserveren. Late aankomst na 18.00 uur dient speciaal met het huis afgesproken te worden. Voor de prijs van een telefoontje kunt u ter plaatse een reservering laten maken naar het volgende huis voor de volgende nacht. Gebruik deze om teleurstelling te voorkomen.

Aankomsttijden

U wordt geadviseerd de eigenaar op de hoogte te stellen van uw aankomsttijd. Een zeer vroege aankomsttijd kan ongelegen komen tenzij voorafgaand afgesproken. Kamers worden normaal tot 6 uur 's avonds vastgehouden. Het is van groot belang dat u de eigenaar op de hoogte stelt van uw oponthoud, zodat uw kamer kan worden vrijgehouden.

Annuleringen

Mocht u de reservering willen annuleren, neem dan zo spoedig mogelijk contact op met de eigenaar van de accommodatie. Gereserveerde kamers die niet bezet worden, kunnen tot verlies leiden, waarvoor u verantwoordelijk kunt worden gesteld.

Maaltijden

Bij veel van onze huizen is het mogelijk een avondmaaltijd te gebruiken, en dit wordt door middel van een symbool aangegeven. High Tea en/of lichte maaltijden ⊠ zijn in sommige accommodaties ook beschikbaar. Let op de symbolen in de gids die dit aangeven. De avondmaaltijd dient doorgaans vóór 12 uur 's middags te worden gereserveerd.

Verwarming

De meeste accommodaties hebben verwarming, meestal centrale verwarming, en veel hebben turf- of houthaarden.

Blindengeleidehonden en huisdieren

Let op het symbool voor blindengeleidehonden ⊅ en huisdieren ✻ in de brochure, en controleer dit bij de boeking.

Korting voor kinderen

Kortingen voor kinderen zijn doorgaans geldig wanneer de kinderen de kamer met de ouders delen, of wanneer drie of vier kinderen een familiekamer delen. Controleer dit bij de boeking.

Reisbureau-vouchers

Uw reisbureau geeft u een gids waarin alle adressen staan vermeld die de vouchers accepteren, deze adressen worden in onze brochure met het 🟢 symbool aangegeven. Vouchers zijn gewoonlijk geldig voor standaardkamers met logies / ontbijt, maar kunnen in sommige gevallen voor privé-faciliteiten geldig zijn. Een toeslag kan in rekening worden gebracht voor privé-faciliteiten indien deze niet inbegrepen zijn. Een toeslag kan worden berekend voor bezetting van een tweepersoonskamer door één persoon.

Gehandicapten

De National Rehabilitation Board geeft een accommodatiegids voor gehandicapten uit. Alle adressen die in deze brochure het symbool ♿ hebben, zijn goedgekeurd als voor gehandicapten geschikte accommodatie door de Farm and Country Standards/NRB.

Klachten en opmerkingen

Klachten moeten in de eerste instantie worden besproken met de eigenaar van de accommodatie. Wanneer de klacht niet naar uw tevredenheid wordt afgehandeld, dient u contact op te nemen met de Voorzitter van de Irish Farmhouse Holidays Association, telefonisch wanneer u nog op vakantie bent, of schriftelijk na uw terugkeer. Wanneer u denkt dat u te veel betaald heeft, bewaar dan de rekening en stuur een afschrift van de rekening met uw klacht. Door uw klachten en opmerkingen kunnen wij ons produkt verbeteren. Wij geven ook graag uw complimenten door aan onze leden.

Beschrijving van Farmhouse

DICHTSTBIJZIJNDE STAD/DORP Afstand in kilometers		LAND	
Familienaam	**Tel:**	**Fax:**	
NAAM VAN BOERDERIJ	**Open:**		
Adres	Aantal Kamers:	Driepersoonskamers:	
	Tweepersoonskamers:	Familiekamers:	
	Eenpersoonskamers:	Met Privé Faciliteiten:	
B&B:	**HBW ES:**	**S.Supp:**	**Dinner:**
B&B ES:	**3 day HB:**	**CSP:**	**High Tea:**
HBW:	**3 day HB ES:**		

 ✕ ⛽ 🖥 ♪ ⭐ ✻ S

AFKORTINGEN

 Reisbureau-vouchers worden geaccepteerd. Een toeslag kan berekend worden voor kamers met privé-faciliteiten. Controleer dit bij het reserveren.

Reisbureau-vouchers worden niet geaccepteerd.

B&B	Standaard kamer. Logies en ontbijt.
B&B ES:	Kamer met privé-bad/douche en toilet.
HBW:	Standaard kamer, 7 logies en ontbijt en 7 diners.
HBW ES:	Eén week halfpension, 7 logies en ontbijt en 7 diners.
3 day HB:	Standaard kamer, 3 logies en ontbijt en 3 diners.
3 day HB ES:	3 dagen halfpension in kamer met privé-bad/douche, 3 logies en ontbijt en 3 diners.
S.Supp:	Toeslag voor bezetting van twee/driepersoonskamer door één persoon.
CSP:	Korting voor kinderen die de kamer met de ouders delen.
Farm Guesthouse	Boerderij Guesthouse (deze huizen beschikken over meerdere gastenverblijven, en zijn meer commercieel aangelegd).

Symbolen: (Beschikbare faciliteiten op de boerderij of in de omgeving)

✕	Diner	⚲	Fietsen te huur
☒	Lichte maaltijden	⚲	Tennisbaan
🐾	Huisdieren toegestaan	🏃	Squashbaan
⬈	Alleen blindengeleidehonden toegestaan	⛳	18 hole golfbaan
S	Eenpersoonskamers	⛳	9 hole golfbaan
⛏	Boerderij in bedrijf	☑	Pitch and putt
⛏	Te bezoeken boerderij	⛳	Midgetgolf
F	Technisch werkende boerderij	↗	Driving range
🏠	Hulp op de boerderij	♞	Ponyrijden voor gasten
♣	Kinderspeelplaats	⊘	Roken verboden
☕	Thee/koffie op de kamer	⬭	Handwerkdemonstraties
⌿	Vissen	BD	Broodbakdemonstraties
⛵	Boten te huur	TV	TV op de kamer
♀	Wijnvergunning	OBA	Reserveringen in het voor/naseizoen mogelijk
♣	Hobbykamer		
✈	32 km van het vliegveld	EC	Eurocheques
⛴	32 km van ferryhaven	AE	American Express
♿	Geschikt voor gehandicapten (goedgekeurd door de NRB)	DC	Diners Club
☀	Organisch geteelde producten	V	VISA/Barclaycard
∪	Paardrijden (goedgekeurd door Aire)	AM	Access/Mastercard
🚶	Georganiseerde wandelingen		

PRENOTAZIONI

Le prenotazioni possono essere effettuate contattando direttamente la casa o tramite un ufficio informazioni turistiche. La prenotazione va confermata per iscritto e allegando il deposito richiesto. Nel caso di un'emergenza con tattare il più vicino rappresentante di contea.

Prenotate sempre la sistemazione per la prima e l'ultima notte in anticipo. Giugno/luglio/agosto - 48 ore in anticipo. Dublino - 2 settimane di anticipo, preferibilmente di più. Confermare la prenotazione entro 7 giorni con il deposito pattuito. Le camere possono essere garantite tramite Carta di Credito - controllate quando prenotate e controllate al momento della preotazione anche la penale e la prassi in casso di annullamento. Arrivi a tarda ora: dopo le ore 18.00 solo previo accordo speciale con i propietari della casa.

Prenotazioni successive verranno fatte al costo dellatelefonata. Per evitare delusioni avvaletevi di questo servizio.

Orario di arrivo

È consigliabile comunicare alla fattoria l'orario di arrivo previsto. Arrivare con forte anticipo senza preavviso potrebbe infatti causare inconvenienti. Le camere vengono di solito riservate fino alle ore 18.00 ed è quindi importante comunicare eventuali ritardi per assicurarsi che la camera non venga ceduta.

Annullamenti

Nel caso si debba annullare la prenotazione, darne immediata comunicazione ai proprietari della fattoria. Le camere riservate e non occupate potrebbero comportare una perdita economica per la quale si può essere ritenuti legalmente responsabili.

Pasti

Vengono serviti pasti serali in molte fattorie della nostra associazione, indicate in questa guida con un simbolo. In alcune fattorie sono anche disponibili spuntini e pasti leggeri ⊠ . Controllare i simboli in questa guida come riferimento. I pasti serali vanno generalmente prenotati entro mezzogiorno.

Riscaldamento

La maggior parte delle case sono fornite di riscaldamento, generalmente centralizzato, e in molte ci sono caminetti a torba o a legna.

Cani guida per ciechi e animali domestici

Cercate in questa guida il simbolo cani guida ⟴ e animali domestici ⟴ e controllate sempre al momento della prenotazione.

Riduzioni per bambini

Generalmente si applicano riduzioni per bambini nel caso essi condividano la camera con i genitori oppure se tre o quattro bambini condividono una camera familiare. Controllare al momento della prenotazione.

Voucher

La vostra agenzia viaggi vi fornirà un elenco delle fattorie che accettano voucher, indicate in questa guida con il simbolo ⟴ . I voucher generalmente includono pernottamento in camera standard e prima colazione, e solo in alcuni casi servizi privati, che richiedono il pagamento di un supplemento se non sono espressamente indicati. Viene richiesto un supplemento nel caso in cui un singolo ospite occupi una camera a due o più letti.

Disabili

Il National Rehabilitation Board (NRB: ente nazionale per la riabilitazione) pubblica una guida delle case attrezzate per l'accoglienza ai disabili. Tutte le fattorie contrassegnate in questa guida dal simbolo ⟴ sono state riconosciute rispondenti agli Standard fattoria e campagna/NRB.

Reclami e commenti

Eventuali reclami vanno rivolti in primo luogo ai proprietari della casa. In caso di mancata soddisfazione, contattare il Presidente dell'Irish Farm Holiday Association, per via telefonica se si è ancora in vacanza o per iscritto se si è già rientrati a casa. Se si ritiene di aver pagato più del dovuto, conservare la ricevuta e allegarne una copia alla lettera di reclamo. Ogni reclamo e critica ci aiuta a migliorare il nostro prodotto. Siamo anche sempre molto lieti di riportare i giudizi positivi ai membri della nostra associazione.

CITTÁ/PAESE PIÚ VICINO Distanza in Km		CONTEA	
Nome della famiglia	Tel:	Fax:	
NOME DELLA FATTORIA	Operto:		
Indirizzo	No Camere:	Triple:	
	Doppie:	Familiari:	
	Singole:	Con Servizi Privati:	
B&B:	HBW ES:	S.Supp:	Dinner:
B&B ES:	3 day HB:	CSP:	High Tea:
HBW:	3 day HB ES:		

✕ ⟴ ⟴ ♪ ⟴ ⟴ S

Descrizione della fattoria

ABBREVIAZIONI

Si accettano voucher di agenzie di viaggio. Possibile supplemento per servizi privati. Controllare al momento della prenotazione.

Non si accettano voucher di agenzie di viaggio.

B&B: Camera standard. Pernottamento e prima colazione.

B&B ES: Camera con bagno/doccia e toilette privati.

HBW: Pernottamento, prima colazione e cena per 7 giorni in camera standard.

HBW ES: Pernottamento, prima colazione e cena per 7 giorni in camera con bagno/doccia.

3 day HB: Pernottamento, prima colazione e cena per 3 giorni in camera standard.

3 day HB ES: Pernottamento, prima colazione e cena per 3 giorni in camera con bagno/doccia.

S.Supp.: Supplemento camera singola.

CSP: Riduzione per bambini in condivisione con i genitori.

Farm Guesthouse Fattoria/Guesthouse (dispongono di solito di più camere del solito e sono operazioni più commerciali.

Simboli: (Servizi disponibili nella fattoria o nelle sue vicinanze)

✘	Cena	⚙	Noleggio biciclette
✖	Spuntini	⚲	Campo da tennis
	Sono ammessi animali domestici	🏃	Squash
	Sono ammessi solo cani guida		Campo da golf a 18 buche
S	Camere uso singola		Campo da golf a 9 buche
	Fattoria operante		Pitch and putt
	Fattoria operante all'aperto		Minigolf
F	Fattoria meccanizzata		Driving range
	Possibilità di partecipare ai lavori della fattoria		Pony ad uso degli ospiti
	Attrezzature per bambini	⊗	Non fumatori
	Bollitore in camera per te o caffè	⃝	Dimostrazioni di attività artigianali
	Possibilità di pesca con la lenza	BD	Dimostrazioni di preparazione del pane
	Noleggio barche	TV	TV nelle camere
	Licenza vini	OBA	Aperto fuori stagione su prenotazione
	Sala giochi		
	20 miglia dall'aeroporto	EC	Eurocheques
	20 miglia da porto traghetti	AE	American Express
&	Accesso disabili approvato dal NRB.	DC	Diners Club
	Prodotti organici	V	VISA/Barclaycard
U	Maneggio approvato dall'Aire (associazione irlandese centri equestri)	AM	Access/Mastercard
	Escursioni a piedi guidate		

COMO HACER LA RESERVA

Las reservas se pueden hacer contactando directamente con la casa o a través de una oficina de información turística. Deberá confirmar su reserva por escrito y adjuntando el depósito necesario. En caso de emergencia, contacte con el representante del área del condado más cercano.

Reserve siempre la primera y la última noche de alojamiento por adelantado, junio/julio/agosto- con 48 horas de antelación. Dublín -2 semanas, preferentemente más, de antelación. Confirme la reserva antes de 7 días con el depósito acordado. Las habitaciones se pueden garantizar mediante tarjeta de crédito -compruébelo al hacer la reserva. Llegadas tardías - después de las 6pm por acuerdo especial con la casa. Las reservas posteriores se realizarán por lo que cuesta una llamada telefónica. Para evitar decepciones, le rogamos se aproveche de este servicio.

Hora de llegada

Es aconsejable informar a la casa en la que se vaya a alojar de la hora de su llegada. Si llega muy pronto, puede ocasionar inconvenientes, a no ser que ésta haya sido avisada. Normalmente las habitaciones se guardan hasta las 6 p.m. Es muy importante que telefonee a la casa si va a llegar con retraso para asegurarse que le guardarán la habitación.

Cancelaciones

En caso de que tuviera que cancelar su reserva, le rogamos se ponga en contacto con la casa tan pronto como sea posible. Las habitaciones reservadas y no ocupadas pueden causar una pérdida de ingresas al propietario, de la cual usted sería el responsable legal.

Comidas

Es posible cenar en muchas de nuestras casas y se encuentran indicadas con un símbolo. En algunas casas también podrá tomar té y/o comidas ligeras ✗. Le rogamos que compruebe los símbolos en la guía de referencia. La cena normalmente se reservará antes de las 12 del mediodía.

Calefación

La mayoría de las casas tienen calefación, normalmente calefación central y muchas tienen turberas abiertas o chimeneas.

Perros guía y animales domésticos

Busque el símbolo de perros guía ⊓ y animales domésticos ⚭ en el folleto y compruébelo cuando realice la reserva.

Tarifa reducida para niños

La tarifa reducida para niños se aplica normalmente cuando éstos comparten habitación con sus padres o cuando tres o cuatro niños comparten una habitación familiar. Le rogamos que lo compruebe cuando realice la reserva.

Bonos de agencias de viajes

Su agencia de viajes le proporcionará una lista de los lugares que aceptan bonos y éstos están indicados en el folleto con el símbolo ⚫. Los bonos normalmente son válidos para alojamiento y desayuno en una habitación estándar, pero en algunos casos puede que incluyan ducha o baño privados. Si estas instalaciones privadas no se incluyen, tendrá que pagar un suplemento por ellas. Cuando una persona ocupe una habitación para dos o tres personas, se le cobrará un suplemento.

Personas con minusvalías

El Consejo de Rehabilitación Nacional (NRB) ha editado la Guía de alojamiento para personas con minusvalías. Todos los lugares con el símbolo ♿ en éste catálogo han sido aprobados por las Normas de las Casa Granja y de Campo/NRB como alojamientos acondicionados para estas personas.

Reclamaciones y otros comentarios

Las reclamaciones se deberán hacer primero ante los propietarios de las casas. Si ésta no es atendida satisfactoriamente, deberá contactar con el presidente de Irish Farm Holidays Association por teléfono si todavía se encuentra de vacaciones, o mediante un escrito si ya ha regresado a su hogar. Si cree que le han cobrado más de lo estipulado, le rogamos que guarde su recibo y adjunte una copia de éste junto con su reclamación. Las reclamaciones y sugerencias nos ayudarán a mejorar nuestro producto. Gustosamente haremos llegar sus comentarios a nuestros miembros.

PUEBLO/CIUDAD MAS CERCANO Distancia en Km		CONDADO	
Apellido	**Tel:**	**Fax:**	
NOMBRE DE LA CASA	**Abierto:**		
GRANJA	No de Habitaciones:	Triple:	
Dirección	Doble/Dos Camas:	Familiar:	
	Individual:	Con Bañ/Ducha Privados:	
B&B:	**HBW ES:**	**S.Supp:**	**Dinner:**
B&B ES:	**3 day HB:**	**CSP:**	**High Tea:**
HBW:	**3 day HB ES:**		

✗ ⚭ ☕ ♪ ⊓ ⚭ S

Descripción de la casa granja

VOUCHERS ACCEPTED

ABREVIATURAS

 Se aceptan bonos de la agencia de viajes. Posible cobro extra por habitaciones con baño privado. Asegúrese al hacer la reserva.

 No se aceptan bonos de la agencia de viajes.

B&B: Habitación estándar en Bed & Breakfast -pensión que ofrece cama y desayuno.

B&B ES: Habitación con baño/ducha y servicio privado.

HBW: Habitación estándar con 7 días de cama, desayuno y cena.

HBW ES: Media pensión en habitación con baño/ducha, 7 días de cama, desayuno y cena.

3 Day HB: Habitación estándar, 3 días de cama, desayuno y cena.

3 Day HB ES: 3 días de media pensión en habitación con baño/ducha, 3 días de cama, desayuno y cena.

S.Supp: Ocupación individual de habitación doble/triple.

CSP: Descuento para niños que comparten con sus padres.

Farm Guesthouse — Casas granja para huéspedes (estas casas suelen tener más habitaciones para huéspedes y son más comerciales en su funcionamiento).

SÍMBOLOS: (Instalaciones disponibles en la proximidad de la casa granja)

- ✗ Cena
- ☒ Comidas ligeras
- Se permiten animales domésticos
- Sólo se permiten perros guías
- S Alquiler individual
- Granja en activo
- Granja en activo abierta
- F Granja en activo técnica
- Participación del huésped en el trabajo de la granja
- Instalaciones para niños
- Té/café (servicios en habitaciones)
- Instalaciones de pesca
- Barcos para alquilar
- Licencia para vender vino
- Habitación de juegos
- A 32 kilometrós del aeropuerto
- A 32 kilometrós del puerto
- Acceso para personas con minusvalías aprobado por NRB
- Granja de productos orgánicos
- U Establos para practicar la hípica aprobados por Aire

- Programas de excursiones organizadas
- Bicicletas para alquilar
- Cancha de tenis
- Cancha de squash
- Campo de golf de 18 agujeros
- Campo de golf de 9 agujeros
- Mini-golf
- Golf loco
- Campo de práctica de tiros de salida
- Ponis para uso de los huéspedes
- ⊗ Prohibido fumar
- CD Demostraciones de artesanía
- BD Demostraciones de cómo hacer pan
- TV TV en las habitaciones
- OBA Reservas fuera de temporada por acuerdo
- EC Eurocheques
- AE American Express
- DC Diners Club
- V VISA/Barclaycard
- AM Access/Mastercard

Bord Fáilte - Irish Tourist Board Offices

IRELAND
Bord Failte Eireann
Baggot Street Bridge
Dublin 2
Tel: 01 602 4000
Tel: 1850 23 03 30
Fax: 01 602 4100
Email: user@irishtouristboard.ie
Web: www.ireland.travel.ie

NORTHERN IRELAND
Bord Failte
53 Castle Street
Belfast BT1 1GH
Tel: 00 44 28 9032 7888
Fax: 00 44 28 9024 0201
Email: info@irishtouristboardni.com
Web: www.ireland.travel.ie

Bord Failte
44 Foyle Street
Derry
BT48 6AT
Tel: 00 44 28 71369501
Fax: 00 44 28 71369501
Web: www.ireland.travel.ie

* if dialling Northern Ireland direct from
Republic of Ireland the code 048 followed by
the tel. no. is sufficient.

EUROPE

AUSTRIA
Irische Fremdenverkehrszentrale
Libellenweg 1
A-1140 Vienna
Tel: 00 43 1 501596060
Fax: 00 43 1 911 3765
Email: bordfailte@aon.at
Web: www.irlandinfo.at

BELGIUM
Irish Tourist Board- Bord Failte
Avenue de Beaulieulaan 25/12
1160 Brussels
Tel: 00 32 02 275 0171
Fax: 00 32 02 672 1066
Email: info@irishtouristboard.be
Web: www.ireland-tourism.be

BRITAIN
Irish Tourist Board
Ireland House
150 New Bond Street
London W1S 2AQ
Tel: 00 44 20 7493 3201
Fax: 00 44 20 7493 9065
Email: info@irishtouristravel.co.uk
Web: www.irelandtravel.co.uk

DENMARK
Det Irske Turistkontor
"Klostergaarden"
Amagertorv 29B,3
DK 1160
Copenhagen K
Tel: 00 45 33 15 8045
Fax: 00 45 33 93 6390
Email: info@irske-turistkontor.dk
Web: www.irland-turisme.dk

FINLAND
Irlannin Matkailutoimisto
Embassy of Ireland
Erottajankatu 7A
PL33, 00130
Helsinki
Tel: 00 358 9 608 966/961
Fax: 00 358 9 646 022
Email: failte@netlife.fi
Web: www.irlanninmatkailu.com

FRANCE
Office National du Tourisme Irlandais
33 rue de Miromesnil
75008 Paris
Tel: 00 33 1 70 20 00 20
Fax: 00 33 1 47 42 01 64
Email: info@irlande-tourisme.fr
Minitel: 3615 Irlande
Web: www.irlande-tourisme.fr

GERMANY
Irische Fremdenverkehrszentrale
Untermainanlage 7
D-60329 Frankfurt am Main
Tel: 0049 69-66 800950
Fax: 0049 69 92318588
Email: info@irishtouristboard.de
Web: www.irland-urlaub.de

ITALY
Ente Nazionale del Turismo Irlandese
Via Santa Maria Segreta 6
20123 Milano
Tel: 00 39 02 48296060
Fax: 00 39 02 8690396
Email: info@turismo.irlandese.it
Web: www.irlanda-travel.com
www.ireland.travel.ie

THE NETHERLANDS
Iers Nationaal Bureau voor Toerisme
Spuistraat 104
1012 VA Amsterdam
Tel: 0031 20 504 0689
Fax: 0031 20 620 8089
Email: info@irishtouristboard.nl
Web: www.ierland.nl

NORWAY
Irlands Turistkontor
Karenslyst alle 9A,
Postboks 295 Skoyen,
0213 Oslo, Norway.
Tel: 0047 - 22563310
Fax: 0047 - 22543120
Email: he-madse@online.no
Web: www.visit-irland.com

PORTUGAL
Delegacao de Turismo Irlandesa
Embaixada da Irlanda
Rua da Imprensa a Estrela 1-4
1200 Lisboa
Portugal
Tel: 00 351 21 392 94 40
Fax: 00 351 21 397 73 63

SPAIN
Oficina de Turismo de Irlanda
Paseo de la Castellana 46, 3(tm) Planta
28046 Madrid
Tel: 00 34 91 745 64 20
Fax: 00 34 91 577 69 34
Email: ireland@ran.es
Web: www.turismodeirlanda.com

SWEDEN
Irlandska Turistbyran
Sibyllegatan 49
PO Box 5292
10246 Stockholm
Tel: 00 46 8 662 8510
Fax: 00 46 8 661 7595
Email: info@irlandskaturistbyran.a.se
Web: www.irlandsinfo.com

SWITZERLAND
Ireland Mailing House
CH-5634 Merenschwand
Switzerland
Tel: 0041 1 2104153
Fax: 056 675 75 80 - Ireland
Web: www.ireland.travel.ie

USA
Irish Tourist Board
345 Park Avenue
New York
NY 10154
Tel: 1800 223 6470
Fax: 001 212 371 9052
Web: www.irelandvacations.com

SOUTH AFRICA
(Physical Address)
Irish Tourist Board
c/o Development Promotions
Everite House, 7th Floor
20 De Korte Street
Braamfontein 2001
Johannesburg
South Africa

(Postal Address)
PO Box 30615
Braamfontein 2017
Johannesburg
Tel: 00 27 011 339 4865
Fax: 00 27 011 339 2474
Email: devprom@global.co.za
Web: www.ireland.travel.ie

NEW ZEALAND
Irish Tourist Board
Dingwall Building
2nd Floor
87 Queen Street
Auckland
Tel: 00 64 9 3798720
Fax: 00 64 9 3022420
Email: patrick.flynn@walshes.co.nz
Web: www.ireland.travel.ie

AUSTRALIA
Irish Tourist Board
5th Level
36 Carrington Street
Sydney
NSW 2000
Tel: 00 61 2 9299 6177
Fax: 00 61 2 9299 6323
Email: itb@bigpond.com
Web: www.ireland.travel.ie

JAPAN
Irish Tourist Board
Ireland House 4f
2-10-7 Kojimachi
Chiyoda-ku
Tokyo 102-0083
Tel: 00 81 3 5275 1611
Fax: 00 81 3 5275 1623
Email: bfejapan@oak.ocn.ne.jp
Web: www.ireland.travel.ie

Tourism Organisations & Information Offices

TOURISM ORGANISATIONS

TOURIST INFORMATION OFFICES

Dublin
Dublin City and County
Dublin Tourism Centre,
Suffolk Street, Dublin 2.
Website: www.visitdublin.com

South-East
Carlow, Kilkenny, South Tipperary,
Waterford, Wexford
South-East Tourism
41 The Quay, Waterford.
Tel: (051) 875823
Fax: (051) 877388

South-West
Cork, South Kerry
Cork-Kerry Tourism
Áras Fáilte,
Grand Parade, Cork.
Tel: (021) 4273 251
Fax: (021) 4273 504

Shannon Development
Clare, North Kerry, Limerick,
South Offaly, North Tipperary
**Shannon Development,
Tourism Division**
Shannon Town Centre,
Co. Clare.
Tel: (061) 361 555
Fax: (061) 363 180

West
Galway, Mayo, Roscommon
Ireland West Tourism
Áras Fáilte, Forster Street,
Galway City.
Tel: (091) 563 081
Fax: (091) 565 201

North-West
Cavan, Donegal, Leitrim,
Monaghan, Sligo
North-West Tourism
Regional Headquarters,
Temple Street, Sligo.
Tel: (071) 612 01
Fax: (071) 603 60
Email: irelandnorthwest@eircom.net
Website: www.irelandnorthwest.travel.ie
Letterkenny: Derry Road
Tel: (074) 211 60
Fax: (074) 251 80
Email: donegaltourism@eircom.net

East Coast & Midlands
Kildare, Laois, Longford,
Louth, Meath, North Offaly,
Westmeath, Wicklow
East Coast & Midlands Tourism
Clonard House,
Dublin Road,
Mullingar, Co. Westmeath.
Tel: (044) 487 61
Fax: (044) 404 13
Email:
midlandseasttourism@eircom.net

Dublin Tourist Offices
Dublin Tourism Centre,
Suffolk Street,
Dublin 2.

Dublin Airport,
Arrivals Hall.

O' Connell Street,
Dublin 1.

Dún Laoghaire
Harbour,
Ferry Terminal
Building.

Tallaght,
The Square
Towncentre.

Baggot Street Bridge,
Dublin 2.

Information line within
Ireland (including
Dublin) 1850 - 230 330
Information line from
UK 0207 493 3201
Reservations Ireland:
00 800 668 668 66
UK: 00 800 668 668 66

South-East
Tourist Offices
(open year round)
Carlow:
College Street.
Tel: (0503) 31554

Clonmel:
Sarsfield Street.
Tel: (052) 229 60
Fax: (052) 263 78

Dungarvan:
The Square.
Tel: (058) 417 41
Fax: (058) 450 20

Gorey:
Town Centre.
Tel: (055) 21248
Fax: (055) 22521

Kilkenny:
Shee Alms House,
Rose Inn Street.
Tel: (056) 515 00
Fax: (056) 639 55

Waterford:
The Granary.
Tel: (051) 875 823
Fax: (051) 876 720
Waterford Crystal,
Cork Road
Tel: (051) 358 397

Wexford:
Crescent Quay.
Tel: (053) 231 11
Fax: (053) 471 43

Cork-Kerry
Tourist Offices
Blarney:
Tel: (021) 4381 624

Cork:
Áras Fáilte,
Grand Parade.
Tel: (021) 4273 251
Fax: (021) 4273 504

Killarney:
Beach Road,
New Street.
Tel: (064) 316 33
Fax: (064) 345 06

Skibbereen:
North Street.
Tel: (028) 217 66
Fax: (028) 213 53

Shannon Region
Tourist Offices
Adare:
Main Street.
Tel: (061) 396 255
Fax: (061) 396 610

Ennis:
Arthur's Row,
(off O'Connell Square)
Town Centre
Tel: (065) 682 8366
Fax: (065) 682 8350

Limerick:
Arthur's Quay
Tel: (061) 317 522
Fax: (061) 317 939

Shannon Airport,
Arrivals Hall,
Tel: (061) 471 664
Fax: (061) 471 661

Tralee:
Ashe Memorial Hall,
Denny Street.
Tel: (066) 712 1288
Fax: (066) 712 1700

Ireland-West
Tourist Offices
Galway:
Áras Fáilte,
Forster Street,
Galway
Tel: (091) 563 081
Fax: (091) 565 201
Email:
info@irelandwesttourism.ie

Aran:
Tel: (099) 612 63
Fax: (099) 614 20

Oughterard:
Tel: (091) 552 808
Fax: (091) 552 811

Westport:
The Mall.
Tel: (098) 257 11
Fax: (098) 267

North-West
Tourist Offices
Cavan:
Farnham Street
Town Centre
Tel: (049) 433 1942

Buncrana:
Shore Road,
Co. Donegal
Tel: (077) 200 20

Bundoran:
Main Street,
Co. Donegal
Tel: (072) 413 50
Fax: (072) 425 39

Donegal Town:
The Quay,
Co. Donegal
Tel: (073) 211 48
Fax: (073) 227 62

Dungloe:
Tel: (075) 212 97

Letterkenny:
Derry Road,
Co. Donegal
Tel: (074) 211 60
Fax: (074) 251 80
Email: donegaltourism
@eircom.net

Leitrim:
The Old Barrel Store
Carrick-on-Shannon,
Tel: (078) 201 70
Fax: (078) 200 89

Monaghan:
Market House,
Monaghan Town,
Tel: (047) 811 22

Sligo:
Temple Street,
Sligo Town
Tel: (071) 612 01
Fax: (071) 603 60
Email: irelandnorthwest
@eircom.net
Website: www.ireland-
northwest.travel.ie

Yeats
Memorial Building:
Hyde Bridge,
Co. Sligo
Tel: (071) 387 72

East Coast & Midlands
Tourist Offices
Athlone:
Athlone Castle,
Athlone,
Co. Westmeath.
Tel: (0902) 946 30

Arklow:
Coach House, Arklow,
Co. Wicklow.
Tel: (0402) 324 84

Clonmacnoise:
Co. Offaly.
Tel: (0905) 741 34

Drogheda:
Bus Eireann Station
Drogheda,
Co. Louth.
Tel: (041) 9837 070

Dundalk:
Jocelyn Street,
Dundalk,
Co. Louth
Tel: (042) 933 5484
Fax: (042) 933 8070
Email: dundalktourist
office@eircom.net

Glendalough:
Co. Wicklow
Tel: (0404) 456 88

Kildare:
Kildare Town,
Co. Kildare
Tel: (045) 522 696

Longford:
Market Square,
Co. Longford
Tel: (043) 465 66

Newgrange:
Brú na Boinne Visitor
Centre, Donore,
Co. Meath.
Tel: (041) 9880 305

Mullingar:
Market House,
Mullingar,
Co. Meath.
Tel: (044) 486 50

Portlaoise:
James Fintan
Lawlor Avenue,
Portlaoise,
Co. Laois.
Tel: (0502) 211 78

Trim:
Mill Street, Trim,
Co. Meath.
Tel: (046) 371 11

Tullamore:
Tullamore Dew
Heritage Centre,
Tullamore,
Co. Offaly.
Tel: (0506) 526 17

Wicklow:
Rialto House,
Fitzwilliam Square,
Wicklow Town.
Tel: (0404) 691 17
Fax: (0404) 691 18
Email:wicklowtouristoffice
@eircom.net

Open your eyes to Ireland's exciting heritage...

Yearly ticket available!

Dúchas offers a guide-information service and visitor facilities at over 65 sites throughout Ireland.
For further information contact:

'Heritage Card'
Education and Visitor Service
Department of Arts, Heritage, Gaeltacht & the Islands
6 Ely Place Upper, Dublin 2, Ireland.

Tel: +353 1 6472461 Fax: +353 1 6616764
email: heritagecard@ealga.ie
web: www.heritageireland.ie

Dúchas The Heritage Service

An Roinn Ealaíon, Oidhreachta, Gaeltachta agus Oileán
Department of Arts, Heritage, Gaeltacht and the Islands

Please send me details about the Heritage Card and Dúchas sites

Name _____

Address _____

_____

Send to :
'Heritage Card',
Education & Visitor Service,
Department of Arts, Heritage, Gaeltacht & the Islands
6 Ely Place Upper,
Dublin 2, Ireland.

IFH 2001

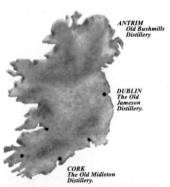

The WATERFORD CRYSTAL Visitor Centre

Watch us shape tomorrow's treasures...

Feel the heat of the furnaces as Masterblowers create elegant shapes at temperatures of 1400°C.

then see us cut the light fantastic

See our Master Craftsmen create beautiful, intricate cuts which are the hallmark of Waterford Crystal.

Opening Hours

Showrooms	Tours
Mar - Dec. 7 days: 8:30am - 6:00pm.	Apr - Oct. 7 days: 8:30am - 4:00pm.
Jan - Feb. 5 days: 9:00am - 5:00pm.	Nov - Mar. 5 days: 9:00am - 3:15pm.

Take a magical factory tour and wonder at the world's largest display of Waterford Crystal. Browse through our jewellery and craft giftstore and then round it off with a relaxing meal in our fine food restaurant.
Experience the Waterford Crystal Visitor Centre. For information call: 051-332500, fax: 051-332720.

Experience the craft, then take some home.

WATERFORD CRYSTAL

Irish Farmhouse Holidays have been welcoming visitors for over three decades to experience the traditional, agricultural and social life of Ireland. A stay in an Irish Farmhouse offers visitors a unique opportunity to get back to nature and the land while staying in a relaxed family environment. Our families have a well deserved reputation for hospitality, service and care which we maintain with pride. The magical scenery combined with the peaceful natural environment and warm hospitality ensures that visitors to our farmhouses will enjoy a truly unforgettable holiday.

All our guests can experience the magical nature of the countryside and enjoy appetising and healthy food in a clean and friendly environment. In addition to this, first time visitors can discover the traditions of Irish agriculture, the precious customs of rural living and also learn to adjust to the slower pace of life. Some of our homes are located near towns, villages and cities while others are situated near our world renowned coastlines.

These homes offer a variety of prices and also a variety of activities to be enjoyed during your stay.

At Irish Farmhouse Holidays we will be delighted to provide you with any information which you may require. In addition to this we would welcome feedback from the visitors which would aid in achieving an even higher standard of service and accommodation.

Finally, I would welcome any additional observations you may have and am looking forward to hearing from you in the near future.

Kathryn M Delany

Kathryn Delany
Chairperson,
Irish Farmhouse Holidays Association
2 Michael Street,
Limerick.
Tel: 061-400700
Fax: 061-400771
Website:
http://www.irishfarmholidays.com
e-mail: farmhols@iol.ie

Good Food

Few things say 'Welcome!' quite as eloquently
as the enticing aroma of a home cooked
meal. Our farmhouses are fortunate to have
a supply of the freshest natural ingredients
always on hand. Ireland has always been
renowned for the quality of its food, and
gourmets recognise the 'Irish Country
House' cuisine has a style all its own.
These days you are as likely as not to
encounter continental and exotic eastern
influences in our food. The flavour and goodness
of natural ingredients, freshly cooked, remains the
same though, and gives that little something extra to the
mouth-watering fruits of our orchards, fields and streams.

Relaxation

The Celtic Tiger may be alive and well, but if there is one thing we know how to do it is relax! Shaking off the stresses and strains of modern living is important on an annual holiday, but equally there are times during the year when we just need to get away from it all. The tranquillity and comfort of an Irish Farmhouse break is a real tonic, offering as it does, fresh air, good food and the opportunity to relax and unwind. During your stay your hosts will be glad to share their knowledge of local events and direct you to places of interest. Whether your holiday is a long break or a weekend away, you will be assured of friendly advice, a homely atmosphere, and the warmest of welcomes.

Leisure

With a rich and fertile soil, and an abundance of rainfall, Ireland is one of the greenest countries on Earth. Naturally, this makes the land ideal for golf and fishing, with some of the world's most beautiful golf courses, and plentiful lakes and rivers. Verdant hills and valleys, and miles of unspoilt coastline, offer a multitude of leisure activities such as swimming, sea-angling, walking and horse riding. In keeping with our Celtic roots, we are also blessed with the finest musicians in the world, and no matter where you go you will find plenty of opportunities to enjoy them. If a relaxing break is more your style, you can choose to explore the countryside from the comfort of your farmhouse base.

Exploration

The rich history of these islands is evident in castles, ruins and heritage sites across the land. Endowed as we are with a country that is a veritable tapestry of artistic, cultural and historic associations, Ireland offers unlimited opportunities for exploration. Whether you wish to immerse yourself in the glorys of the past, or simply relax and take in some sightseeing, you will find a wealth of local knowledge and the warmest of welcomes in an Irish Farmhouse Holiday.

HONOURARY PRESIDENT:
Mrs. Nancy Fitzgerald

EXECUTIVE COMMITTEE

CHAIRPERSON:
Mrs. Kathryn Delany
Gaulstown House,
Dunshaughlin,
Co. Meath.
Tel: 01-8250240
Fax: 01-8259147

VICE CHAIRPERSONS
Mrs. Dympha Crowley
Dromloc House,
Bantry, Co. Cork
Tel: 027-50030
Fax: 027-50030

Mrs. Imelda McMahon
Gortmor House,
Lismakeegan,
Carrick-on-Shannon,
Co. Leitrim.
Tel: 078-20489
Fax: 078-21439

COMPANY SECRETARY:
Mrs. Sheila O'Donoghue
Valley View Farmhouse,
Gortdromakerry,
Muckross, Killarney,
Co. Kerry.
Tel: 064-31206
Fax: 064-31206

TREASURER
Mrs. Catherine Liston
Kyle Farmhouse
Glenbevan, Croom
Co. Limerick.
Tel: 061-397598

AREA REPRESENTATIVES

WATERFORD/WEXFORD
Mrs. Brede Merrigan
Milltown House.
New Ross,
Co. Wexford.
Tel: 051-880294
Fax: 051-880294

CARLOW/KILKENNY/TIPPERARY
Mrs. Maureen Walsh,
Killamaster House,
Carlow, Co. Carlow.
Tel: 0503-63654
Fax: 0503-63654

CORK (WEST)
Mrs. Teresa Crowley
Bunalun, Skibbereen,
Co. Cork.
Tel: 028-21502
Tel: 028-21241

CORK (EAST)
Mrs. Bernadette Murphy
Ardfield, Goggins Hill,
Ballinhassig, Co. Cork.
Tel: 021-885723
Fax: 021-885723

KERRY (NORTH)
Mrs. Brid Moriarty
Moriarty's Farmhouse,
Rahaane, Ventry,
Tralee, Co. Kerry.
Tel: 066-9159037
Fax: 066-9159037

KERRY (SOUTH)
Mrs. Dorothea Stephens
Hill View Farmhouse,
Milltown P.O. Co. Kerry.
Tel: 066-9767117
Fax: 066-9767910

DUBLIN/KILDARE/MEATH/WICKLOW/LOUTH
Mr. Vincent Gorman
Ballindrum Farm,
Ballindrum,
Athy, Co. Kildare.
Tel: 0507-26294
Fax: 0507-26296

CLARE
Mr. John Daly
Clonmore Lodge,
Quilty, Co. Clare.
Tel: 065-7087020
Tel: 065-7087270

Mrs. Anne O'Halloran
Elmdale, Barefield,
Ennis, Co. Clare.
Tel: 065-6827151
Fax: 065-6827151

GALWAY
Mrs. Kathleen Griffin
Rockfield House
New Town, Moycullen
Co. Galway.
Tel: 091-555586

LIMERICK
Mrs. Kathleen Fitzgerald
Fitzgeralds Farmhouse,
Mount Marian,
Abbeyfeale Hill,
Abbeyfeale, Co. Limerick.
Tel: 068-31217
Fax: 068-31558

DONEGAL/SLIGO
Mrs Rosemary Crawford
Gleanna Oir Farmhouse,
Ards, Ramelton
Co. Donegal.
Tel: 074-51187

LONGFORD/OFFALY/WESTMEATH/LAOIS
Mrs Veronica Minnock
Minnock's Farmhouse,
Roscrea Road, Birr,
Co. Offaly.
Tel: 0509-20591
Tel: 0509-21684

CAVAN/MONAGHAN/LEITRIM
Mrs Una Smith
Riverside Farmhouse,
Coote Hill,
Co. Cavan.
Tel: 049-5552150
Fax: 049-5552150

MAYO/ROSCOMMON
Mrs Teresa Sammon
Cuaneen House
Carramore
Louisburgh, Co. Mayo
Tel: 098-66460

Ireland

Legend

National Primary Routes	
National Secondary Routes	
Other Routes (selected)	
Railways	
County Boundary	
Northern Ireland Border	
Coastal Sandy Beach	
Airports	
International Car Ferry	
Local Car / Passenger Ferry	
Tourist Information Offices	

Whilst every care has been taken to
ensure accuracy in the compilation of this map,
Bord Fáilte – Irish Tourist Board cannot accept
responsibility for errors or omissions.
Because of the small scale of this map, not all holiday centres
can be shown. The information on this map is
correct at the time of going to press.

© July 1998 Bord Fáilte – Irish Tourist Board

KILOMETRES
0   20   40   60   80km

MILES
0   10   20   30   40   50mls

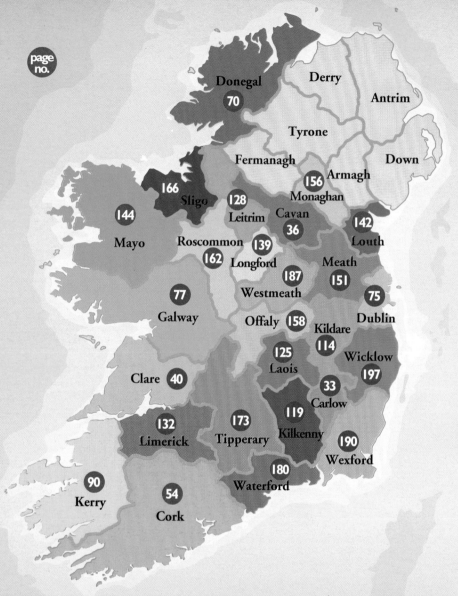

Carlow

Carlow is known as 'The Celtic Centre of Ireland' because of its wealth of ancient monuments and heritage sites. Its famous cathedral is also well worth a visit. A haven for game anglers, the county is traversed by the two great rivers Barrow and Slaney which wind their way past old stone bridges and picturesque villages.

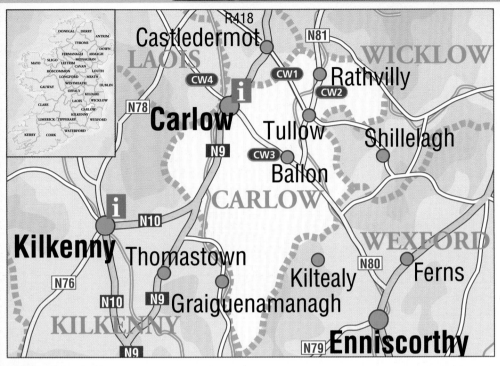

CASTLEDERMOT 5 km   Carlow CW1

Maureen Walsh
KILLAMASTER HOUSE
Killamaster
Carlow, Co Carlow

Tel: 0503-63654   Fax: 0503-63654
Open: March - October

OBA

AM
EC

No Rooms:	3		Triple:	–		
Twin/Double:	3		Family:	–		
Single:	_		En suite:	3		

B&B:	-	HBW ES:	-	-	S.Supp: £6.50 €8.25	Dinner: -	-
B&B ES: £20/22	€25.39/27.93	3 day HB:	-	-	CSP: 25%	High Tea:-	-
HBW:	-	3 day HB ES: -					

Luxury farmhouse with beautiful garden, in view of Wicklow mountains and historic Duckettsgrove Castle. Tea/coffee making facilities in bedrooms. Horse riding, golf, game and coarse fishing nearby. Situated on R418 Castledermot-Tullow Road, off main N9 road. Signposted from Castledermot & Tullow. Midway between Dublin & Rosslare. Email: mairinwalsh@eircom.net Website: http://homepage.eircom.net/~mairin

RATHVILLY 4 km   Carlow CW2

Mrs Mina Corrigan
BAILE RICÉAD
Rathvilly
Co Carlow

Tel: 0503-61120   Fax: –
Open: 17th March – 31st October

OBA

AM
V

No Rooms:	4		Triple:	1		
Twin/Double:	2		Family:	–		
Single:	1		En suite:	2		

B&B: £20	€25.39	HBW ES:	-	-	S.Supp: £6.50 €8.25	Dinner: -	-
B&B ES: £22.50	€28.57	3 day HB:	-	-	CSP: 25%	High Tea:-	-
HBW:	-	3 day HB ES: -					

Scenically set in peaceful countryside with beautiful view of Wicklow Mountains. Comfortable farm house with delicious home baking and log fires. Situated 4 km from Rathvilly off N81, 1 1/2 hours drive from Dublin and Rosslare, 10 km from Castledermot on N9. Mountain climbing, fishing, golf and horse riding nearby. AA selected QQQ award. Mobile: 087-2440622. Website: www.carlowtourism.com/bailericead.html

TULLOW 8 km

	Carlow CW3

Patrick & Maureen Owens
SHERWOOD PARK HOUSE
Kilbride, Ballon
Co Carlow

Tel: 0503-59117   Fax: 0503-59355
Open: All Year

OBA

No Rooms:	4	Triple:	3
Twin/Double:	1	Family:	-
Single:	-	En suite:	4

B&B:	-	-	**HBW ES:**	-	-	**S.Supp:** £6.50 € 8.25	**Dinner:** £20 € 25.39
B&B ES: £30	€ 38.09		**3 day HB:**	-	-	**CSP:** 25%	**High Tea:** -
HBW:	-	-	**3 day HB ES:**	-	-		

🗶 🗶 ⛺ 🐾 S 🕤 🖵

Timeless elegance and a warm family welcome await you at Sherwood - a period Georgian residence built by Arthur Baillie circa 1700, set in rolling parklands and tranquil countryside just off the N80 mid-way Dublin Rosslare. Open fires, romantic bedrooms & canopy beds. Excellent home cooking. Fishing, horse riding, pet farm & golfing at prestigious Mount Wolseley. Beside Altamont Gardens. Bring own wine. Email: info@sherwoodparkhouse.ie. Website: www.sherwoodparkhouse.ie

Vouchers Not Accepted

BALLYLINAN 4 km

	Carlow CW4

Mrs Bernadine Mulhall
COOLANOWLE HOUSE
Ballickmoyler
Carlow

Tel: 0507-25176   Fax: 0507-25176
Open: 1st January – 24th December

No Rooms:	3	Triple:	–
Twin/Double:	3	Family:	–
Single:	–	En suite:	2

B&B: £18	€ 22.86	**HBW ES:** £210	€ 266.64	**S.Supp:** £6.50 € 8.25	**Dinner:** £15 € 19.05
B&B ES: £20	€ 25.39	**3 day HB:** £95	€ 120.63	**CSP:** 50%	**High Tea:** £10 € 12.70
HBW: £195	€ 247.60	**3 day HB ES:** £100	€ 126.97		

🗶 S 🕤 🖵 U ⚲ 👓 🏌

A warm welcome awaits you at Coolanowle Farmhouse, with fully equipped gymnasium, sauna & steamroom. Surrounded by 3 acres of beechwood gardens, lawn tennis court & 18th Century flax ponds all on a real working farm. Ideal for touring the South East and Midlands, Dublin 1 hour, Kilkenny 40mins, Portlaoise 25mins, Carlow/Athy 10 mins and Rosslare 1.5hrs. Also available 2 * 2 ensuite bedroomed 4 star s/c cottages. Email: coolanowle@eircom.net. Website: www.coolanowle.com

VOUCHERS ACCEPTED

Approved Accommodation Sign
This sign will be displayed at most premises which are approved by Tourism Accommodation Approvals Ltd. under licence from Bord Fáilte – Irish Tourist Board.

Panonceau indiquant les hébergements homologués
Ce panonceau sera mis en vue dans la plupart des établissements homologués par Tourism Accommodation Approvals Ltd. sous brevet de Bord Fáilte-Office National du Tourisme Irlandais.

Zeichen für anerkannte Unterkünften
Sie werden das Zeichen an den meisten bei Tourism Accommodation Approvals Ltd. unter Lizenz von Bord Fáilte.

Erkende Accomodatie teken
Dit teken wordt vertoond bij de meeste gelegenheden die erkend zijn door Tourism Accommodation Approvals Ltd. gevolmachtigd door Bord Fáilte-de Ierse toeristen-organisatie.

Insegne indicante Alloggi Approvati
Questa insegna sarà esposta nella maggior parte dei locali che sonno approvati dal Tourism Accommodation Approvals Ltd. su licenza da Bord Fáilte-commissione Irlandese per il turismo.

Simbolo homologado de hospedaje
Este símbolo será expuesto en la gran mayoría de los alojamientos aprobados por Tourism Accommodation Approvals Ltd. bajo licencia de Bord Fáilte-Oficina de Turismo de Irlanda.

Cavan

Dotted with some of the world's most famous fishing lakes and rivers, Cavan is an angler's paradise. Gently rolling hills and an unspoiled natural environment provide an attractive setting for pretty villages and towns. Even if fishing is not your choice of pastime, the peaceful landscape and relaxing atmosphere provide the perfect get-away-from-it-all destination.

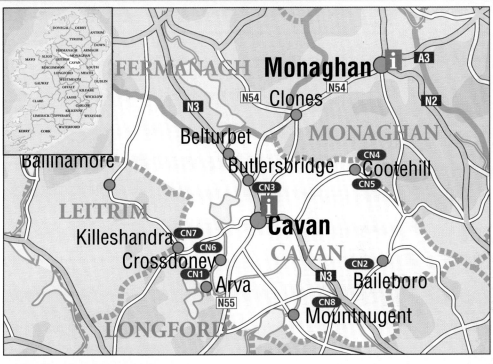

ARVA 5km

Cavan CN1

Mrs. Pearl Kells
"THE ARCHES"
Drumyouth
Arva, Co. Cavan

Tel: 049-4335460   Fax: -

Open: Open all year

OBA

	No Rooms:	4	Triple:	2
	Twin/Double:	2	Family:	-
	Single:		En suite:	4

		HBW ES:	£185	€234.90	S.Supp: £6.50 €8.25	Dinner: £12 €15.24
B&B:	- -					
B&B ES: £19	€24.13	3 day HB:	-	-	CSP: 25%	High Tea: -
HBW:	- -	3 day HB ES: £90		€114.27		

"The Arches" offers luxury farmhouse accommodation only 500 metres from Ardra Lake. Set in a peaceful panoramic setting in the heart of Cavan's Lakeland. Ideal base for fishing, touring, walking, golfing and horse riding. Welcoming cup of tea, friendly atmosphere, good home cooking guaranteed to make your holiday enjoyable.

VOUCHERS ACCEPTED

BAILIEBORO 6.4 km

Cavan CN2

Maureen Willock
MANOR HOUSE
Drumanespic P.O.
Bailieboro, Co Cavan

Tel: 042-9665101/9666680 Fax: –

Open: All year round

	No Rooms:	4	Triple:	–
	Twin/Double:	4	Family:	–
	Single:	–	En suite:	4

		HBW ES:		S.Supp: - -	Dinner: - -
B&B:	- -				
B&B ES: £20	€25.39	3 day HB:	-	CSP: - -	High Tea: -
HBW:	- -	3 day HB ES:			

Beautiful renovated 18th century farmhouse while maintaining the historic character of the house and grounds. Quiet scenic countryside on R165. Friendly and comfortable. Private car park. 6 km from Bailieborough and 20 km from Cavan town. Disabled facilities.

VOUCHERS ACCEPTED

BELTURBET 5 km | Cavan CN3

Mrs Catherine Smith
FORTVIEW HOUSE
Drumbran, Cloverhill
Belturbet, Co Cavan

Tel: 049-4338185   Fax: 049-4338834
Open: All year

No Rooms:	6	Triple:	4
Twin/Double:	2	Family:	–
Single:	–	En suite:	3

B&B:	£18	€ 22.85	HBW ES:	£196	€ 248.87	S.Supp: £6.50 € 8.25	Dinner: £14	€ 17.78
B&B ES:	£20	€ 25.39	3 day HB:	-	-	CSP:	25%	High Tea:-	-
HBW:	£182	€ 231.09	3 day HB ES:	£88	€ 111.74		

A warm welcome with turf fire awaits you at our working farmhouse where fresh vegetables and dairy products are served. Course fishing on 365 lakes and 5 rivers. Bait stockist, cold room, log book, fishing videos and courier escorted fishing tours. Expert angling guide available. Pub, pool room, entertainment 300 yards away. 3 km off N54 at Cloverhill. Mobile: 0872776358. Email:fortviewhouse@hotmail.com

---

COOTEHILL 1.5 km | Cavan CN4

Mrs Marion Fay
CABRAGH HOUSE
Cavan Road
Cootehill, Co Cavan

Tel: 049-5552153   Fax: 049-5552156
Open: 1st May – 31st October   OBA

No Rooms:	5	Triple:	1
Twin/Double:	4	Family:	–
Single:	-	En suite:	2

B&B:	£19	€ 24.13	HBW ES:	-	-	S.Supp: £6.50 € 8.25	Dinner:	-
B&B ES:	£21	€ 26.66	3 day HB:	-	-	CSP:	20%	High Tea:-	-
HBW:	-	-	3 day HB ES:	-	-		

Pleasant 18th century farmhouse, set in scenic surroundings on Cavan/Cootehill road. 1.5 km from Cootehill. Unrivalled angling facilities with numerous lakes and rivers. Bait stockist, boats for hire. Equestrian centres, golf and driving range locally. Walking and cycling maps available. Bicycles for hire. Gym. Car parking. Garden for visitors use. Heritage/cultural centre 6km. Email: cabraghhouse@oceanfree.net.

COOTEHILL 1.5 km | Cavan CN5

Mrs Una Smith
RIVERSIDE FARMHOUSE
(off Cavan Road)
Cootehill, Co Cavan

Tel: 049-5552150/5559950   Fax:049-5559950
Open: 10th January – 20th December

AM
V
EC

No Rooms:	6	Triple:	1
Twin/Double:	3	Family:	1
Single:	1	En suite:	5

B&B:	£17	€ 21.59	HBW ES:	£200	€ 253.95	S.Supp: £6.50 € 8.25	Dinner: £12	€ 15.24
B&B ES:	£19	€ 24.13	3 day HB:	£85	€ 107.93	CSP:	20%	High Tea:£8	€ 10.16
HBW:	£180	€ 228.56	3 day HB ES:	£90	€ 114.28		

Victorian house overlooking the river Annalee. 1.5 km from Cootehill. Original plasterwork and fireplaces. A fisherman's paradise for coarse pike and trout, walking and cycling area, working Dairy farm. Golf 16 km. Horse riding. outdoor pursuit centre, art/culture/IT centre 3km and Pitch & Putt 5km. Swimming pool & Genealogy centre 24km. Entertainment and restaurant locally 24hr taxi. Email: unasmith@eircom.net

---

CAVAN 7 km | Cavan CN6

Bert & Iris Neill
LISNAMANDRA
Crossdoney
Co Cavan

Tel: 049-4337196   Fax: -
Open: Easter – 1st November   OBA

AM
V

No Rooms:	4	Triple:	–
Twin/Double:	2	Family:	2
Single:	–	En suite:	3

B&B:	£17	€ 21.58	HBW ES:	-	-	S.Supp:	-	Dinner:	-
B&B ES:	£19	€ 24.13	3 day HB:	-	-	CSP:	Negot.	High Tea:Variable	
HBW:	-	-	3 day HB ES:	-	-		

Spacious, centuries-old farmhouse with a warm, welcoming atmosphere where guests can relax & absorb tranquility & gentle charm of North Midlands. Dairy farm S.W. of Cavan, on R198 Forest Park. Equestrian and golf nearby. Ironing facilities, electric blankets, tea/coffee. hairdryers. Varied breakfast menu.

KILLESHANDRA 4 km | Cavan CN7

Mrs Geraldine O'Reilly
EONISH LODGE
Killeshandra
Co Cavan

Tel: 049-4334487	Fax: -	
Open: 1st January – 20th December		OBA
No Rooms: 4	Triple: 2
Twin/Double: 2	Family: –
Single: –	En suite: 4

B&B:	£20	€25.39	HBW ES:	£196	€248.86	S.Supp: £10 €12.70	Dinner: £15 €19.05
B&B ES: £20	€25.39		3 day HB:	-	-	CSP: 20%	High Tea:£10 €12.70
HBW:	-	-	3 day HB ES: £90	€114.28			

Eonish Lodge is set in the heart of the Lake District, overlooking Lough
Oughter, close to Killykeen Forest Park. rooms ensuite. Excellent home produced food and homely
atmosphere assured. Golf and horse riding locally. Ideal location for fishing, walking or relaxing in
peaceful surroundings. Entertainment in pubs in Killeshandra.

VOUCHERS ACCEPTED

MOUNT NUGENT 5 km | Cavan CN8

Ursula Liebe-Harkort
ROSS HOUSE
Mount Nugent
Co Cavan

Tel: 049-8540218	Fax: 049-8540218	
Open: Open all year		OBA
No Rooms: 6	Triple: -	AM V EC
Twin/Double: 1	Family: 5
Single: -	En suite: 6

B&B:	-	-	HBW ES:	-	-	S.Supp: £10 €12.70	Dinner: £14/20€17.78/25.39
B&B ES: £20/30	€25.39/38.01		3 day HB:	-	-	CSP: 30/75%	High Tea: £10/14 €12.7/17.78
HBW:	-	-	3 day HB ES: -				

Charming old manor house, neighbouring Ross Castle. Spacious rooms en-suite
with TV, telephone and tea making facilities, some with fireplace and conservatory. Base of Lough Sheelin
Equestrian centre with extensive trails along lake and mature forests, 30 fence-cross-country-course. Private
pier, boats, tennis court, sauna & jacuzzi. Email: rosshouse@eircom.net Website: welcome.to/rosshouse

Vouchers Not Accepted

Clare

Located between the majestic river Shannon
and the Atlantic ocean, Clare is famous for its
towering cliffs and sparkling beaches. The
heart-stopping beauty of the cliffs of Moher
and Ailwee Caves, and the natural wonder of
the Burren National Park are famed
world-wide. Music lovers come here in throngs
to delight in the best traditional music and
dance to be found anywhere.

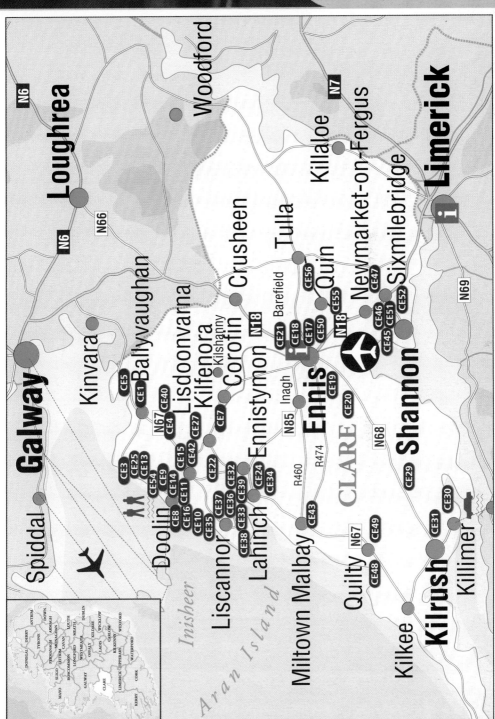

BALLYVAUGHAN 15 km   Clare CE25

Anne & Patrick Carrucan
ANNALY HOUSE
Fanore, Ballyvaughan,
Co Clare

Tel: 065-7076154   Fax: –
Open: 16th March – 16th October

	No Rooms:	3	Triple:	–
	Twin/Double:	3	Family:	–
	Single:	–	En suite:	1

AM V EC

B&B:	£17	€ 21.58	HBW ES:	£200	€ 253.95	S.Supp: £6.50 € 8.25	Dinner: £12 € 15.24
B&B ES: £19		€ 24.13	3 day HB:	–		CSP: 30%	High Tea: £10 € 12.70
HBW: £193		€ 245.06	3 day HB ES: £87		€ 110.47		

✗ ☒ ⛾ ♪ ∪ S ▣ ⚲

A working farm in the Burren on the scenic route R477 between Doolin and Ballyvaughan overlooking the Aran Islands, Galway Bay and Connemara. Ideal for walking, biking, fishing, surfing and pony trekking. Traditionl music played by family. Extensive breakfast menu. Guide du Routard and Michelin recommended Email: annalyhs@gofree.indigo.ie

---

BALLYVAUGHAN 1 km   Clare CE1

Mrs Mary Kyne
DOLMEN LODGE
Tonarussa
Ballyvaughan, Co Clare

Tel: 065-7077202   Fax: 065-7077202
Open: 17th March – 20th October

OBA

	No Rooms:	4	Triple:	–
	Twin/Double:	3	Family:	1
	Single:	–	En suite:	4

EC V AM

B&B:	-	HBW ES:	-	S.Supp: £6.50 € 8.25	Dinner: -
B&B ES: £20	€ 25.39	3 day HB:	-	CSP: 33.3%	High Tea: -
HBW: -		3 day HB ES: -			

🐾 ⛾ 🛋 ☕ ⚲ 🚲

Elegant farmhouse, scenic setting. Panoramic views of Galway Bay and Burren. Quiet, peaceful, 1 km from Ballyvaughan. Dillard/Causin recommended. Ideal for walking/cycling the Burren. Safe sandy beach 3km. Convenient to Cliffs of Moher and Aran Islands. Signposted on N67, Ballyvaughan/Galway road. Irish spoken. Garden for visitors use. "A lovely home in a beautiful place." Email: dolmenlodge@eircom.net

---

BALLYVAUGHAN 14 km   Clare CE3

Ita Linnane & Noel Walsh
ROCKY VIEW FARMHOUSE
Fanore, Ballyvaughan
Co Clare

Tel: 065-7076103   Fax: –
Open: 1st March – 30th November

OBA

	No Rooms:	6	Triple:	1
	Twin/Double:	3	Family:	1
	Single:	1	En suite:	6

EC V AM

B&B:	-	HBW ES:	-	S.Supp: £6.50 € 8.25	Dinner: £13 € 16.50
B&B ES: £19	€ 24.13	3 day HB:	-	CSP: 20%	High Tea: £9.50 € 12.06
HBW: -		3 day HB ES: £93	€ 118.09		

✗ S ∪ ⚲ ⚙ ⊘

Farmhouse situated in heart of Burren region. Burren Way Walks nearby, guided walking tours available on request. Superb view of Burren Hills and Galway Bay. Ideal base for walkers and nature enthusiasts. Traditional and vegetarian meals available. Breakfast menu. Dinner on Request. Non-smoking. Email: rockyview@tinet.ie

---

BALLYVAUGHAN 7 km   Clare CE4

Mrs Teresa McDonagh
ROCKHAVEN
Cahermacnaughton
Ballyvaughan, Co Clare

Tel: 065-7074454   Fax: –
Open: 1st April – 30th September

	No Rooms:	3	Triple:	–
	Twin/Double:	2	Family:	1
	Single:	–	En suite:	2

B&B:	£17	€ 21.58	HBW ES:	£190	€ 241.25	S.Supp: -	Dinner: £12 € 15.23
B&B ES: £19		€ 24.13	3 day HB:	£76	€ 96.50	CSP: 50%	High Tea: -
HBW: £180		€ 228.55	3 day HB ES: £86		€ 109.19		

✗ ▶ ⚲ ⛾ 🍴 ⚙ ∪ 📝

Modern spacious family run farmhouse in the Burren with scenic view, situated 1 km off N67, 7 km south of Ballyvaughan and 7 km north of Lisdoonvarna. Centrally located for visiting places of historical interest. Organic farm produce. Home baking. Tea/coffee on arrival. Recommended guide du Routard, Tom Lawton Walking Ireland.

BURREN 4 km — Clare CE5

Michael & Patricia Flaherty
BURREN OAKS
Oughtmama, Bellharbour
Co Clare

Tel: 065-7078043   Fax: 065-7078043
Open: 1st April – 30th September

No Rooms:	4	Triple:	–
Twin/Double:	3	Family:	1
Single:		En suite:	4

B&B:	-	HBW ES:	-	S.Supp: £6.50 €8.25	Dinner:	-
B&B ES: £19	€24.13	3 day HB:	-	CSP: 33.3%	High Tea:	-
HBW:	-	3 day HB ES: -				

Spacious farmhouse in the Burren. Located between Ballyvaughan and Kinvara off N67 at Bellharbour and Cocker Pass. Ideally situated for visiting Corcomroe Abbey, Coole Park, Aran Islands, Cliffs of Moher and Connemare. Convenient to beaches and restaurants. Medieval banquets in nearby Dunguaire Castle. Private car park. T.V. lounge. Tea/coffee on arrival.

COROFIN 3 km — Clare CE7

Mrs Betty Kelleher
INCHIQUIN VIEW
Kilnaboy, Corofin
Co Clare

Tel: 065-6837731   Fax: –
Open: April – 1st October

No Rooms:	4	Triple:	2
Twin/Double:	2	Family:	
Single:		En suite:	4

EC V

B&B: £19	€24.13	HBW ES: £260	€330.13	S.Supp: £8/10 €10.16/	Dinner: £19	€24.13
B&B ES: £22	€27.93	3 day HB: £110	€139.67	€12.70	High Tea:	
HBW: £230	€292.4	3 day HB ES: £115	€146.02	CSP:		

Spacious well-appointed farmhouse in impressive surroundings, beside the Burren National Park. Situated 2 miles north of Corofin on L53 road. Renowned fishing lakes, Burren walks and easy access to beaches and the attractions of Clare's Atlantic coast. Established reputation for good food in relaxing accommodation. AA listed. Email: bkellinchfmho@tinet.ie

---

DOOLIN 3 km — Clare CE8

Mrs Bridie Browne
BAY VIEW
Cliffs of Moher Road
Doonagore, Doolin, Co Clare

Tel: 065-7074325   Fax: –
Open: 1st April - 1st November

No Rooms:	3	Triple:	–
Twin/Double:	3	Family:	
Single:	–	En suite:	2

B&B: £17	€21.58	HBW ES:	-	S.Supp: £6.50 €8.25	Dinner: -
B&B ES: £19	€24.13	3 day HB:	-	CSP: 25%	High Tea: -
HBW:	-	3 day HB ES:	-		

Family run farmhouse. Panoramic view of Aran Islands, Galway Bay. Traditional music nightly in Doolin pubs. Touring base for Cliffs of Moher and the Burren. Boat trips to Aran Islands. Scenic cliff walks. Tea/coffee served on arrival. Orthopaedic beds/hair dryers in all rooms. Warm Irish hospitality.

DOOLIN 2 km — Clare CE9

Mrs Maria Canavan
ST CATHERINES
Doolin
Co Clare

Tel: 065-7074103   Fax: 065-7074103
Open: 1st March - 1st November

OBA
EC

No Rooms:	4	Triple:	–
Twin/Double:	4	Family:	
Single:	–	En suite:	4

B&B:	-	HBW ES:	-	S.Supp: £6.50 €8.25	Dinner: £15 €19.50
B&B ES: £19	€24.13	3 day HB:	-	CSP: 25%	High Tea: £10 €12.60
HBW:	-	3 day HB ES: -			

Family run rural farmhouse, set in tranquil surroundings. Ideal base for trips to Aran Islands, Cliffs of Moher and the Burren. Turf fires. Breakfast menu. Dinner on request. Music nightly in village pubs. Home baking. Warm welcome awaits you. Stay with us and relax with quiet walks through farm. Email: mcanavan@eircom.net

DOOLIN 3 km | Clare CE10

Mrs Margaret Carey
EMOHRUO
Cliffs of Moher Road
Luogh North, Doolin, Co Clare

Tel: 065-7074171   Fax: 065-7074171
Open: 1st March – 1st November

No Rooms:	4	Triple:	1
Twin/Double:	3	Family:	–
Single:	–	En suite:	3

OBA
AM V

			HBW ES:	-	-	S.Supp: £6.50 €8.25	Dinner: -	-
B&B:	£17	€21.58						
B&B ES:	£19	€24.13	3 day HB:	-	-	CSP: 25%	High Tea:-	
HBW:			3 day HB ES: £55	€69.84				

Modern bungalow in scenic setting within walking distance of the Cliffs of Moher. Convenient to the Burren, Ailwee Cave, Boat Trips to Aran Islands. Traditional music locally. 1 hour drive – Shannon Airport and Killimer Car Ferry. Fishing, horse riding, pitch & putt. laundry service locally. Marian Reisefurther recommended. Email: mgtcarey@eircom.net.

DOOLIN 2 km | Clare CE54

Mrs Josephine Clarke
BRIDGE HOUSE
Gortaclob, Doolin,
Co Clare

Tel: 065-7074534   Fax: -
Open: 1st March - 30th November

No Rooms:	3	Triple:	–
Twin/Double:	3	Family:	–
Single:	–	En suite:	3

EC

			HBW ES:	-	-	S.Supp: £6.50 €8.25	Dinner: £15	€19.50
B&B:	-	-						
B&B ES:	£19	€24.13	3 day HB:	-	-	CSP: -	High Tea:-	
HBW:	-	-	3 day HB ES: -					

Comfortable family home. Ideal for touring Burren, Aran Island & Cliffs of Moher. Home baking, turf fires, refreshments on arrival. Breakfast menu. Dinner on request. Music in all pubs locally.

DOOLIN 2 km | Clare CE11

Mrs Mary Fitzgerald
RIVERDALE FARM
Gortaclob
Doolin, Co Clare

Tel: 065-7074257   Fax: –
Open: 1st March – 1st November

No Rooms:	4	Triple:	–
Twin/Double:	4	Family:	–
Single:	–	En suite:	2

OBA
EC

			HBW ES:	-	-	S.Supp: £6.50 €8.25	Dinner: £15	€19.04
B&B:	£17	€21.58						
B&B ES:	£19	€24.13	3 day HB:	-	-	CSP: 25%	High Tea:-	
HBW:	-	-	3 day HB ES: -					

Comfortable 4th generation family home. Suitable base for touring Clare, the Burren, Cliffs of Moher, Ailwee Caves. Boat trips to Aran Islands. Traditional music in Doolin. Turf fires, breakfast menu, refreshments on arrival. A warm welcome awaits you.

DOOLIN 5 km | Clare CE13

The Linnane Family
FERNHILL FARM
Doolin, Lisdoonvarna
Co Clare

Tel: 065-7074040   Fax: 065-7074040
Open: 1st March – 30st November

No Rooms:	6	Triple:	1
Twin/Double:	4	Family:	1
Single:	-	En suite:	6

OBA
EC

			HBW ES:	-	-	S.Supp: £6.50 €8.25	Dinner: £16	€20.33
B&B:	£19	€24.13						
B&B ES:	£22	€27.93	3 day HB:	-	-	CSP: 15%	High Tea: £12	€15.25
HBW:	-	-	3 day HB ES: -					

Fernhill is a luxurious house on a working farm, adjacent to Doolin and the famous spa town and health centre. Situated close to the cliffs of Moher and the Burren region, it has won several awards and is highly recommended by travel writers and TV personnel. All meals served on request.

DOOLIN

Clare CE14

Mr & Mrs Pat O'Connor
O'CONNORS FARMHOUSE
Doolin
Co Clare

Tel: 065-7074314		Fax: 065-7074498	
Open: 1st February – 30th November			
No Rooms:	4	Triple:	1
Twin/Double:	2	Family:	1
Single:	–	En suite:	4

AM / V / EC

B&B:	-	HBW ES:	-	S.Supp: £6.50 €8.25	Dinner: -	-
B&B ES: £20	€25.39	3 day HB:	-	CSP: 50%	High Tea: -	-
HBW:	-	3 day HB ES: -				

Modern farmhouse situated in the heart of Doolin, within 5 minutes stroll from traditional pubs, shops and restaurants. Homebaking. Tea/coffee facilities. Breakfast menu, laundry. Recommended La Guide du Routard Ireland, Golden Thought Tourism Award Winners. ITB approved. Riverside caravan and camping within the farm grounds.

VOUCHERS ACCEPTED

DOOLIN

Clare CE15

Mrs Mary O'Donoghue
ASHLING FARMHOUSE
Road Ford
Doolin, Co Clare

Tel: 065-7074342		Fax: 065-7074342	
Open: 1st January – 31st December			OBA
No Rooms:	3	Triple:	–
Twin/Double:	2	Family:	1
Single:	–	En suite:	2

AM / V / EC

B&B: £17	€21.58	HBW ES:	-	S.Supp: £7 €8.88	Dinner: -	-
B&B ES: £19	€24.13	3 day HB:	-	CSP: 30%	High Tea: -	-
HBW:	-	3 day HB ES: -				

Situated in the centre of Doolin, pitch & putt course nearby. Ideal base for touring the Burren, Cliffs of Moher. Home baking, tea/coffee on arrival. Irish music in local pubs. Pets allowed. Breakfast menu.

VOUCHERS ACCEPTED

DOOLIN 3 km

Clare CE16

Patrick & Mary Sweeney
DOONAGORE FARMHOUSE
Cliffs of Moher Road
Doonagore, Doolin, Co Clare

Tel: 065-7074170		Fax: 065-7074170	
Open: 1st January – 31st December			
No Rooms:	4	Triple:	–
Twin/Double:	4	Family:	–
Single:	–	En suite:	4

AM / V

B&B:	-	HBW ES:	-	S.Supp: £6.50 €8.25	Dinner: -	-
B&B ES: £19	€24.13	3 day HB:	-	CSP: Negot.	High Tea: -	-
HBW:	-	3 day HB ES: -				

Three generation family run farmhouse, overlooking the Aran Islands. Walking distance from Cliffs of Moher. Touring base for the Burren, Ailwee Caves, daily boat trips to the Aran Islands. Traditional music nightly in Doolin pubs. Shannon Airport, Killimer Car Ferry one hour. Horse riding, Lahinch Golf Course, Pitch & Putt locally. A warm Irish welcome awaits you.

VOUCHERS ACCEPTED

ENNIS 1 km

Clare CE17

Mrs B. Barron & Family
NEWPARK HOUSE
Tulla Road
Ennis, Co Clare

Tel: 065-6821233		Fax: –	
Open: Easter – 31st October			OBA
No Rooms:	6	Triple:	4
Twin/Double:	1	Family:	1
Single:	–	En suite:	6

EC

B&B:	-	HBW ES:	-	S.Supp: £10 €12.70	Dinner: £17.50 €22.22
B&B ES: £25/30	€31.74/38.09	3 day HB:	-	CSP:	High Tea: -	-
HBW:	-	3 day HB ES: -				

Come and stay in one of Ireland's oldest houses of historic interest (1650). Woodland setting, large comfortable rooms with modern facilities, furnished with antiques, some canopy beds. Good food and homebaking. Convenient to Shannon, Bunratty, Knappogue, Cliffs of Moher and Lakelands, Ennis 2 km turn off R352 opposite Roselevan Arms. Email: newparkhouse.ennis@eircom.net

VOUCHERS ACCEPTED

ENNIS 8 km   Clare CE21

Thomas & Anne O'Halloran
ELMDALE
Barefield
Ennis, Co Clare

Tel: 065-6827151	Fax: 065-6827151	
Open: 30th March – 30th November		OBA

No Rooms:	5	Triple:	1
Twin/Double:	1	Family:	2
Single:	1	En suite:	3

B&B:	£19/20	€24.13/25.39	HBW ES:	-	-	S.Supp: £7	€8.89	Dinner: £15	€19
B&B ES: £21/22	€26.67/27.93	3 day HB:	£96	€122	CSP:	33%	High Tea:£11.50 €15
HBW:	-	-	3 day HB ES: £96	€122			

Experience Irish hospitality at its best at Elmdale, on 120 acre's with impressive surroundings and convenience to Castles, Burren, Atlantic coast, Golf course's, angling & Shannon airport. Resident harpist and Irish step dancing in home. Home cooking available daily. Delightful welcome awaits you here. Email: itselmdale@hotmail.com

VOUCHERS ACCEPTED

ENNIS 7 km   Clare CE18

Anne & Martin McLoughlin & Family
BURREN CRAG
Barefield
Ennis, Co Clare

Tel: 065-6827267	Fax: 065-6827267	
Open: 1st January – 20th December		EC

No Rooms:	4	Triple:	1
Twin/Double:	2	Family:	1
Single:	—	En suite:	4

B&B:	-	-	HBW ES:	£210	€266.64	S.Supp: £6.50	€8.25	Dinner: £17	€21.59
B&B ES: £19/20	€24.13/25.39	3 day HB:	-	-	CSP:	33.3%	High Tea: £10	€12.70
HBW:	-	-	3 day HB ES: £100	€126.97			

Warm Irish welcome with refreshments to our refurbished farmhouse on N18 north of Ennis. Relax in our spacious garden. Children's pony, cattle, farmyard, fowl & rabbit. Local traditional music, golf, fishing and boat hire arranged. Check out our special weekly family rates. Self-catering accommodation on grounds. Email: burrencrag@esatclear.ie Website: http://www.iolfree.ie/burrencrag.farmhouse

VOUCHERS ACCEPTED

ENNIS 3 km   Clare CE19

Mrs Maureen Moran
EDEN HILL HOUSE
Kilmorane, Kilrush Road (N68)
Ennis, Co Clare

Tel: 065-6824285	Fax: –	
Open: 1st February – 1st December		

No Rooms:	4	Triple:	1
Twin/Double:	2	Family:	1
Single:	—	En suite:	4

B&B:	-	-	HBW ES:	-	-	S.Supp: £6.50 €8.25	Dinner: -	-
B&B ES: £19	€24.13	3 day HB:	-	-	CSP:	50%	High Tea: -
HBW:	-	-	3 day HB ES: -	-			

Luxury farmhouse in peaceful rural setting, 3 km from Ennis town. Less than 30 minutes drive to Shannon Airport, the Cliffs of Moher and castles. Horses and cattle on farm. Home baking and breakfast menu. Large bedrooms with TV.

VOUCHERS ACCEPTED

ENNIS 8 km   Clare CE20

Marian & Pat Nolan
HAWTHORNS
Bansha, Darragh
Kilrush Road, Ennis, Co Clare

Tel: 065-6838221	Fax: –	
Open: 1st March – 30th November		EC

No Rooms:	3	Triple:	—
Twin/Double:	2	Family:	1
Single:	—	En suite:	3

B&B:	-	-	HBW ES:	-	-	S.Supp: £6.50 €8.25	Dinner: -	-
B&B ES: £19	€24.13	3 day HB:	-	-	CSP:	50%	High Tea: -
HBW:	-	-	3 day HB ES: -	-			

Modern bungalow on car ferry road N68. Breakfast menu. Airport 30 minutes. Convenient cliffs, caves, banquets, golf, angling, horse riding, traditional music locally. Spacious gardens. Open peat fires. Warm welcome. Suckler herd on farm. Taxi Service arranged. Mobile: 088-2730526.

VOUCHERS ACCEPTED

ENNISTYMON 6 km — Clare CE22

Mrs Eileen Carroll
TULLAMORE FARMHOUSE
Kilshanny, Ennistymon
Co Clare

Tel: 065-7071187   Fax: 065-7072023
Open: 1st March – 31st October

V EC AM

No Rooms:	5	Triple:	1
Twin/Double:	2	Family:	1
Single:	1	En suite:	4

B&B:	£19	€24.13	HBW ES:	-	-	S.Supp: £6.50 €8.25	Dinner:	-	-
B&B ES: £20		€25	3 day HB:	-	-	CSP: -	High Tea:	-	
HBW:	-	-	3 day HB ES:	-					

Elegant refurbished farmhouse, located on a beautiful scenic setting overlooking
Lahinch Golf Links and countryside. Signposted on Cliffs of Moher Road, also on Ennistymon - Lisdoonvarna Road.
Trout fishing in river flowing through farm. Irish music, swimming. Established reputation for fine food. Winner of
Galtee Breakfast Award and BHS Award. Email: info@tullamorefarm.com Website: www.tullamorefarm.com

S ⚓ U ☕ 🍴 ✕

ENNISTYMON 1.5 km — Clare CE24

Houlihan Family
HILL BROOK FARM
Lahinch Road
Ennistymon, Co Clare

Tel: 065-7071164   Fax: -
Open: 16th March - 31st October

OBA AM EC V

No Rooms:	4	Triple:	–
Twin/Double:	3	Family:	1
Single:	–	En suite:	4

B&B:	-		HBW ES:	-	-	S.Supp: £6.50 €8.25	Dinner:	-	-
B&B ES: £19/20	€24.13/25.39	3 day HB:	-	-	CSP: 33.3%	High Tea:	-	
HBW:	-	-	3 day HB ES:	-					

Spacious comfortable farmhouse on elevated site with lovely view of
countryside and the Inagh River. Situated on the N67 approx. 100 metres off road. Family run farm
close to Lahinch, Cliffs of Moher, the Burren, Aran Islands and Bunratty. Restaurants, golf and beach
nearby. Email: hillbrookfarm@eircom.net Website: www.hillbrookfarm.com

⚓ ☕ ♿ 🍴 ✓ ⊗ 👓 TV

KILFENORA 4 km — Clare CE27

Mrs Eileen O'Brien
LAKESIDE LODGE
Lickeen
Kilfenora Co Clare

Tel: 065-7071710   Fax: 065-7071182
Open: 17th March - 31st October

OBA AM V EC

No Rooms:	4	Triple:	–
Twin/Double:	4	Family:	–
Single:	–	En suite:	3

B&B:	£17	€21.58	HBW ES:	£220	€279.34	S.Supp: £6.50 €8.25	Dinner: £14	€17.77
B&B ES: £19	€24.13	3 day HB:	£93	€118.09	CSP: 30%	High Tea: £10	€12.70
HBW: £200	€253.94	3 day HB ES: £93	€118.09				

A warm friendly welcome awaits you at Lickeen, famous trout lake.
Convenient for touring the Burren, Aran Islands, Cliffs of Moher and Doolin. Signposted from Kilfenora
village and from the N67 between Ennistymon and Lisdoonvarna. Traditional music and dancing in
Kilfenora. Family interests include the Burren, fishing, walks, cooking. Email: lakesidelodge@eircom.net

✕ ⚓ 🎣 🖥 🍴 👓 S

KILLIMER 5 km — Clare CE29

Mrs Carmel Kelly
WOODLANDS FARM
Drumdigus, Kilmurray McMahon
Kilrush, Co Clare

Tel: 065-9053033   Fax: –
Open: 1st April – 31st October

No Rooms:	3	Triple:	1
Twin/Double:	1	Family:	–
Single:	1	En suite:	2

B&B:	£17	€21.58	HBW ES:	£184	€233.63	S.Supp: £6.50 €8.25	Dinner:	-	-
B&B ES: £19	€24.13	3 day HB:	£75	€95.23	CSP: 30%	High Tea: £9	€11.43
HBW: £170	€215.85	3 day HB ES: £81	€102.85				

Woodlands Farm is a modern spacious bungalow situated in woodland
surroundings, visitors welcome on dairy farm. 10 minutes drive to Shannon Car Ferry. Traditional
Music nightly on request. Home made brown bread served each morning with breakfast. Beautiful
tarmacadam tennis court. TV in rooms.

✕ 👓 🖥 S ⚓ ☕ TV

KILRUSH 5 km | Clare CE30

Seán & Bríd Cunningham
FORTFIELD FARM
Donail
Killimer/Kilrush, Co Clare

Tel: 065-9052533/51457   Fax: 065-9052908
Open: 1st March - 1st November

No Rooms:	5	Triple:	–
Twin/Double:	3	Family:	2
Single:	–	En suite:	3

AE AM V

B&B:	£17	€21.58	HBW ES:	-	S.Supp: £6.50 €8.25	Dinner:	-	-
B&B ES:	£19	€24.13	3 day HB:	-	CSP:	30%	High Tea:£7	€8.88
HBW:	-		3 day HB ES:	-				

Modern spacious Mansard residence. Regional Award winning family farm 1999. Tranquil elevated site with panoramic views. Relax in our conservatory, with tea & scones on arrival, or in our spacious garden. Working dairy farm incorporating visitor pet farm with Llamas, Wallabies, Rheas & Swans etc. Family traditional music only on request. Located 1km off Killimer ferry/Kilrush N67 road (signposted) for ferry passengers; Killimer car ferry 3 mins drive. Ennis-Kilrush N68 road 3km. Direct dial from bedrooms. Seaside, music & excellent restaurant locally. Email: fortfield@eircom.net

VOUCHERS ACCEPTED

KILRUSH 6 km | Clare CE31

Mrs. Maureen Troy
KNOCKERRA HOUSE
Knockerra
Kilrush, Co Clare

Tel: 065-9051054   Fax: –
Open: 1st April - 30th September

No Rooms:	3	Triple:	–
Twin/Double:	2	Family:	1
Single:	–	En suite:	3

B&B:	-		HBW ES:	-	S.Supp: £6.50 €8.25	Dinner:	-	-
B&B ES:	£25	€31.74	3 day HB:	-	CSP:	25%	High Tea:£10	€12.70
HBW:	-		3 day HB ES:	-				

Georgian style manor, situated on extensive private grounds in tranquil, peaceful setting with gardens for visitors, Ideal stop off – Galway-Kerry or vice versa. 3 km off N67. 7 minutes drive from Killimer Car Ferry. 1 km off N68.

VOUCHERS ACCEPTED

LAHINCH 2 km | Clare CE32

John & Mary Lucas
SANDFIELD LODGE
Lahinch
Liscannor, Co Clare

Tel: 065-7081010   Fax: –
Open: Easter – September 30th

OBA
V
AM

No Rooms:	4	Triple:	–
Twin/Double:	4	Family:	–
Single:	–	En suite:	4

B&B:	-		HBW ES:	-	S.Supp: £6.50 €8.25	Dinner:	-
B&B ES:	£19	€21.58	3 day HB:	-	CSP:	High Tea:	-
HBW:	-		3 day HB ES:	-			

Charming 300 year old former hunting lodge. 5th generation family home, 0.6 km off main coast road, nestling on elevated wooded site with avenue of mature trees overlooking Liscannor Bay and Lahinch golf links. Mixed working farm, open log fires, home baking, posturepaedic beds, antique furnishings. Central to Cliffs of Moher, Burren, Doolin, Aran Islands. Sandy beaches. Shore angling. Email: sandfield@eircom.net

VOUCHERS ACCEPTED

LAHINCH 1.5 km | Clare CE33

Eamonn & Ann Slattery
SANDFIELD HOUSE
Liscannor
Co Clare

Tel: 065-7081603   Fax: 065-7081619
Open: 1st May – 1st October

OBA

No Rooms:	3	Triple:	–
Twin/Double:	3	Family:	–
Single:	–	En suite:	3

B&B:	-		HBW ES:	-	S.Supp: £8 €10.16	Dinner:	- -
B&B ES:	£20/25	€25.39/31.74	3 day HB:	-	CSP:	High Tea:	- -
HBW:	-		3 day HB ES:	-			

Sandfield House is an elegant Georgian residence just off main N67 Lahinch to Cliffs of Moher Road. Overlooking Liscannor Bay and Lahinch Golf Links. It stands amid a working suckling and sheep farm with its own links pitch & putt course. Enjoy pony trekking, horse riding, golf and sea fishing. Central to Cliffs of Moher, Doolin, Aran Islands, Burren & Ailwee caves. 3 bedrooms en suite individually decorated incorporating many antiques. Email: sandfieldhouse@esatclear.ie

Vouchers Not Accepted

LAHINCH 0.5km — Clare CE34

Mary Shannon
CLOVERFIELD
Station Road
Lahinch, Co. Clare

Tel: 065-7081170 Fax: -
Open: 1st May - 30th September

No Rooms:	4	Triple:	2
Twin/Double:	2	Family:	-
Single:		En suite:	4

B&B:	-	-	HBW ES:	-	-	S.Supp: £6.50 €8.25	Dinner: -	-
B&B ES: £19	€24.13	3 day HB:	-	-	CSP: 50%	High Tea: -	
HBW:	-	3 day HB ES: -					

Comfortable and friendly farmhouse with scenic view on a working dairy farm. Walking distance (0.5km) from Lahinch Village, sandy beach, restaurants and world famous golf course. Ideal base for touring Cliffs of Moher, Burren, Doolin, Aran Islands and Bunratty. Email: cloverfieldbnb@hotmail.com

---

LISCANNOR 3km / Cliffs of Moher 1 km — Clare CE35

Mrs Mary Considine
MOHER LODGE FARMHOUSE
Cliffs of Moher
Liscannor, Co Clare

Tel: 065-7081269 Fax: 065-7081589
Open: 1st April – 1st November

No Rooms:	4	Triple:	2
Twin/Double:	2	Family:	-
Single:		En suite:	4

EC

B&B:	-	-	HBW ES:	-	-	S.Supp: £6.50 €8.25	Dinner: -	-
B&B ES: £20/22	€25.39/27.93	3 day HB:	-	-	CSP: -	High Tea: -	
HBW:	-	3 day HB ES: -					

Moher Lodge is superbly situated, 1 km from Cliffs of Moher on R478. 3 km from Liscannor. Beautiful views of sea and countryside. Mixed working farm. Peat fires. Breakfast menu. Touring base for Cliffs of Moher, Aran Islands, Burren, Doolin, Limerick and Galway. Travel Writers recommended. Shannon Airport and Killimer Car Ferry 1 hour drive. Email: moherlodge@eircom.net

---

LISCANNOR 2 km — Clare CE36

John & Geraldine Greene
ARD NA MARA FARMHOUSE
Loughloon
Liscannor, Co Clare

Tel: 065-7081387 Fax: 065-7081387
Open: 1st April – 1st October

OBA
V

No Rooms:	3	Triple:	1
Twin/Double:	2	Family:	-
Single:		En suite:	3

B&B: £17	€21.58	HBW ES:	-	-	S.Supp: £7 €8.89	Dinner: -	-
B&B ES: £19	€24.13	3 day HB:	-	-	CSP: 25%	High Tea: -	
HBW:	-	3 day HB ES: -					

Modern farmhouse overlooking Lahinch & Liscannor Bay. Some bedrooms with sea view. Convenient to the Cliffs of Moher, Burren, Doolin, Aran Islands and Lahinch Sea World. French/Irish languages spoken. Breakfast menu. Recommended in Le Guide du Routard & Reisen.

LISCANNOR 3 km — Clare CE37

Kathleen & Tom O'Connor
BAY VIEW FARMHOUSE
Loughloon
Liscannor, Co Clare

Tel: 065-7081523 Fax: –
Open: 1st April - 15th October

No Rooms:	4	Triple:	1
Twin/Double:	2	Family:	1
Single:	–	En suite:	3

B&B: £17	€21.58	HBW ES:	-	-	S.Supp: £6.50 €8.25	Dinner: -	-
B&B ES: £19	€24.13	3 day HB:	-	-	CSP: 25%	High Tea: £10 €12.97
HBW:	-	3 day HB ES: -					

Bayview Farmhouse is superbly situated with exhilarating views of Lahinch and Liscannor Bay and surrounding countryside. Golf course and sandy beach. Excellent home produced food and homely atmosphere assured. Broad range of outdoor pursuits in area. Central to Cliffs of Moher, Burren, Doolin, Bunratty, Lahinch Sea World, Aran Islands.

LISCANNOR 2 km — Clare CE38

Mrs. Patsy O' Connor	Tel: 065-7081590	Fax: –	
CASTLEVIEW	Open: 1st April - 15th October		AM
Cliffs of Moher Road	No Rooms: 5	Triple: –	V
Clahane, Liscannor, Co Clare	Twin/Double: 3	Family: 2	EC
	Single: –	En suite: 5	

B&B: -	-	HBW ES: -	-	S.Supp: £7.50 €9.52	Dinner: -	-
B&B ES: £19	€24.13	3 day HB: -	-	CSP: 50%	High Tea: -	
HBW: -	-	3 day HB ES: -				

✗ ⊠ S ⓶ ⌧ ▶.

Modern spacious family run farmhouse situated in quiet scenic countryside overlooking Clahane Beach. Convenient to Burren Way walks, Cliffs of Moher, Burren, restaurants, golf, pitch & putt. Lahinch Water World. Le Guide de Routard Ireland recommended. Home baking, peat fires, breakfast menu. Tea/coffee making facilities. Email: castleviewfarmhouse@tinet.ie

---

LISCANNOR 2 km — Clare CE39

Bridget O'Gorman & Family	Tel: 065-7081039	Fax: 065-7081039	
HARBOUR SUNSET	Open: 15th May-15th September		OBA
FARMHOUSE, Rannagh	No Rooms: 3	Triple: –	AM
Liscannor, Co Clare	Twin/Double: 2	Family: 1	V
	Single: –	En suite: 3	EC

B&B: £20	€25.39	HBW ES: £270	€342.82	S.Supp: £6.50 €8.25	Dinner: £18	€22.85
B&B ES: £22	€27.93	3 day HB: £110	€139.67	CSP: 25%	High Tea: £10	€12.69
HBW: £250	€317.43	3 day HB ES: £115	€146.01			

✗ ⊠ S ⓶ ⌧ ❄ ⚙ ✓ ▶.

200 year old restored farmhouse in tranquil surroundings set on 86 acre dairy farm with friendly pet animals. 1 km off Cliffs of Moher Road. Panoramic view of golf course and beach. Award winning family play Irish music around peat fire. On parle Français. Home baking. Hair dryers. Irish crochet. Colourful garden. Putting green. Base for Cliffs of Moher, Doolin, Burren, Aran Islands. Recommended Frommers. Airport 45 minutes. Email: harbsunfarmhse@eircom.net

---

LISDOONVARNA 6 km — Clare CE40

Mrs Bríd Casey	Tel: 065-7074059	Fax: 065-7074457	
BENRUE FARMHOUSE	Open: 1st April – 30th November		OBA
Lisdoonvarna	No Rooms: 6	Triple: 1	EC
Co Clare	Twin/Double: 2	Family: 1	V
	Single: 2	En suite: 4	AM

B&B: £17	€21.58	HBW ES: -	-	S.Supp: £6.50 €8.25	Dinner: -
B&B ES: £19	€24.13	3 day HB: -	-	CSP: 50%	High Tea: -
HBW: -	-	3 day HB ES: -			

∪ ▶. ❄ å ↝ ⏚ BD S

Warm & welcoming family home in quiet scenic area. Explore limestone pavements, flora /fauna & stone fort on our farm in the heart of the Burren. House located 6 km from Lisdoonvarna, 12 km from Ballyvaughan off N67. Convenient to Cliffs of Moher, Aillwee Caves, beaches, Spa Wells, Burren Centre, Aran Islands. Guide du Routard, Tom Lawton Walking Ireland & Ramblers Guide recommended. Extensive breakfast menu. Tea/coffee & scones on arrival. Email: benrue@eircom.net

---

LISDOONVARNA 2 km — Clare CE42

Teresa Donnellan	Tel: 065-7074318	Fax: 065-7074318	
SLIEVE ELVA	Open: All Year		EC
Kilmoon	No Rooms: 6	Triple: 1	AM
Lisdoonvarna, Co Clare	Twin/Double: 2	Family: 2	V
	Single: 1	En suite: 4	

B&B: £17.50	€22.22	HBW ES: -	-	S.Supp: £6.50 €8.25	Dinner: £15.50	€19.68
B&B ES: £19	€24.13	3 day HB: -	-	CSP: 50%	High Tea: -	
HBW: -	-	3 day HB ES: £101	€128			

⚲ ∪ ☎ å ▶. ✓ ⌧ ❄

Comfortable spacious farmhouse in the Burren region. Located 2 km north of Lisdoonvarna. Scenic country walks, close to the Burren Way Walking Route with maps provided. Excellent cuisine, open turf fires, extensive breakfast menu. Refreshments served on arrival. Ideal base for touring the Cliffs of Moher, Burren and Aran Islands. Recommended in Guide du Routard, New York Times and BHS Regional Winner. Email: slieveelva@tinet.ie Website: http://tinet.ie/~slieveelva/

MILTOWN MALBAY 3 km   Clare CE43

Ms Rita Meade
BERRY LODGE
Annagh
Miltown Malbay, Co Clare

Tel: 065-7087022	Fax: 065-7087011	
Open: 14th February – 6th January		OBA
No Rooms: 5	Triple: –	
Twin/Double: 5	Family: –	
Single: –	En suite: 5	

B&B: -	-	HBW ES: -	-	S.Supp: £10	€ 12.70	Dinner: £24	€ 30.47	
B&B ES: £22/25	€ 27.93/31.74	3 day HB: -	-	CSP: -		High Tea:-	-	
HBW: -	-	3 day HB ES: £130	€ 165.08					

✗ 🖵 ♀ 🖼 ⚙ ▸ B D

Berry Lodge is a recently renovated Victorian Country House overlooking the sea. This charming residence blends old world style with the comfort of today. The peaceful atmosphere is enhanced by excellent accommodation and superb food. Rita Meade teaches country cooking during the Autumn and Spring. "Hands On" cookery mornings with lunch can be arranged during season. Special breaks at Christmas and New Year. Recommended by Travellers & Diners guide. Email: rita.meade@esatclear.ie

VOUCHERS ACCEPTED

NEWMARKET-ON-FERGUS 1.5 km   Clare CE45

Mrs B. Conheady
BEECHGROVE FARMHOUSE
Knocknagun
Newmarket-on-Fergus, Co Clare

Tel: 061-368140	Fax: –	
Open: 1st April – 1st November		OBA
No Rooms: 4	Triple: –	
Twin/Double: 3	Family: 1	
Single: –	En suite: 2	

B&B: £17	€ 21.58	HBW: £210	€ 266.64	S.Supp: £7	€ 8.88	Dinner: £16	€ 20.31	
B&B ES: £19	€ 24.13	3 day HB: £95	€ 120.62	CSP: 50%		High Tea:£12	€ 15.23	
HBW: £200	€ 253.59	3 day HB ES: £100	€ 126.97					

✗ ✗ 🔥 🐟 🔟 S

Family run farmhouse on elevated site with magnificent view of River Fergus. 1km off Limerick-Ennis N18 road. Shannon Airport and Bunratty Castle 10 minutes drive. House set amid 120 acre working farm with cattle, sheep and horses. Dillard and Causin Guide recommended. Peaceful location.

VOUCHERS ACCEPTED

NEWMARKET-ON-FERGUS 5 km   Clare CE46

Mrs Mary McCormack
MOOGHAUN FARMHOUSE
Newmarket-on-Fergus
Co Clare

Tel: 065-6825786	Fax: 065-6825786	
Open: 1st April – 1st November		OBA
No Rooms: 4	Triple: -	
Twin/Double: 3	Family: -	
Single: 1	En suite: 3	

B&B: £17	€ 21.58	HBW ES: £200	€ 253.94	S.Supp: £7	€ 8.89	Dinner: £15	€ 19.05	
B&B ES: £19	€ 24.13	3 day HB: £90	€ 114.27	CSP: 33⅓%		High Tea:£10	€ 12.70	
HBW: -	-	3 day HB ES: £95	€ 120.62					

✗ 🔥 ✗ 🗡 🐴 U S

Traditional family farmhouse on working dairy farm situated in scenic countryside with relaxing walking trails through the farm. Close to Mooghaun Hillfort, Quin Abbey, Knappogue Castle, Craggaunowen Project, Bunratty Castle & Shannon Airport. 5km from Newmarket-on-Fergus. Tea/Coffee on arrival.

VOUCHERS ACCEPTED

NEWMARKET-ON-FERGUS 0.5 km   Clare CE47

Mrs Pauline O'Leary
WEAVERS LODGE
Newmarket-on-Fergus
Co Clare

Tel: 061-368348	Fax: –	
Open: 1st March – 15h November		
No Rooms: 3	Triple: –	
Twin/Double: 2	Family: 1	
Single: –	En suite: 2	

B&B: £17	€ 21.85	HBW ES: -	-	S.Supp: £6.50	€ 8.25	Dinner: -		
B&B ES: £19	€ 24.13	3 day HB: -	-	CSP: 50%		High Tea:£8	€ 10.16	
HBW: -	-	3 day HB ES: £100	€ 126.97					

S 🐟 U 🗡 ▸ ▸ ✓ 🔥

Modern farm bungalow 0.5 km off N18 in village of Newmarket-on-Fergus. Shannon Airport 15 minutes drive. Convenient to Bunratty, Knappogue and Dromoland Castles and Clare Inn Hotel. Riding, golf and fishing locally. Top class restaurants within 5minute walk. Credit cards accepted. Email: olearyfarm@eircom.net

VOUCHERS ACCEPTED

QUILTY 3 km — Clare CE48

John & Máire Daly
CLONMORE LODGE
Quilty
Co Clare

Tel: 065-7087020 Fax: 065-7087270
Open: 1st March – 4th November

No Rooms:	6	Triple:	–
Twin/Double:	4	Family:	2
Single:	–	En suite:	6

AM / V / EC

B&B:	-	-	HBW ES:	£28/34	€ 35.85/41.93	S.Supp: £6.50	€ 8.25	Dinner: £12	€ 15.24
B&B ES: £19/22	€ 22.85/28	3 day HB:	-	-	CSP:	50%	High Tea: -	-
HBW:	-	-	3 day HB ES: £90	€ 114.28					

Working farm overlooking Atlantic off N67 one mile from sandy beach. Scenic walks, local pubs, pitch & putt, tennis, crazy golf and pony riding for childern. All rooms en suite with tv, tea/coffee. Ideal stop between Kilimer car ferry to Kerry from Galway, Cliffs of Moher, and Burren. Email: clonmorelodge@hotmail.com Website: www.visitwestclare.com

VOUCHERS ACCEPTED

QUILTY 4 km — Clare CE49

Theresa & Tim Donnellan
FIONNUAIRE
Mullagh
Quilty, Co Clare

Tel: 065-7087179 Fax: 065-7087179
Open: 1st June – 15th September

No Rooms:	4	Triple:	-
Twin/Double:	2	Family:	2
Single:	-	En suite:	4

AM / V / EC

B&B:	-	-	HBW ES:	£220	€ 279	S.Supp: £7	€ 9	Dinner: £15	€ 19.04
B&B ES: £20	€ 25.39	3 day HB:	-	-	CSP:	50%	High Tea: £10	€ 12.70
HBW:	-	-	3 day HB ES: £95	€ 120					

Working dairy farm, set in quiet countryside. Attractive farmhouse with sweeping views of rural/coastal landscape. The Donnellans entice you to experience life on a dairy farm. Farm pets and pony. Games/leisure room. Cycling, country walks and seaside strolls. Music in village pubs, within walking distance. Families welcome. Comfortable, relaxing. Guest participation in farm work. Mobile: 087-239 8236. Email: fionnuaire@eircom.net

VOUCHERS ACCEPTED

QUIN 6 km — Clare CE50

Mrs. Aida Enright-O'Brien
CASTLEFERGUS FARM
Quin
Co Clare

Tel: 065-6825914 Fax: 065-6825914
Open: 1st February - 1st December *OBA*

No Rooms:	3	Triple:	–
Twin/Double:	2	Family:	1
Single:	–	En suite:	3

B&B:	-	-	HBW ES:	£220	€ 279.34	S.Supp: £6.50	€ 8.25	Dinner: £16	€ 20.32
B&B ES: £19	€ 24.13	3 day HB:	-	-	CSP:	30%	High Tea: £10	€ 12.70
HBW:	-	-	3 day HB ES: £100	€ 126.97					

Charming 19th century farmhouse offering a high standard of accommodation situated in secluded grounds on a working farm with cows, sheep, horses and geese. Approved riding stables offering hunting and riding holidays. Trekking and riding instruction for beginners or competent riders by qualified instructor. Ideal touring base, convenient to Cliffs of Moher, Burren region, banquets at Bunratty and Knappogue Castles. Shannon Airport 15 mins.

VOUCHERS ACCEPTED

QUIN 1 km — Clare CE55

The Hannon Family
ARDSOLLUS FARM
Ardsollus, Quin, Ennis,
Co. Clare

Tel: 065-6825601 Fax: 065-6825959
Open: 1st May - 1st November *OBA*

No Rooms:	4	Triple:	–
Twin/Double:	4	Family:	
Single:	-	En suite:	2

V / AM

B&B:	£20	€ 26	HBW ES:	-	-	S.Supp: £7	€ 8.89	Dinner:	-
B&B ES: £25	€ 32	3 day HB:	-	-	CSP:	-	High Tea:	-
HBW:	-	-	3 day HB ES:	-				

A spacious Agri-Tourism Award Winning 300 year old Farmhouse on 120 acre working dairy farm, overlooking Dromoland Estate. Fifth generation family home. There are show jumping horses on farm. Shannon airport, Bunratty and Knappogue 15 minutes. One mile off N18. Turn at Clare Inn Hotel. Email: ardsollusfarm@ireland.com

Vouchers Not Accepted

SHANNON 5 km

Noreen & Michael McInerney
CAHERGAL FARM HOUSE
& RIDING CENTRE
Newmarket-on-Fergus
Co Clare

Tel: 061-368358   Fax: 061-368805
Open: 1st February – 1st December   OBA

No Rooms:	4	Triple:			
Twin/Double:	3	Family:	1		
Single:	–	En suite:	4		

B&B:	-	-	HBW ES:		-	S.Supp:	-	Dinner:	£18 €22.56
B&B ES: £20	€25.39	3 day HB:		-	CSP:	-	High Tea:£10	€12.69
HBW:	-	3 day HB ES:	-					

Luxury secluded Farmhouse in the centre of a national award winning farm offering
excellent standards of accommodation, emphasis on delicious home cooking & baking. Highly recommended in many
travel guides. Private registered Equestrian centre. Full size tennis court. Convenient to Dromoland, Bunratty &
Knapogue Castles. 10 mins drive from Shannon airport Email: cahergal@eircom.net Website: http://come.to/cahergal

SIXMILEBRIDGE 1 km

Veronica O'Dea
FORTWILLIAM
Sixmilebridge
Co Clare

Tel: 061-369216   Fax: -
Open: 1st May – 1st October

No Rooms:	4	Triple:	-		
Twin/Double:	3	Family:	1		
Single:	-	En suite:	-		

B&B:	-	HBW ES:		-	S.Supp:£6.50 €8.25	Dinner: £17 €21.58
B&B ES: £19	€24.13	3 day HB:		-	CSP:	-	High Tea:£11 €13.96
HBW: £210	€266.44	3 day HB ES: £100	€126.97				

Fortwilliam farmhouse is situated in lovely scenic area. Knapogue, Bunratty,
Craganowen are all within 4km. Comfortable lounge looking onto lovely gardens. Golf, pitch and putt locally.
Lovely country walks. Our farmhouse has got two awards for the best in our locality. Hospitality guaranteed.

TULLA 7 km

The Hoey Family
GORTEEN FARMHOUSE
Dangan, Tulla,
Co Clare

Tel: 065-6835140   Fax: -
Open: 1st April – End of October   OBA

No Rooms:	3	Triple:	-		
Twin/Double:	2	Family:	1		
Single:	-	En suite:	3		

B&B:	-	-	HBW ES:		S.Supp:£6.50 €8.25	Dinner: £15 €19.04
B&B ES: £20	€25.39	3 day HB:		-	CSP:	25%	High Tea:£10 €12.69
HBW:	-	3 day HB ES:	-				

Enjoy blissful peace and tranquillity in recently refurbished farmhouse on Beef and
Dairy farm. 3km North of Craggaunowen, off the R352. Home cooking, breakfast menu. Warm spacious
rooms. Farm walk. Local fishing. Central for visiting Bunratty, Knappogue, The Burren, Mountshannon, Killaloe.
40mins Shannon Airport. Email: mary_hoey@hotmail.com

Cork

The county offers a great diversity of cultural and leisure activities and is famous for its many festivals including: the Kinsale Gourmet Festival; the International Choral Festival; Bantry Mussel Fair; and the Cork Film and Jazz Festivals. Cork's rich heritage and varied landscapes make it a delight to explore. Don't miss famous Blarney Castle where visitors can kiss the Blarney Stone which bestows the 'gift of the gab'!

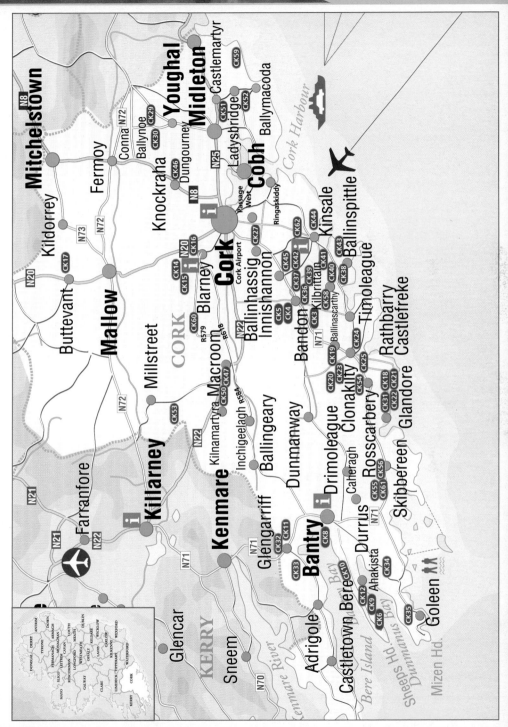

BANDON 5 km — Cork CK3

Mrs Kathleen Crowley
HILLCREST
Knockbrown, Bandon
Co Cork

Tel: 023-41488   Fax: –
Open: 1st June - 30th September

	No Rooms:	4	Triple:	-
	Twin/Double:	3	Family:	-
	Single:	1	En suite:	2

AM / V / EC

B&B: £17	€21.58	HBW ES:	-	-	S.Supp: £6.50 €8.25	Dinner: -	-
B&B ES: £19	€24.13	3 day HB:	-	-	CSP: 50%	High Tea: -	-
HBW: -	-	3 day HB ES: -	-				

Modern farmhouse in peaceful rural setting offering comfortable accommodation and home baking. Signposted at Oldchapel (1 km west of Bandon) on N71 Bandon-Clonakilty Road. Ideally suited to touring West Cork and Kerry. Horse riding, golf, fishing and sandy beaches all within 10 km. Convenient to Cork Airport and Ferryport. Taxi service arranged. TV in bedrooms.

BANDON 1 km — Cork CK4

O'Brien Family
OAKGROVE HOUSE
Kilbrogan, Bandon
Co Cork

Tel: 023-41962   Fax: 023-41962
Open: 6th January - 20th December

	No Rooms:	3	Triple:	–
	Twin/Double:	2	Family:	1
	Single:	–	En suite:	2

AM / V / EC

B&B: £17	€21.58	HBW ES:	-	-	S.Supp: £6.50 €8.25	Dinner: £13/16 €16.5/20.3
B&B ES: £19	€24.13	3 day HB:	-	-	CSP: 30%	High Tea: £12 €15.2
HBW: -	-	3 day HB ES: -	-			

Warm and welcoming family home in quite scenic area 1/4 mile from Bandon town. Signposted on R589 Bandon-Macroom Road. Convenient to airport and ferryport. Ideally situated for touring Cork and Kerry. Kinsale, Blarney and sandy beaches 20 minutes drive. Golf, pitch & putt, indoor swimming pool, fitness studio and facilities 3 minutes drive.

BANDON 4 km — Cork CK5

Frankie Perrott
ACORN LODGE
Littlesilver
Bandon, Co Cork

Tel: 023-41262   Fax: 023-43636
Open: 1st May - 20th September

OBA

	No Rooms:	3	Triple:	–
	Twin/Double:	2	Family:	1
	Single:	–	En suite:	3

AM / V

B&B: -		HBW ES:	-	-	S.Supp: £6.50 €8.25	Dinner: £16 €20.32
B&B ES: £20	€25.39	3 day HB:	-	-	CSP: 20%	High Tea: £10 €12.97
HBW: -	-	3 day HB ES: £100	€126.97			

Enjoy a peaceful stay at Acorn Lodge in beautiful countryside 4km from Bandon, off R590 (main Bandon Macroom Killarney Rd.) Ideal base for touring West Cork, Kerry, Cork City. Golfing in Bandon, fishing and sailing in Kinsale. Wooded walks, traditional music and dancing locally. Convenient to Cork airport and ferry port.

BANTRY 21 km — Cork CK6

Mrs Jennie Barry
REENMORE FARMHOUSE
Ahakista, Durrus
Bantry, Co Cork

Tel: 027-67051   Fax: –
Open: 1st April - 1st November

OBA

	No Rooms:	6	Triple:	–
	Twin/Double:	5	Family:	1
	Single:	–	En suite:	4

B&B: £17	€21.59	HBW ES:	-	-	S.Supp: £6.50 €8.25	Dinner: £14 €17.78
B&B ES: £19	€24.13	3 day HB:	-	-	CSP: 25%	High Tea: £12 €15.24
HBW: -	-	3 day HB ES: £97	€123.16			

Seaside traditional style farmhouse, 14 km west of Durrus, Sheep's Head Peninsula. 2 km west of Ahakista Village. Fourth generation home. Dairy and sheep farming. Home cooking. Fresh farm produce. Open fires. Complimentary refreshments. Le Guide du Routard recommended. Long distance walk. Swimming, fishing and boating locally. Email: jenniebarry@oceanfree.net

BANTRY 4 km   Cork CK8

Mrs Dympna Crowley
DROMCLOC HOUSE
Bantry
Co Cork

Tel: 027-50030   Fax: 027-50030
Open: 1st March - 1st November

No Rooms:	6	Triple:	2
Twin/Double:	4	Family:	–
Single:	–	En suite:	5

B&B:	£17	€21.59	HBW ES:	-	-	S.Supp: £7	€8.89	Dinner: £14	€17.78
B&B ES:	£19	€24.13	3 day HB:	-	-	CSP: 25%		High Tea: £10	€12.70
HBW:	-	-	3 day HB ES:	-	-				

Seaside dairy farm at Relane Point. Signposted 2km southwest of Bantry off N71 at Westlodge Hotel on Sheepshead Walk/Cycle route. Magnificent views, shingle beaches, shore fishing/farm walks, own boat, private tennis court, Irish music. Bantry House, swimming pool, bar 2km, horse riding 3km, golf 6km. Email: dromcloc@indigo.ie Website: www.cork-guide.ie/bantry/dromclochouse/welcome.html

BANTRY 19 km   Cork CK9

Mrs Agnes Hegarty
HILLCREST FARM
Ahakista, Durrus
Bantry, Co Cork

Tel: 027-67045   Fax: –
Open: 1st April - 1st November

No Rooms:	4	Triple:	1
Twin/Double:	2	Family:	1
Single:	–	En suite:	3

B&B:	£18	€22.86	HBW ES:	£224	€284.42	S.Supp: £6.50	€8.25	Dinner: £15	€19.05
B&B ES:	£20	€25.39	3 day HB:	£90	€114.28	CSP: 25%		High Tea: £12	€15.24
HBW:	£210	€266.64	3 day HB ES:	£96	€121.89				

Traditional style farmhouse, tastefully restored, on farm with superb views of sea and mountains. 11km west of Durrus on 'Sheeps Head Peninsula'. Ahakista Village 1 km. Short walk to beach, fishing, boating, pubs with Irish music on 'Sheep's Head Way', mature gardens, peat fires, games room, antiques. Tea/Coffee making in bedrooms, hairdryers, breakfast menu. Email: agneshegarty@oceanfree.net

BANTRY 12 km   Cork CK10

Mrs Julia McCarthy
SEA MOUNT FARMHOUSE
Goats Path Road, Glenlough West
Bantry, Co Cork

Tel: 027-61226   Fax: 027-61226
Open: 1st April - 10th october   EC

No Rooms:	6	Triple:	–
Twin/Double:	6	Family:	–
Single:	–	En suite:	6

B&B:	£17	€21.58	HBW ES:	£220	€279.34	S.Supp: £6.50	€8.25	Dinner: £14	€17.78
B&B ES:	£19	€24.13	3 day HB:	-	-	CSP: -		High Tea: £11	€13.97
HBW:	-	-	3 day HB ES:	£97	€123.17				

Scenically set with interesting garden restored 7 generation farmhouse. Magnificent views overlooking Bantry Bay, traditional stone farm buildings, historical/archaeological information. 12 km west of Bantry on 'Sheep's Head Peninsula' beautiful hill/sea walks. Complimentary tea/scones on arrival. Homely atmosphere, guaranteed home baking, electric blankets, hairdryers. Email: seamountfarmhouse1@eircom.net

BANTRY 6 km   Cork CK11

Mrs Noreen Mullins
LEACA HOUSE
Snave, Bantry
Co Cork

Tel: 027-51792   Fax: 027-51792
Open: 1st March-31st October   OBA

No Rooms:	3	Triple:	–
Twin/Double:	3	Family:	–
Single:	–	En suite:	3

B&B:	-	-	HBW ES:	-	-	S.Supp: £6.50 €8.25	Dinner: -
B&B ES:	£19/20	€24.13/25.39	3 day HB:	-	-	CSP: -	High Tea: -
HBW:	-	-	3 day HB ES:	-	-		

Modern bungalow situated 6km from Bantry, signposted on main Bantry-Glengarriff road (N71). Peaceful, tranquil setting. Breathtaking scenery overlooking Bantry and miles of countryside. Fishing, swimming, hill walking, restaurants and bars with nightly entertainment all nearby. Home baking. Breakfast menu. Email: leacahousebb@hotmail.com

BANTRY 19 km — Cork CK12

Mrs Mary O'Mahony
GROVE HOUSE
Ahakista, Durrus
Bantry, Co Cork

Tel: 027-67060 Fax: –
Open: 1st May - 30th October

OBA
EC

No Rooms:	5
Twin/Double:	3
Single:	1

Triple:	–
Family:	–
En suite:	2

B&B:	£18	€22.86	HBW ES:	-	-	S.Supp: £6.50 €8.25	Dinner: -	-
B&B ES: £20		€25.39	3 day HB:	-	-	CSP: 50%	High Tea: £13 €16.51
HBW:	-	-	3 day HB ES:	-			

Old style farmhouse in quiet wooded location with magnificent views of sea and mountains on Sheep's Head Peninsula. Private coastline, safe swimming, own boat. Bicycle hire can be arranged. Hill walking trips planned, maps provided. Own honey (in season). Log fires. 10 km from Durrus. Dry stock herd.

VOUCHERS ACCEPTED

BLARNEY 6 km — Cork CK14

Dawson Family
BIRCH HILL FARM HOUSE
Grenagh
Blarney, Co Cork

Tel: 021-4886106 Fax: –
Open: 1st May - 31st October

No Rooms:	6
Twin/Double:	4
Single:	1

Triple:	-
Family:	1
En suite:	2

B&B:	£17	€21.58	HBW ES:	-	-	S.Supp: £6.50 €8.25	Dinner: -
B&B ES: £19		€24.13	3 day HB:	-	-	CSP: 25%	High Tea: -
HBW:	-	-	3 day HB ES:	-			

Victorian (1874) family home. Signposted from Blarney (6 km) and from N20 (3 km). Comfortable, peaceful accommodation overlooking mature trees and river. Log fires, home baking, Frommers recommended. Dairy and cattle farm. Pony trekking, golf, driving range, fishing, Irish music, restaurants in Blarney. Convenient to Car Ferry and Airport.

VOUCHERS ACCEPTED

BLARNEY 9 km — Cork CK60

Mrs Eileen Desmond
BALLYANLY HOUSE
Inniscarra,
Co Cork

Tel: 021-7332440 Fax: -
Open: All Year

No Rooms:	3
Twin/Double:	3
Single:	

Triple:	–
Family:	–
En suite:	3

B&B:	-	-	HBW ES:	-	-	S.Supp: £7 €8.89	Dinner: -
B&B ES: £19		€24.13	3 day HB:	-	-	CSP: 50%	High Tea: £10 €12.70
HBW:	-	-	3 day HB ES:	-			

Bright and spacious farmhouse on a dairy/beef farm. Elevated site with breathtaking scenery in a peaceful rural and tranquil setting. Cork airport and Cork ferryport within 30 minutes drive. Ideal touring centre for South West. Restaurants and bars with nightly entertainment nearby. Enjoy tea/coffee and home baking on arrival and throughout stay. Signposted on the R579

VOUCHERS ACCEPTED

BLARNEY 5 km — Cork CK15

The Hallissey Family
GARRYCLOYNE LODGE
Garrycloyne
Blarney, Co Cork

Tel: 021-4886214 Fax: –
Open: 20th April - 1st November

AM V

No Rooms:	4
Twin/Double:	3
Single:	

Triple:	-
Family:	1
En suite:	4

B&B:	-	-	HBW ES:	-	-	S.Supp: £6.50 €8.25	Dinner: -
B&B ES: £19		€24.13	3 day HB:	-	-	CSP: 33%	High Tea: -
HBW:	-	-	3 day HB ES:	-			

Friendly, comfortable accommodation and a warm welcome assured. Family home for four generations on a working dairy farm. Mature gardens. Ideal holiday base for families. Blarney Castle 5Km. Complimentary tea/coffee and scones on arrival. Four bedrooms en suite on ground floor. Signposted on Waterloo Road out of Blarney.

VOUCHERS ACCEPTED

BLARNEY 2.5 km

Cork CK16

Mrs Vera Quill
GREEN GROVE
Stone View
Blarney, Co Cork

Tel: 021-4385167   Fax: 021-4385167
Open: 1st March - 30th November

	No Rooms:	4	Triple:	1
	Twin/Double:	2	Family:	–
	Single:	1	En suite:	1

AM V

						S.Supp: -	-	Dinner: -	-
B&B:	£17	€21.58	HBW ES:	-	-				
B&B ES:	£19	€24.13	3 day HB:	-	-	CSP:	20%	High Tea:-	-
HBW:	-	-	3 day HB ES:-	-					

Comfortable modern farmhouse on elevated scenic location overlooking the world famous Blarney Castle. Central heating. Ideal base for touring the south west. Blarney golf course bar and restaurant 100yds. Pitch and Putt on farm. Blarney village 2.5km has shops, restaurants, pubs and traditional music. Cork City 8Km, Airport 12 km, Ferryport 20 km. Email: greengrove@eircom.net

BUTTEVANT 1 km

Cork CK17

Pat & Annemaire O'Brien
SPITALFIELDS
Buttevant
Mallow, Co Cork

Tel: 022-23184   Fax: –
Open: 1st February - 31st October

	No Rooms:	4	Triple:	1
	Twin/Double:	2	Family:	1
	Single:		En suite:	4

V

					S.Supp: £6.50	€8.25	Dinner: £18	€23
B&B:	-	-	HBW ES:	-	-			
B&B ES:	£20	€26	3 day HB:	-	-	CSP:	25%	High Tea:-	-
HBW:	-	-	3 day HB ES:	£100	€126.97			

Spitalfields, built in 1765, is a charming Georgian house with period en suite bedrooms. Set in its own farmland with horses, sheep and cows, it provides a peaceful haven for a restful break - enjoy gracious living with modern conveniences. An hour's drive to most of Munster's top tourist attractions, with golf, horse riding and hill walking nearby. Email: spitalfields@oceanfree.net

CLONAKILTY 6 km

Cork CK19

Norma Walsh
ARD NA GREINE
Ballinascarthy
Clonakilty, Co Cork

Tel: 023-39104   Fax: 023-39397
Open: 1st January - 31st December.

	No Rooms:	6	Triple:	1
	Twin/Double:	3	Family:	1
	Single:	1	En suite:	5

AM V EC

						S.Supp: £6.50	€8.25	Dinner: £12/20	€15/25
B&B:	-	-	HBW ES:	-	-				
B&B ES:	£22.50/25	€28.57/31.74	3 day HB:	-	-	CSP:	50%	High Tea:£12	€15.24
HBW:	-	-	3 day HB ES:	£130	€165.07				

A warm welcome awaits you in this comfortable home with a spectacular view of the countryside.
With emphasis on Norma's delicious home cooking and baking. Vegetarians and coeliacs are catered for. À la carte dinner served each day. Galtee Breakfast Awards, Le Guide du Routard, Ireland's Best B & B's, Bern Baums Ireland, RAC Guide recommended. Signposted on N71. Near Ballinascarthy village. Very central for Kinsale, West Cork and Blarney. Email: normawalshi@eircom.net Website: ardnagreine.com

CLONAKILTY/CASTLEFREKE 1.5 km

Cork CK18

Mrs Eleanor O'Donovan
KILKERN HOUSE
Rathbarry, Castlefreke
Clonakilty, Co Cork

Tel: 023-40643   Fax: 023-40643
Open: All Year

	No Rooms:	5	Triple:	–
	Twin/Double:	4	Family:	1
	Single:	–	En suite:	3

V EC

						S.Supp: £6.50	€8.25	Dinner: £15	€19.05
B&B:	£18	€22.85	HBW ES:	-	-				
B&B ES:	£20	€25.39	3 day HB:	£96	€121.89	CSP:	50%	High Tea:-	-
HBW:	-	-	3 day HB ES:	£102	€129.51				

Beautifully situated seaside home on shores of Kilkern Lake (50 metres). Sandy beaches 1 km. Rathbarry Tidy Towns Award winning village 1 km. Signposted on Clonakilty/ Skibbereen N71. 5 km west of Clonakilty. Dairy/tillage farm. Horse & pony, farm animals. Hard tennis court. Seafood, home baking & fresh farm produce. Forest walks, leisure activities locally. 'Le Guide du Routard' recommended. TV in bedrooms & tea/coffee. Babysitting service. Mobile: 086-8566616

CLONAKILTY 9.5 km — Cork CK20

Mrs Phil Beechinor
LISCUBBA HOUSE
Rossmore
Clonakilty, Co Cork

Tel: 023-38679   Fax: –
Open: 1st January - 31st December   OBA

No Rooms:	4	Triple:	2
Twin/Double:	1	Family:	–
Single:	1	En suite:	1

B&B:	£17	€21.58	HBW ES:	£225	€285.69	S.Supp:£6.50	€8.25	Dinner: £15	€19.05
B&B ES: £19	€24.13	3 day HB:	£90	€114.28	CSP:	50%	High Tea:£10	€12.7
HBW:	£210	€166.64	3 day HB ES:£96	€124.59				

Old style farm house on beef and tillage farm off the beaten track.
Comfortable accommodation in relaxed and homely atmosphere. Central for day tours of West
Cork. Landscaped garden. Own produce and home baking. Sandy beaches 20 minutes drive. Heated
swimming pool 15 minutes drive. Pottery lessons by request. Signposted on N71 & R588 roads.

CLONAKILTY/RATHBARRY 1.5 km — Cork CK21

John & Maureen Callanan
SPRINGFIELD HOUSE
Kilkern, Castlefreke
Clonakilty, Co Cork

Tel: +353 023-40622 Fax: +353 023-40622
Open: March 1st - October 31st   OBA

No Rooms:	4	Triple:	–
Twin/Double:	2	Family:	2
Single:	–	En suite:	3

B&B:	£17/19	€21.59/24.13	HBW ES:	-	S.Supp: £6.50	€8.25	Dinner: £15	€19.05
B&B ES:£19/22.50	€24.13/28.57	3 day HB:	-	CSP:	50%	High Tea:£10	€12.70
HBW:	-	3 day HB ES:	-				

Enjoy a real homely holiday where a warm welcome awaits you in this beautiful Georgian
farmhouse, spacious rooms, some with TV. Peaceful location on dairy farm with panoramic view of the Atlantic Ocean.
Signposted on Clonakilty-Skibbereen N71 road. Ideal for touring West Cork and Kerry. All leisure activities nearby. Fresh farm
produce. Home cooking a speciality. AA & QQQ ◆◆◆ approved. Tea & coffee on arrival. Email: jandmcallanan@eircom.net

CLONAKILTY/RATHBARRY 1 km — Cork CK22

Mrs. E.J. Calnan
AN GARRÁN CÓIR
Rathbarry, Clonakilty
West Cork

Tel: 023-48236   Fax: 023-48236
Open: 1st January - 31st December

No Rooms:	4	Triple:	1
Twin/Double:	2	Family:	1
Single:	–	En suite:	4

B&B:	-	B&B W ES:	-	S.Supp: £6.50	€8.25	Dinner: £15	€19.05
B&B ES: £19/23	€24.13/25.39	3 day HB:	-	CSP:	50%	High Tea: -	-
HBW:	-	3 day HB ES:	£105	€133.32			

Luxurious family farmhouse in scenic peaceful walking area. Sandy beaches 1km. Spacious en-suite rooms
with TV, *tennis court on premises. Award winning breakfast menu, delicious meals from organic produce with herbs and fruit from garden.
Seafood specialities. Michael Collins home and Castlefreke Castle, Rathbarry award winning village/pub-1 mile. All arrangements made for
golfing, walking, horse riding, fishing and cycling. AA, ◆◆◆◆ selected premises. Refreshments on arrival. Email: angarrancoir@eircom.net

CLONAKILTY 4 km — Cork CK23

Bella Helen
HILLSIDE FARM
Kilgarriffe
Clonakilty, Co Cork

Tel: 023-33139   Fax: –
Open: 20th May - 20th September   OBA

No Rooms:	4	Triple:	1
Twin/Double:	2	Family:	1
Single:	–	En suite:	2

B&B:	£17	€21.58	HBW ES:	£200	€354	S.Supp: £7	€8.25	Dinner: -	-
B&B ES: £19	€24.13	3 day HB:	£85	€165.10	CSP:	50%	High Tea:£10	€12.70
HBW:	£190	€251.30	3 day HB ES:£95	€120.63			

Old style farmhouse, working dairy farm (pedigree friesians). 4 km North West of Clonakilty on
Enniskeane Road (R588). Signposted on N71 from Bandon at Clonakilty RFC pitch. 45 minutes drive from Cork Airport and Ringaskiddy
Ferryport. Templebryan & Lisnagun stone circles nearby. Traditional cooking, produce from farm. Rare fowl farm walks. All leisure activities
nearby, horse riding, sandy beaches, Irish music, restaurants, model village & swimming pool. Email: richardhelen@eircom.net

CLONAKILTY 1 km

Cork CK24

Mrs Dorothy Jennings
DESERT HOUSE
Clonakilty
Co Cork

Tel: 023-33331		Fax: 023-33048	
Open: 1st January - 31st December			
No Rooms:	5	Triple:	–
Twin/Double:	5	Family:	–
Single:	–	En suite:	4

AE / AM / V / EC

B&B:	£17	€21.59	HBW ES:	-	S.Supp: £6.50 €8.25	Dinner: -
B&B ES:	£19	€24.13	3 day HB:	-	CSP: Negot.	High Tea:£11 €13.97
HBW:	-		3 day HB ES: -			

Georgian style farmhouse on dairy farm overlooking Clonakilty Bay. Signposted on N71 East of Clonakilty at roundabout. AA Listed. Birdwatching on estuary, sandy beaches, tennis, fishing, golf, pitch and putt, model village, watersports, horse riding locally. Gault Millau and Lonely Planet Guide recommended. TV & tea/coffee in bedrooms. Credit cards accepted. Email: deserthouse@eircom.net

VOUCHERS ACCEPTED

CLONAKILTY 2 km

Cork CK25

Noreen McCarthy
DUVANE FARM
Ballyduvane
Clonakilty, Co Cork

Tel: 023-33129		Fax: 023-33129	
Open: 15th March - 15th November			
No Rooms:	4	Triple:	1
Twin/Double:	2	Family:	1
Single:	–	En suite:	4

B&B:	-	HBW ES:	-	S.Supp: £6.50 €8.25	Dinner: £15 €19.05
B&B ES:	£22.50/25 €28.57/31.74	3 day HB:	-	CSP: 50%	High Tea:£10 €12.97
HBW:	-	3 day HB ES: -			

Elegant Georgian House situated on beef farm 2km from Clonakilty on N71, Skibbereen side of town. Comforting, relaxing accommodation where a warm welcome awaits you. Period furniture, Brass and Canopy Beds. TV, tea/coffee in bedrooms. Galtee Award Winner. Best B/B's Elsie Dillard, Susan Causin Irl. All meals local produce, own honey. Very central for Kinsale, West Cork and Blarney. AA QQQQ selected house. R.A.C. Listed. Tea and coffee on arrival.

VOUCHERS ACCEPTED

CORK 10 km

Cork CK27

Bernadette Murphy
ARDFIELD
Goggins Hill, Ballinhassig
Co Cork

Tel: 021-4885723		Fax: 021-4885723	
Open: 17th March - 31th October			*OBA*
No Rooms:	4	Triple:	2
Twin/Double:	2	Family:	–
Single:	–	En suite:	4

AM / V / EC

B&B:	-	HBW ES:	-	S.Supp: £6.50 €8.25	Dinner: £16 €20.32
B&B ES:	£19/21 €24.13/26.66	3 day HB:	-	CSP: 30%	High Tea:-
HBW:	-	3 day HB ES: -			

Peaceful residence with breathtaking views of Owenabue Valley. Breeding and training of top class show jumping and event horses. 300 metres off R613. Near Halfway village. 1km off N71. Close to Cork airport. 15km from Ringaskiddy Ferry Port and Kinsale. 10km from Cork City. Regular bus service. Early breakfasts. Email: ardfieldaccomm@eircom.net Website: http://homepage.eircom.net/~ardfield

VOUCHERS ACCEPTED

FERMOY 20 km

Cork CK29

Mrs Wendy England
BEECHFIELD
Ballynoe (near Conna),
Fermoy, Co Cork

Tel: 058-59358/59213		Fax: 058-59358	
Open: 1st May - 31st September			
No Rooms:	3	Triple:	–
Twin/Double:	3	Family:	–
Single:	–	En suite:	3

B&B:	-	HBW ES:	£200 €253.95	S.Supp: £6.50 €8.25	Dinner: £13 €16.51
B&B ES:	£19 €24.13	3 day HB:	-	CSP: 50%	High Tea:£8 €10.16
HBW:	-	3 day HB ES: £90 €114.28			

350 year old farmhouse on working dairy and poultry farm, situated 8kms from Conna, fishing on the Bride. 20kms from Fermoy, fishing on Blackwater. Peaceful setting with large garden. Dinners a speciality, 5 course meals. Visitors may bring own wine. Owner qualified chef. Facilities for fishermen. Ideal stop off from Rosslare to tour the west. Breakfast menu. No extra charge for ensuite on vouchers. Tea on arrival. Email: awengland@eircom.net

VOUCHERS ACCEPTED

FERMOY 20 km | Cork CK30

Mrs Mary Mulcahy
BOULTA HOUSE
Boulta, Ballynoe
Conna, Fermoy, Co Cork

Tel: 058-59247   Fax: –
Open: 1st January-31st December

No Rooms:	3	Triple:	–
Twin/Double:	2	Family:	–
Single:	1	En suite:	–

B&B	£18	€ 22.86	HBW ES:	-	-	S.Supp: £15 € 19.05	Dinner: £15 € 19.05
B&B ES: -			3 day HB:	-	-	CSP: 25%	High Tea: £12 € 15.24
HBW:			3 day HB ES: -				

200 year old farmhouse, located in idyllic surroundings. Family home since 1865 on dairy/tillage farm. 12 km from Lismore Heritage Town. Fota Wildlife Park and Cobh Heritage Centre within easy reach. Golf at Lismore, Fermoy, Midleton, Youghal. Angling on Bride and Blackwater rivers.

GLANDORE 2 km | Cork CK31

Margaret Mehigan
KILFINNAN FARM
Glandore
Co Cork

Tel: 028-33233   Fax: 028-33233
Open: 1st January-31st December.

No Rooms:	4	Triple:	–	EC
Twin/Double:	2	Family:	2	
Single:	–	En suite:	2	

B&B	£17	€ 21.59	HBW ES:	-	-	S.Supp: £6.50 € 8.25	Dinner: -
B&B ES: £20		€ 25.39	3 day HB:	-	-	CSP: 10%	High Tea: £8 € 10.16
HBW:	-	-	3 day HB ES: £105		€ 133.32		

Family run farmhouse in peaceful surroundings, overlooking picturesque Glandore Harbour. Meat, eggs, milk, fruit and vegetables produced on the farm. Sandy beaches and Drombeg Stone Circle within 2 km. Ideal location for country walks, fishing and water sports. Pony trekking and golf nearby. Garden for visitors use.

GLENGARRIFF 2 km | Cork CK32

Mrs Mary Harrington
THE HEIGHTS
Carrigrour
Glengarriff, Co Cork

Tel: 027-63088   Fax: –
Open: Easter - 31st October

No Rooms:	4	Triple:	1
Twin/Double:	3	Family:	–
Single:	–	En suite:	4

B&B	£19	€ 24.13	HBW ES:	-	-	S.Supp: -	Dinner: -
B&B ES: -			3 day HB:	-	-	CSP: 10%	High Tea: £10 € 12.97
HBW:	-	-	3 day HB ES: -				

Elevated two storey farmhouse providing exceptional views of Glengarriff Harbour and Bantry Bay. Signposted on the N71 at the Bantry side of Glengarriff, 1.6 km off main road. Scenic surroundings and views extending south to Mount Gabriel. Golf, fishing and horse riding locally.

GLENGARRIFF 3 km | Cork CK33

Mrs Bridget O'Shea
MAGANNAGAN FARM
Derryconngry, Glengarriff
Beara, Co Cork

Tel: 027-63361   Fax: –
Open: 31th March - 31st October

No Rooms:	3	Triple:	–
Twin/Double:	3	Family:	–
Single:	–	En suite:	2

B&B	£17	€ 21.58	HBW ES:	-	-	S.Supp: £6.50 € 8.25	Dinner: -
B&B ES: £19		€ 24.13	3 day HB:	-	-	CSP: 50%	High Tea: £10 € 12.69
HBW:	-	-	3 day HB ES: -				

Farm bungalow in scenic mountainous setting, 3km from Glengarriff village on Castletownbere road. Ideal location for touring Rings of Beara and Kerry - perfect base for walking - Beara way walk, passing Magannagan farm. Magnificent views of Sugar Loaf Mountain and surrounding countryside. Home baking and refreshments on arrival.

GOLEEN 9 km

Cork CK34

Mrs Violet Connell
FORTVIEW HOUSE
Gurtyowen, Toormore
Goleen, Co Cork

Tel: 028-35324   Fax: 028-35324
Open: 1st March - 1st November   *OBA*

No Rooms:	5	Triple:	-
Twin/Double:	4	Family:	-
Single:	1	En suite:	5

B&B:	-	-	HBW ES:	-	-	S.Supp: £10	€13	Dinner: £20	€25.39
B&B ES: £25/30	€31.74/38.09	3 day HB:	-	-	CSP:	25%	High Tea:-	-
HBW:	-	-	3 day HB ES: £135/150	€171.41/190.46				

Traditional stone built house on dairy farm. Furnished in antique country pine, brass and iron beds. Extensive breakfast menu. Tea/coffee facilities. National agricultural tourism award winners. AA ◆ ◆ ◆ ◆ 'Bridgestone 100 Best places to stay in Ireland.' Located 2km from Toormore on main Bantry road R591, Goleen 9km. Schull 9km. Ideal base for touring West Cork and Mizen Peninsula. **Vouchers Not Accepted**

GOLEEN 5km

Cork CK35

Mary Sheehan
LAKE VIEW HOUSE
Letter, Goleen,
Co. Cork

Tel: 028-35494   Fax: -
Open: May 1st - September 30th   *OBA*   *EC*

No Rooms:	3	Triple:	-
Twin/Double:	1	Family:	2
Single:	-	En suite:	2

B&B: £17	€21.58	HBW ES:	-	-	S.Supp: £6.50	€8.25	Dinner: £12	€15.24
B&B ES: £19	€24.13	3 day HB:	-	-	CSP:	50%	High Tea:-	
HBW:	-	-	3 day HB ES: £90	€114.30				

Modern farmhouse, in peaceful setting overlooking Lissagriffin Lakes. Breakfast menu. Tea/coffee facilities. Situated 5kms west of Goleen village. 6kms from Mizen Head. 0.8km off Goleen/Mizen Head road. Convenient to Barley Cove beach, Crookhaven village, pony trekking, sailing and golf. Email: tsandms@eircom.net

KINSALE 15 km

Cork CK36

Mrs Sheila Connolly
FARNAGOW LODGE
Innishannon
Co Cork

Tel: 021-4775671   Fax: 021-4775671
Open: 1st January - 23th December   *OBA*   *V*

No Rooms:	4	Triple:	-
Twin/Double:	3	Family:	1
Single:	-	En suite:	3

B&B: £18	€22.86	HBW ES:	-	-	S.Supp: £6.50	€8.25	Dinner: £16	€20.23
B&B ES: £19	€24.13	3 day HB:	-	-	CSP:	20%	High Tea:£10	€12.97
HBW:	-	-	3 day HB ES: -					

Working farm situated in beautiful rural landscape. Warm, homely atmosphere with friendly family. Ideally situated for touring West Cork. Convenient to Kinsale (15 km), airport, ferry and Cork city. Signposted off the N71 at Innishannon Bridge. Complimentary tea/coffee and home baking on arrival. Email: farnagowlodge@eircom.net Website: www.dirl.com/cork/farnagow-lodge.htm

INNISHANNON 3 km

Cork CK37

Tim & Sheila Cummins
BALLYMOUNTAIN HOUSE
Innishannon (near Kinsale)
Co Cork

Tel: 021-4775366   Fax: 021-4775366
Open: 1st January - 31st December

No Rooms:	6	Triple:	2
Twin/Double:	3	Family:	1
Single:	-	En suite:	5

B&B: £17/19	€21.6/24.13	HBW ES: £235	€298.39	S.Supp: £6.50	€8.25	Dinner: £13/15	€16.5/19
B&B ES: £19/21	€24.13/26.68	3 day HB: £94/98	€119.3/124.43	CSP:	50%	High Tea: £12	€15.24
HBW: £220	€279.34	3 day HB ES: £99/105	€125.7/133.32				

Pre-1800 period residence. Signposted on N71 on bridge west of Innishannon. Ideal location for visiting Kinsale, Blarney, Cork City & many beaches, all 15-30 km drive. Convenient to airport & ferryport. Early breakfast available. Recommended by many travel guides. Email: ballymountain@eircom.net Website: http://www.dirl.com/cork/ballymountain.htm

KINSALE 10 km   Cork CK38

Mrs. Eileen Fielding
SEAFIELD FARMHOUSE
Harbour View
Kilbrittain, Co Cork

Tel: 023-49818   Fax: 023-49818
Open: 1st March - 1st November

No Rooms:	6	Triple:	–	AE
Twin/Double:	3	Family:	2	AM V
Single:	1	En suite:	4	EC

B&B:	£17	€21.58	HBW ES:	£196	€248.87	S.Supp: £6.50	€8.25	Dinner: £12 €15.24
B&B ES:	£20	€25.39	3 day HB:	£80	€101.58	CSP:	50%	High Tea:£8 €10.16
HBW:	£190	€241.25	3 day HB ES:	£90	€114.28			

Elevated farmhouse overlooking beach. Breathtaking views of sea and
countryside. Situated 10 km from Kinsale, Bandon and Clonakilty on R600 road. Gourmet restaurant
and pub within walking distance. All amenities locally. Homely atmosphere. Cork Airport and
Ringaskiddy Ferryport 1 hours drive. Old Head of Kinsale Golf Course 4 miles. Beef/tillage farm.

KINSALE 12km   Cork CK39

Helen S. Forde
LOCHINVER FARMHOUSE
Ballinadee (near Kinsale)
Bandon, Co Cork

Tel: 021-4778124   Fax: –
Open: 16th March - 31st October

No Rooms:	5	Triple:	–	AM V
Twin/Double:	4	Family:	–	EC
Single:	1	En suite:	3	

B&B:	£18	€22.86	HBW ES:	£240/250	€304.7/317.4	S.Supp: £7	€8.88	Dinner: £16 €20.32
B&B ES:	£19/21	€24.13/26.66	3 day HB:	£98	€124.43	CSP:	20%	High Tea:–
HBW:	£230	€292.04	3 day HB ES:	£98	€124.43			

Comfortable farmhouse on dairy farm in scenic location overlooking
Bandon River. 8 km off the N71 at Innishannon Bridge. 12 kms from Kinsale via Ballinadee Road.
Mature gardens, home baking, fresh produce, open fires, orthopaedic beds. Convenient to all leisure
activities, airport, ferryport. Tea/coffee refreshments on request. Email: hsforde@indigo.ie

KINSALE 13 km   Cork CK40

Mrs Nan McCarthy
HARBOUR CREST
Rathclaren, Kilbrittain
(near Kinsale) Co Cork

Tel: 023-49676   Fax: 023-49676
Open: 1st March - 1st November

No Rooms:	4	Triple:	–	V
Twin/Double:	3	Family:	1	EC
Single:		En suite:	3	

B&B:	£17	€21.59	HBW ES:	£210	€266.64	S.Supp: £6.50	€8.25	Dinner:£14 €17.8
B&B ES:	£19	€24.13	3 day HB:	£90	€114.3	CSP:	50%	High Tea: - -
HBW:	-	-	3 day HB ES:	£95	€120.63			

Family run farmhouse providing home cooking & fresh farm produce. Situated on elevated site
overlooking Courtmacsherry Bay, spectacular views of countryside, midway between Kinsale, Clonakilty & Bandon 0.3Km off R600.
Excellent choice of high class restaurants nearby. Convenient to golf, pitch & putt, forest walks, birdwatching, safe sandy beaches. Le
Guide de Routard recommended. Ideal touring base. 45 mins drive from airport & car ferry. Website: www.harbourcrest.com

KINSALE 1.5 km   Cork CK62

The Murphy Family
MURPHY'S FARMHOUSE
Kinsale,
Co Cork

Tel: 021-4772229   Fax: 021-4774176
Open: 1st March - 31st October

No Rooms:	3	Triple:	–	
Twin/Double:	3	Family:	–	
Single:		En suite:	3	

B&B:	-	-	HBW ES:	-	-	S.Supp: -	-	Dinner: - -
B&B ES:	£20	€25.39	3 day HB:	-	-	CSP:	Negot. 25%	High Tea:- -
HBW:	-	-	3 day HB ES:	-				

Modern Farmhouse, 1.5km from Kinsale, looking over the Bandon river. Set
in scenic and tranquil countryside. Cork airport and ferryport within 30 minutes drive. Horse riding,
golf, fishing, sailing, walking and sandy beaches nearby. Within the beautiful town of Kinsale, Murphy's
offers you a warm welcome. Email: murphysfarmhouse@europe.com

Vouchers
Not Accepted

KINSALE 12.5 km   `Cork CK41`

Marion Moloney
BRIDGEVIEW FARMHOUSE
Harbour View, Kilbrittain
(near Kinsale) Co Cork

Tel: 023-49723   Fax: –
Open: 1st March - 31st October

No Rooms:	4	Triple:	1
Twin/Double:	1	Family:	-
Single:	2	En suite:	2

B&B: £17	€21.85	HBW ES: -	-	S.Supp:£6.50 €8.25	Dinner: -
B&B ES: £19	€24.13	3 day HB: -	-	CSP: 50%	High Tea: -
HBW: -		3 day HB ES: -			

Situated midway between Kinsale and Clonakilty, 500 m off R600. Scenic surroundings and views overlooking Courtmacsherry Bay. Warm family welcome. Home baking. Within walking distance of Gourmet Restaurants. Ideal centre for wind surfing, fishing, golf, horse riding and walking. Convenient to sandy beaches. 40 minutes from Cork Airport and Ringaskiddy Ferryport. Ideal base for touring West Cork. Email: bridgeviewfarmhouse@eircom.net

VOUCHERS ACCEPTED

KINSALE 7 km   `Cork CK42`

Dominique O'Sullivan-Vervaet
LEIGHMONEYMORE
Dunderrow
Kinsale, Co Cork

Tel: 021-775312   Fax: 021-775692
Open: 15th March - 30th November

No Rooms:	4	Triple:	–
Twin/Double:	3	Family:	1
Single:		En suite:	4

AM / V / EC

B&B:		HBW ES:	-	S.Supp: £10 €12.7	Dinner: -
B&B ES: £30	€38.09	3 day HB:	-	CSP: 25%	High Tea: -
HBW: -		3 day HB ES: -			

Period house on the banks of the Bandon River off R605 Innishannon-Kinsale road. Spacious rooms with antique furniture, brass beds, TV and hairdryer. Easy access to West Cork. Convenient to Cork airport and Ringaskiddy ferryport. Sea angling, horse riding, golf (special concessions for guests at local course) and sailing available locally. Working farm. French, Dutch, German, Italian Spanish & Japanese spoken. Email:leighmoneymore@eircom.net

Vouchers Not Accepted

KINSALE 10 km   `Cork CK43`

Mrs Maria Sweetnam
RAHEEN HOUSE
Kilgobbin, Ballinspittle
Kinsale, Co Cork

Tel: 021-4778173   Fax: 021-4778173
Open: 1st May- 30th September   *OBA*

No Rooms:	3	Triple:	–
Twin/Double:	3	Family:	–
Single:		En suite:	1

B&B: £18	€22.86	HBW ES:	-	S.Supp:£6.50 €8.25	Dinner: -
B&B ES: £20	€25.40	3 day HB:	-	CSP: 25%	High Tea:£10 €12.70
HBW: -		3 day HB ES: -			

Luxury farmhouse with view of the Old Head of Kinsale. Situated 10 km from Kinsale via Ballinadee Road. Horse riding, golf, sea angling, sailing, beaches locally. Convenient to Cork Airport and Ringaskiddy Ferryport. Email: raheenhouse@eircom.net website: www.dragnet-systems.ie/dira/raheen

VOUCHERS ACCEPTED

KINSALE 3.2 km   `Cork CK44`

Nigel & Siobhan Sweetnam
HARBOUR HILL FARM
Knockduff
Kinsale, Co Cork

Tel: 021-4774479   Fax: 021-4774479
Open: 1st March - 1st November   *OBA*

No Rooms:	4	Triple:	1
Twin/Double:	3	Family:	-
Single:	–	En suite:	4

B&B: -	-	HBW ES:	-	S.Supp:£6.50 €8.25	Dinner: -
B&B ES: £20/22	€25.39/28.57	3 day HB:	-	CSP: 25%	High Tea: -
HBW: -		3 day HB ES: -			

Modern farmhouse, 3·2 km from Kinsale, overlooking harbour and Charles Fort. Set in scenic countryside. Dairy and sheep farm. Ideal centre for sailing, fishing, golf, horse-riding and walking. Convenient to sandy beaches. 20 minutes from Cork airport and 35 minutes from Ringaskiddy carferry. Signposted off R600 on approach to Kinsale town. Mobile phone 087-2796821.

VOUCHERS ACCEPTED

KINSALE 12 km   Cork CK45

Mrs Eleanor Tutty
GREY GABLES
Innishannon
Co Cork

Tel: 021-4775124   Fax: –
Open: 1st June - 15th September   OBA

No Rooms:	4	Triple:	
Twin/Double:	3	Family:	–
Single:	1	En suite:	2

B&B:	£18	€22.85	HBW ES:	-	-	S.Supp: £6.50 €8.25	Dinner: -	-
B&B ES:	£20	€25.39	3 day HB:	-	-	CSP: 20%	High Tea: -	-
HBW:			3 day HB ES:	-				

Comfortable farmhouse in peaceful countryside 1 km off main Cork-Bantry (N71), 12 miles from Cork City (signposted). Cork Airport and Cork Ferryport within 30 minutes drive. Horse riding, golf, fishing, and sandy beaches nearby. Kinsale within 7 miles with its excellent restaurants. A warm welcome awaits you.

KNOCKRAHA/WATERGRASSHILL 6.5 km   Cork CK46

Ms Fiona Walsh
SILVER SOUTH FARM
Knockraha
Co Cork

Tel: 021-4889470   Fax: –
Open: 1st March - 31st November

No Rooms:	3	Triple:	–
Twin/Double:	3	Family:	
Single:	–	En suite:	2

B&B:	£17	€21.58	HBW ES:	-	-	S.Supp: £6.50 €8.25	Dinner: -	-
B&B ES:	£19	€24.13	3 day HB:	-	-	CSP: 50%	High Tea: -	-
HBW:	-	-	3 day HB ES:	-				

Luxury farmhouse situated in peaceful surroundings. Sign posted on main Cork-Dublin Road N8, 11 km north of Cork, 6.5 km south of Watergrasshill. Convenient to Airport via Tunnel nearby Fota Wildlife Park, Jameson Heritage Centre, Cobh - The Queenstown story, Golf courses and kart-track. Brochure available. Breakfast menu.

MACROOM 9 km   Cork CK47

Mrs Ann Marie Corkery
HILLTOP FARMHOUSE
Ballyvoige, Kilnamartrya
Macroom, Co Cork

Tel: 026-40154   Fax: –
Open: 1st April - 1st October   OBA

No Rooms:	3	Triple:	–
Twin/Double:	2	Family:	1
Single:		En suite:	3

B&B:	-	-	HBW ES:	-	-	S.Supp: £6.50 €8.25	Dinner: -	-
B&B ES:	£19	€24.13	3 day HB:	-	-	CSP: 50%	High Tea: -	-
HBW:	-	-	3 day HB ES:	-				

Situated 3 km off N22 Killarney Road. 9 km from Macroom. Modern dormer bungalow in pleasant, peaceful surroundings. Walks with magnificent panoramic views of scenic Cork/Kerry countryside. Ideal base for touring, fishing, golfing. Within 50 km of Blarney, Bantry, Kenmare, Killarney and Ring of Kerry. Ground floor rooms. Music in village pubs 200 metres. Families welcome. Email: amfcorkery@eircom.net

MACROOM 9.5 km   Cork CK50

Mary & Michael O'Sullivan
FINDUS HOUSE
Ballyvoige, Kilnamartyra
Macroom, Co Cork

Tel: 026-40023   Fax: 026-40023
Open: 1st March - 1st November

AE
AM
V
EC

No Rooms:	6	Triple:	1
Twin/Double:	4	Family:	
Single:	1	En suite:	6

B&B:	-	-	HBW ES:	£220	€279.34	S.Supp: £6.50 €8.25	Dinner: £17	€21.59
B&B ES:	£19	€24.13	3 day HB:	-	-	CSP: 50%	High Tea: £11	€013.97
HBW:	-	-	3 day HB ES:	-				

A warm welcome awaits you at this award winning farm guesthouse, with the best of Irish hospitality, spectacular views and walks featuring delicious home cooking, salmon a speciality. Relax chat and enjoy a sing song in our comfortable lounge. Signposted on Killarney N22 road. Recommended by Frommers & Ireland's best B&B Guide.

MIDLETON 3.5 km   Cork CK51

The de Cogan's
KILLAMUCKEY HOUSE
Castlemartyr, Midleton
Co Cork

Tel: 021-4667266   **Fax:** –
Open: 1st June - 1st November

No Rooms:	3	Triple:	–
Twin/Double:	3	Family:	–
Single:	–	En suite:	–

B&B: £20	€25.39	HBW ES: -	-	S.Supp: £6.50 €8.25	Dinner: £20	€25.39
B&B ES: -	-	3 day HB: -	-	CSP: -	High Tea: £10	€12.70
HBW: -	-	3 day HB ES: -	-			

✕ ✕ S 👣 💻 ⊗ C D

A period house of old world charm and character. Spacious rooms. Craft studio featuring local craft. Nice breakfast menu. "A perfect, relaxed & peaceful location" on a pedigree dairy & beef farm. Signposted at Castlemartyr Cross. Recommended by travel writers & selected by Brittany Ferries. Convenient to Cork City, Fota Park, Jameson Heritage, Ballymaloe Cookery School, Irish lace making.

VOUCHERS ACCEPTED

MIDLETON 14 km   Cork CK52

Marian and Pat Moloney
MOLONEY'S FARMHOUSE
Garryvoe Upper
Ladysbridge, Co Cork

Tel: 021-4667421   **Fax:** –
Open: 1st January - 31st December

No Rooms:	3	Triple:	–
Twin/Double:	2	Family:	1
Single:	–	En suite:	3

B&B: £17	€21.58	HBW ES: -	-	S.Supp: £6.50 €8.25	Dinner: -	-
B&B ES: £19	€24.13	3 day HB: -	-	CSP: -	High Tea: -	-
HBW: -	-	3 day HB ES: -	-			

👣 ⊗ 🛏 ⚲ 🐾 🐾 ✕ S

Modern farmhouse, uniquely situated overlooking Ballycotton Bay and Garryvoe Beach. Lush greenfields surround our farm to emphasise the sound of silence. Situated 6 km off N25 route Cork-Rosslare at Castlemartyr. Visit: Ballymaloe House, Jameson, Cobh Heritage Centres, Trabolgan, Fota, Cork Airport and Ferryport. Complimentary tea/coffee. Home baking. Email: maripat@gofree.indigo.ie

VOUCHERS ACCEPTED

MILLSTREET 4 km   Cork CK53

Mrs Jytte Storm
BALLINATONA FARM
Ballinatona
Millstreet Town, Co Cork

Tel: 029-70213   **Fax:** 029-70940
Open: 1st January - 15th December

No Rooms:	6	Triple:	2
Twin/Double:	4	Family:	–
Single:	-	En suite:	6

OBA
AM V

B&B: -	-	HBW ES: -	-	S.Supp: £7.50 €09.52	Dinner: -	-
B&B ES: £19.50	€24.76	3 day HB: -	-	CSP: -	High Tea: -	-
HBW: -	-	3 day HB ES: -	-			

🔲 👣 💻 👤 ✕ ✅ ⊗ TV

Truly the hidden Ireland. Guesthouse 800 feet above sea level. Working dairy farm. Stunning view, mountain forest walks, Coomatroosh Lake and Waterfall. A world of peace. Bright spacious rooms en suite with TV family rooms, triple rooms, double rooms. Spacious dining room, conservatory, lobby, sun lounge. Central heating. Recommended by Frommers and Bed and Breakfast Ireland.

VOUCHERS ACCEPTED

ROSSCARBERY 2 km   Cork CK54

Mrs. Catherine O'Sullivan
"ROSALITHIR"
Frehanes
Rosscarbery, Co Cork

Tel: 023-48136   **Fax:** 023-48136
Open: 1st March - 31st October

No Rooms:	4	Triple:	1
Twin/Double:	2	Family:	1
Single:	–	En suite:	3

OBA
EC

B&B: £20/23	€25.40/29.20	HBW ES: -	-	S.Supp: £7 €8.90	Dinner: -	-
B&B ES: £20/23	€25.40/29.20	3 day HB: -	-	CSP: 50%	High Tea: -	-
HBW: -	-	3 day HB ES: -	-			

S 👣 🐕 U 👓 ⚲ 🐾 ✅

A warm welcome awaits you in this charming family run country residence on dairy farm overlooking tranquil countryside, offering a high standard of accommodation and cooking. Le Guide du Routard and Hidden Ireland Recommended. Signposted on Clonakilty-Rosscarbery N71. Convenient to Glandore, Clonakilty and Skibbereen. Sandy beaches, horse riding, marine activities, pitch & putt, use of hotel leisure facilities nearby. Tea/coffee on request.

VOUCHERS ACCEPTED

SKIBBEREEN 11 km

Cork CK55

Mrs Nora Collins
FLOWER LODGE
Caheragh North
Drimoleague, Co Cork

Tel: 028-31440   Fax: –
Open: 1st April - 30th September   *OBA*

No Rooms:	3
Twin/Double:	2
Single:	–

Triple:	1
Family:	–
En suite:	2

B&B:	£17	€21.58	HBW ES:	-	-	S.Supp: £6.50 €8.25	Dinner: -	-
B&B ES:	£19	€24.13	3 day HB:	-	-	CSP: 25%	High Tea:-	-
HBW:	-	-	3 day HB ES:	-	-			

A warm welcome awaits you at 'Flower Lodge'. A working dairy farm, located on R594, 11km from Skibbereen. Visitors are welcome to relax in our garden or have a woodland/hill walk with magnificent views of the countryside. Shops, pubs, restaurants nearby. Tea/Coffee on arrival. Email: info@flowerlodge.com Website: www.flowerlodge.com

SKIBBEREEN 4 km

Cork CK56

Mrs Teresa Crowley
BUNALUN
Skibbereen
Co Cork

Tel: 028-21502   Fax: 028-21241
Open: 1st May - 1st November   [V]

No Rooms:	4
Twin/Double:	4
Single:	–

Triple:	–
Family:	–
En suite:	3

B&B:	£18	€22.86	HBW ES:	-	-	S.Supp: £6.50 €8.25	Dinner: -	-
B&B ES:	£20	€25.39	3 day HB:	-	-	CSP: -	High Tea: -	-
HBW:	-	-	3 day HB ES:	-	-			

Environmental award winning 19th Century Farmhouse on Dairy Farm. Comfortable rooms in a friendly family run establishment. Home baking and fresh organic food. Clearly signposted off N71, (direction R593). Bunalun is 4 km from Skibbereen where there are excellent restaurants and pubs. There are also beaches, golf, horse riding, fishing and forest walks nearby. Email: crowleys@iol.ie

SKIBBEREEN 8 km

Cork CK61

Padraig & Eileen O'Driscoll
COOLBAWN LODGE
FARMHOUSE
Caheragh, Drimoleague,
Skibbereen, Co Cork

Tel: 028-38166   Fax: -
Open: Easter - 1st October   [V]

No Rooms:	3
Twin/Double:	3
Single:	–

Triple:	–
Family:	–
En suite:	3

B&B:	£18	€22.86	HBW ES:	-	-	S.Supp: £8 €10.16	Dinner: -	-
B&B ES:	£20	€25.39	3 day HB:	-	-	CSP: -	High Tea:-	-
HBW:	-	-	3 day HB ES: -					

A hearty Céad Míle Fáilte awaits you at this family run luxurious farmhouse on dairy and beef farm signposted off N71, 9km west of Skibbereen. Ideal location for touring West Cork and South Kerry. Shops, Restaurants, Fishing, Sports Centre, Golf, Beaches all nearby. Email: info@coolbawnlodge.com Web Address: www.coolbawnlodge.com

TIMOLEAGUE 2 km

Cork CK58

Mrs Mary Dinneen
KILSHINIHAN CROSS
Timoleague
Bandon, West Cork

Tel: 023-46156   Fax: –
Open: 1st May - 31st October

No Rooms:	3
Twin/Double:	2
Single:	1

Triple:	–
Family:	–
En suite:	3

B&B:	£17	€21.58	HBW ES:	-	-	S.Supp: £6.50 €8.25	Dinner: -	-
B&B ES:	£19	€24.13	3 day HB:	-	-	CSP: 50%	High Tea:-	-
HBW:	-	-	3 day HB ES: -					

A comfortable farm House with warm family welcome and homebaking. Golf, horse riding, fishing, bird watching, leisure centre and a selection of safe, sandy beaches. On the R602 road from Bandon to Timoleague village where there is a beautiful abbey situated. Also convenient to airport and ferryport.

YOUGHAL 12 km

Cork CK59

Mrs Margaret Leahy
CASTLE FARM
Ballycrenane, Ballymacoda
Youghal, Co Cork

Tel: 024-98165		Fax: –	
Open: 15th March - 31st October			OBA
No Rooms:	5	Triple:	–
Twin/Double:	4	Family:	1
Single:	–	En suite:	5

B&B:	-	HBW ES:	-	S.Supp: £7 €8.89	Dinner:	-
B&B ES: £20-22 €25.39-27.93	3 day HB:	-	CSP: 50%	High Tea:	-
HBW:	-	3 day HB ES:	-			

1780 Georgian house with sea view overlooking Ballycotton Bay on 75 acre dairy farm. Located on coast road off N25 at Youghal. Signposted from Ballymacoda village. Convenient to Jameson and Cobh Heritage Centres, Fota Wildlife Park, Cork Airport, Ferryport. Tea/Coffee facilities in bedrooms. 5 mins walk to beach. Email: shleahy@gofree.indigo.ie Website: www.dragnet-systems.ie/dira/castlefarm

---

Important note re: e-mail addresses

From September 2000, Telecom Eireann is changing

its existing email access address '**tinet**'.

The new access address will become '**eircom**'.

For example, an existing email address

'**customer@tinet.ie**'

will become '**customer@eircom.net**'

Your hosts will be happy
to make reservations for you and
help you plan your itinerary

Donegal

The North West of Ireland is a favourite
location for those who like their holidays
with a touch of adventure. From the
mountainous skylines of the coast to the soft
colours of the inland areas, Donegal offers
variety and contrast in scenery and activity.
An unrivalled choice of things to do and
see, and the genuine charm and hospitality
of the people, are just some of the reasons

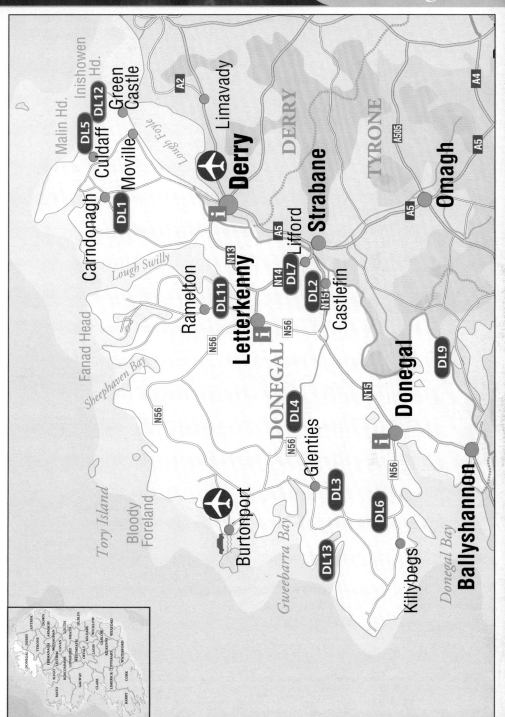

ARDARA 4 km

Donegal DL13

The Boyd Family
CASTLE VIEW
Kilcashel, Loughros Point,
Co. Donegal

Tel: 075-41212 Fax: -
Open: 1st January - 1st December *OBA*

No Rooms:	3	Triple:	–
Twin/Double:	2	Family:	1
Single:	–	En suite:	3

B&B:	£19	€24.13	HBW ES:	-	-	S.Supp: -	-	Dinner: -	-
B&B ES:	£19	€24.13	3 day HB:	-	-	CSP: -	-	High Tea: -	-
HBW:	-	-	3 day HB ES:	-			

Peaceful country home in quiet location. Ideal touring base for North West. Friendly atmosphere and a warm welcome awaits you.

CARNDONAGH 1 km

Donegal DL1

Sharon & Wilson Moore
ASHDALE FARMHOUSE
Malin Road, Carndonagh,
Inishowen, Co Donegal

Tel: 077-74017 Fax: –
Open: Easter – October

No Rooms:	3	Triple:	–
Twin/Double:	3	Family:	–
Single:	–	En suite:	2

AM
V
EC

B&B:	£17	€21.58	HBW ES:	-	-	S.Supp: £6.50 €8.25	Dinner: -	-
B&B ES:	£19	€24.125	3 day HB:	-	-	CSP: 25%	High Tea: -	-
HBW:	-	-	3 day HB ES:	-			

This attractive country house has a homely atmosphere, providing tea and home baking on arrival. Good location for touring Inishowen Penninsula, historical sites, fishing, golf and bike hire available locally. We are situated 1 km from Carndonagh town, on route to Malin Head. Email: ashdalehouse@eircom.net

---

CASTLEFINN 2 km

Donegal DL2

Mrs D. Taylor
GORTFAD
Castlefinn, Lifford
Co Donegal

Tel: 074-46135 Fax: -
Open: Easter – Mid September *OBA*

No Rooms:	5	Triple:	-
Twin/Double:	3	Family:	2
Single:	-	En suite:	4

B&B:	£17	€21.58	HBW ES:	-	-	S.Supp: £6.50 €8.25	Dinner: -	-
B&B ES:	£19	€24.13	3 day HB:	-	-	CSP: 20%	High Tea: -	-
HBW:	-	-	3 day HB ES:	-			

300 year old farmhouse, the home of the same family for seven generations. Quiet and secluded in its own grounds. Landscaped gardens. Good location for touring Glenveigh Castle and Giant's Causeway. Gault Millau recommended.

GLENTIES 2 km

Donegal DL3

Mrs Teresa O'Donnell
OAKDALE FARMHOUSE
Derries, Donegal Road
Glenties, Co Donegal

Tel: 075-51262 Fax: 075-51262
Open: 1st March - 1st November *OBA*

EC

No Rooms:	4	Triple:	-
Twin/Double:	4	Family:	-
Single:	-	En suite:	3

B&B:	£17	€21.58	HBW ES:	£200	€253.95	S.Supp: £6.50 €8.25	Dinner: £13	€16.51
B&B ES:	£19	€24.13	3 day HB:	-	-	CSP: 33.3%	High Tea: £10	€12.70
HBW:	-	-	3 day HB ES:	£90	€114.28			

Comfortable farmhouse situated in scenic area 2 km from Glenties on N56 road to Donegal Town. Ideal for touring Ardara, Glencolmkille, Slieve League and Glenveigh National Park. Beach, country walks. Enjoy home cooking and traditional Irish hospitality, turf fires, en suite rooms, orthopaedic beds. Email: oakdale@eircom.net

GLENTIES 3 km | Donegal DL4

Mrs Mary Ward
PINEWOOD FARMHOUSE
Straboy, Glenties
Co Donegal

Tel: 075-51223		Fax: 075-51223	*OBA*
Open: Easter – November			
No Rooms:	4	Triple:	-
Twin/Double:	3	Family:	1
Single:	-	En suite:	4

EC V AM

B&B:	-		HBW ES:	-		S.Supp: £6.50 €8.25	Dinner: £13 €16.51
B&B ES: £19	€24.13		3 day HB:	-		CSP: 33.3%	High Tea: -
HBW: £200	€253.95		3 day HB ES: £90	€114.28			

Modern farmhouse in scenic mountainous setting, 3 km from Glenties, the 1995 Tidy Towns winner, on main Letterkenny R250 road. Central to Glenveigh National Park, Slieve League, Bloody Foreland, beaches etc. Home baking, fresh seafood. TV lounge, orthopaedic beds. Frommers Guide recommended. Tour advice available. Email: pinewood@eircom.net

VOUCHERS ACCEPTED

INISHOWEN PENINSULA | Donegal DL12

Martha McConway
KINNAGOE BAY HOUSE
Kinnagoe Bay, Lecamy
Inishowen, Co. Donegal

Tel: 077-81280		Fax: 077-81280	
Open: Easter – October.			
No Rooms:	4	Triple:	–
Twin/Double:	2	Family:	1
Single:	1	En suite:	2

AM V EC

B&B: £17	€21.58		HBW ES:	-		S.Supp: £6.50 €8.25	Dinner: -	-
B&B ES: £19	€24.13		3 day HB:	-		CSP: 33.3%	High Tea: -	-
HBW: -			3 day HB ES: -					

Modern farmhouse overlooking beautiful sandy beach of Kinnagoe Bay. On "Inishowen 100 Scenic Route". Located in peaceful countryside and in special areas of conservation (SAC) and National Heritage Areas (NHA). Scenic hill walking, fishing, golf, horse riding available locally. Excellent restaurants and traditional music nearby. Email: mconway1@iol.ie Website: http://www.iol.ie/~kinnagoebayhouse

VOUCHERS ACCEPTED

INISHOWEN PENINSULA | Donegal DL5

Joyce & Mervyn Norris
TREAN HOUSE
Tremone, Lecamy,
Inishowen, Co Donegal

Tel: 077-67121		Fax: 077-67227	*OBA*
Open: 1st March – 31th October.			
No Rooms:	4	Triple:	1
Twin/Double:	1	Family:	1
Single:	1	En suite:	2

AM V EC

B&B: £17	€21.59		HBW ES:	-		S.Supp: £6.50 €8.25	Dinner: £13 €16.51
B&B ES: £19	€24.13		3 day HB: £79	€100.31		CSP: Negotiable	High Tea: -
HBW: -			3 day HB ES: £90	€114.28			

Charming farmhouse in stone walled countryside beside the sea. Family run farm. Historical sites, fishing, treking, golf, bike hire available locally. From Moville follow R238 towards Gleneely 5km, turn right at crossroads following signs to Carrowmena 4km. Then follow sign for Tremone Bay. Trean House 1st on left. Email: treanhouse@oceanfree.net

VOUCHERS ACCEPTED

KILLYBEGS 4 km | Donegal DL6

The Henry Family
CASTLEREAGH HOUSE
Castlereagh, Bruckless
Co Donegal

Tel: 073-37202		Fax: 073-37202	*OBA*
Open: Easter – 1st October			
No Rooms:	3	Triple:	1
Twin/Double:	2	Family:	-
Single:	-	En suite:	3

AM V EC

B&B:	-		HBW ES:	-		S.Supp: £6.50 €8.25	Dinner: -	-
B&B ES: £20	€25.39		3 day HB:	-		CSP: 20%	High Tea: -	-
HBW: -			3 day HB ES: -					

A warm family welcome awaits you from Beth, Ernest and son Howard at their comfortable early 20th Century farmhouse situated on elevated scenic site with beautiful views of sea and countryside. Ideal location 4km from Killybegs on N56 coast road to Donegal town for touring Slieve League, Glencolmkille, Ardara and Glenveigh National Park. Excellent restaurants and trad. music nearby.

VOUCHERS ACCEPTED

LIFFORD 3 km
Donegal DL7

Mervyn & Jean McKean
THE HALL GREENE
Porthall, Lifford
Co. Donegal

Tel: 074-41318 Fax: –
Open: 5th January – 18th December

OBA

No Rooms:	4	Triple:	-
Twin/Double:	2	Family:	2
Single:	-	En suite:	2

B&B: £17	€21.58	HBW ES:	-	-	S.Supp: £6.50 €8.25	Dinner: -	-
B&B ES: £19	€24.13	3 day HB:	-	-	CSP: 50%	High Tea:-	-
HBW: -	-	3 day HB ES: £100	€126.97			

Experience a warm Irish welcome in one of the oldest houses in Ireland, built in 1611. Working beef and sheep farm situated on the River Foyle with farm walks. Ideal for touring Northern Ireland and Donegal. Unsolicited recommendations in several guide books. Home cooking, central heating. Signposted on N14, 1.5 km from Lifford. Email: hallgreenfarmhouse@eircom.net

VOUCHERS ACCEPTED

PETTIGO 1 km
Donegal DL9

Mrs Mary Leonard
AVONDALE
Lough Derg Road
Pettigo, Co Donegal

Tel: 072-61520 Fax: 072-61787
Open: 1st April – 30th September

OBA

No Rooms:	4	Triple:	1
Twin/Double:	3	Family:	–
Single:	–	En suite:	2

B&B: £17	€21.58	HBW ES:	-	-	S.Supp: -	-	Dinner: -	-
B&B ES: £19	€24.13	3 day HB:	-	-	CSP: Negot.	High Tea: £7.50/9.50 €9.52/12.07
HBW: -	-	3 day HB ES: -				

Modern farmhouse on mixed farm, located in scenic and tranquil surroundings. Close to Lough Derg and Lough Erne. Central location for touring Donegal, Tyrone and Fermanagh. Situated on main route from south to both Dublin and Belfast. Several amenities nearby. Landscaped gardens. All enquiries welcome.

VOUCHERS ACCEPTED

RAMELTON 3 km
Donegal DL11

Mrs Rosemary Crawford
GLEANN ÓIR FARMHOUSE
Ards, Ramelton
Co Donegal

Tel: 074-51187 Fax: –
Open: 1st April – 31st October

OBA

No Rooms:	4	Triple:	1
Twin/Double:	2	Family:	1
Single:	–	En suite:	3

B&B: £17	€21.58	HBW ES:	-	-	S.Supp: £6.50 €8.25	Dinner: -	-
B&B ES: £19	€24.13	3 day HB:	-	-	CSP: 50%	High Tea:-	-
HBW: -	-	3 day HB ES: -				

Enjoy a warm welcome on our mixed farm with panoramic views of the meandering River Lennon and the Hills of Donegal. Explore the beauty and amenities of Donegal and Northern Ireland from here. Situated 10 km from Letterkenny (off N56 at Ellistrin) and 3 km from Ramelton (off R245 at Ramelton). Email: gleannoir@ireland.com

VOUCHERS ACCEPTED

Dublin

Dublin is a unique blend of urban dynamism and rural charm. Its people are witty and friendly, and have a well deserved reputation for irrepressible joie de vivre! The city is Europe's most popular destination for visitors, combining stunning architecture, a great artistic heritage, and a lively social scene. Dublin is a riot of sights, sounds and characters, and if shopping is your cup of tea you will find a fantastic variety of shops and markets in the city. County Dublin is ideal walking terrain, and the coastline provides opportunities for yachting, sailing, wind-surfing and fishing.

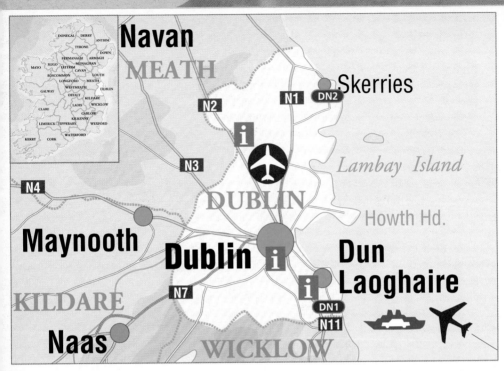

Navan

MEATH

Skerries

N2

N1

DN2

Lambay Island

N3

N4

DUBLIN

Howth Hd.

Maynooth

Dublin

Dun Laoghaire

KILDARE

N7

DN1

N11

Naas

WICKLOW

SHANKILL 4 km   Dublin DN1

Mrs Betty Stevenson
BRIDE'S GLEN FARMHOUSE
Loughlinstown
Shankill, Co Dublin

Tel: 01–2822510   Fax: 01–2827485
Open: 1st April – 30th September

No Rooms:	6	Triple:	–
Twin/Double:	5	Family:	–
Single:	1	En suite:	4

AE AM V EC

				HBW ES:	-	-	S.Supp:	-	Dinner:	-	-
B&B:	£18.00	€22.86									
B&B ES:	£20.00	€25.39	3 day HB:	-	-	CSP:	20%	High Tea:	-	-
HBW:	-	-	3 day HB ES:	-							

Extended farmhouse, on working beef farm overlooking lovely glen and
stream. Convenient for touring Co. Wicklow and Dublin City, all amenities within easy reach. Situated
2km off N11, Dublin to Wexford road. 16km from city centre. Go to Loughlinstown roundabout, beside
Loughlinstown hospital, take exit in direction of Dublin, at "Silver Tassie" turn left and proceed for 2km.

VOUCHERS ACCEPTED

SKERRIES 4 km   Dublin DN2

Mrs Mary Clinton
WOODVIEW FARMHOUSE
Margaretstown
Skerries, Co Dublin

Tel: 01–8491528   Fax: –
Open: 1st March – 31st October

No Rooms:	6	Triple:	1
Twin/Double:	4	Family:	1
Single:	-	En suite:	4

V

			HBW ES:	£220	€279.36	S.Supp: £6.50	€8.25	Dinner:	£14	€17.8
B&B:	£18	€22.85								
B&B ES:	£20	€25.39	3 day HB:	-		CSP:	50%	High Tea: £11	€13.6
HBW:	£210	€266.66	3 day HB ES: £95	€120.63						

Large comfortable farmhouse, est. 1983. Located 4 km west of seaside resort of
Skerries. Follow signs for Ardgillan Castle and Park-house is located 0.5 km from entrance. Turn left off Lusk–Skerries
Road (coming from Dublin). Also 2 km off Balbriggan–Skerries Road (under railway bridge). Very convenient to
Dublin airport and to Dublin ferries. Secure base for visiting city and north Co. Dublin. Email: clintonj@indigo.ie

VOUCHERS ACCEPTED

Galway

The wild and rocky shoreline of the western
counties of Ireland are pitched in constant
battle with the restless Atlantic ocean. The
resulting cliffs, coves and fine beaches provide
a dramatic setting for some of the most
attractive towns in the country. Galway city,
brimming with life, is a centre for the visual
and performing arts. It plays host to the
Galway Arts Festival as well as the world
famous Galway Races.

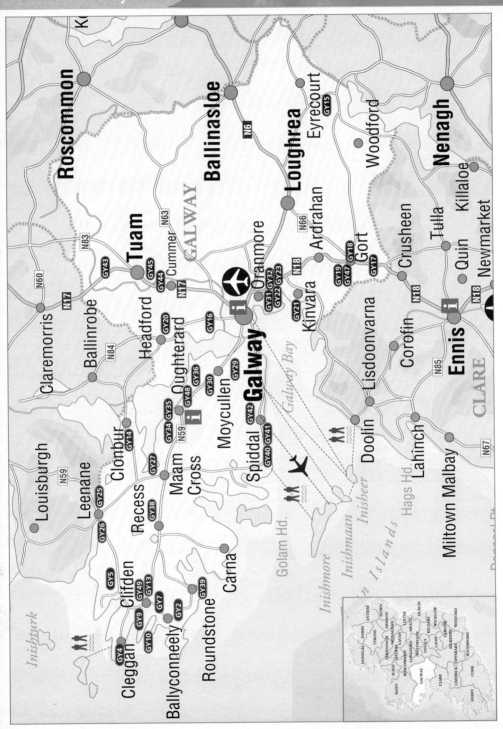

BALLYCONNEELY 1 km | Galway GY2

Mrs Carmel Joyce
TEACH AN EASARD
Ballyconneely, Co Galway

Tel: 095-23560		Fax: 095-23560
Open: 1st January – 15th December		

No Rooms:	6	Triple:	2
Twin/Double:	2	Family:	1
Single:	1	En suite:	6

B&B:	£20	€25.39	HBW ES:	£220	€279.40	S.Supp: £6.50 €8.25	Dinner:	£20	€25
B&B ES:	£20	€25.39	3 day HB:	-		CSP: 25%	High Tea:	£12	€15.24
HBW:	-		3 day HB ES: £110	€139.70					

Old fashioned house with a large garden 1 mile from Ballyconneely village. Close to Connemara golf course. Fishing trips and coastal island and mountain walking tours arranged for guests. Seafood suppers. Award winning Farmhouse. ✗ ⊠ 🛏 ☕ 🍷 🚶 🐾

VOUCHERS ACCEPTED

CLEGGAN | Galway GY4

Mrs Josephine de Courcey
HAZELBROOK
Cleggan, Clifden,
Connemara, Co Galway

Tel: 095-44646		Fax: 095-44646
Open: 15th March – 30th October		

OBA

No Rooms:	6	Triple:	-
Twin/Double:	3	Family:	3
Single:	-	En suite:	5

B&B:	£18	€22.86	HBW ES:	£220	€279.34	S.Supp: £6.50 €8.25	Dinner:	£16	€20.32
B&B ES:	£20	€25.39	3 day HB:	-		CSP: 25%	High Tea:	£10	€12.70
HBW:	£210	€266.64	3 day HB ES: £95	€120.63					

Friendly spacious farmhouse beside fishing village 5km off N59. Panoramic views of sea, mountains, islands. Sea-angling, island hopping tours, boat trips to Inishboffin arranged. Guided heritage walking tours, trips to Connemara National Park with private coach. Pony trekking on sandy beaches. Groups catered for. Recommended Le Guide de Routard and other guides. Email: decourceyhazelbrook@eircom.net Website: www.connemara-tourism.net ✗ ⊠ ∪ ⚓ 🐾 🚶 🎵

VOUCHERS ACCEPTED

CLEGGAN 6 km | Galway GY5

Mrs Marian Feeney
THE OCEAN WAVE
Sellerna, Cleggan
Co Galway

Tel: 095-44775		Fax: 095-44775
Open: 1st May - 1st November		

No Rooms:	3	Triple:	-
Twin/Double:	2	Family:	1
Single:	-	En suite:	3

B&B:	-	-	HBW ES:	£210	€266.64	S.Supp: £6.50 €8.25	Dinner:	£15.50 €19.68
B&B ES:	£19.00	€24.12	3 day HB:	-	-	CSP: 33%	High Tea:	-
HBW:	-		3 day HB ES: £105	€133.32				

Peaceful and relaxing farmhouse, close to fishing village, 6 km off N59. Situated on edge of Cleggan Bay Beach. Breathtaking views of the islands and mountains. See Dolphins 'leap', fishing trips, angling, golfing, pony trekking, mountain climbing. Guided heritage tours. "A home from home stay assured". Traditional music in village pub. ✗ 🍴 ∪ 🎵 🐾 🚴 ♿ ✓

VOUCHERS ACCEPTED

CLIFDEN 6 km | Galway GY13

Mrs Nora Breathnach
DAN O'HARA'S FARMHOUSE
Lettershea
Clifden, Co Galway

Tel: 095-21246/21808	Fax: 095-22098
Open: 1st April – 31st October	

AM V

No Rooms:	4	Triple:	—
Twin/Double:	4	Family:	—
Single:	—	En suite:	4

B&B:	-	-	HBW ES:	-	S.Supp: £6.50 €8.25	Dinner:	-
B&B ES:	£19/20	€24.13/25.39	3 day HB:	-	CSP: Negot.	High Tea:	-
HBW:	-		3 day HB ES: -				

Exclusive country residence attached to traditional working farm and heritage centre. AA listed QQQ. Scenic location on the N59 - main Galway-Clifden Road. 6 km from Clifden. Elegant ensuite bedrooms with phone, TV, coffee/tea making facilities. Breakfast menu. Homebaking. Guests have access to heritage centre and farm walks with superb views. E mail: danohara@eircom.net 🛏 ☕ ∪ 🐾 ✓ 🚴 ♿ TV

VOUCHERS ACCEPTED

CLIFDEN 0.5 km   Galway GY49

Mrs Mary Coyne
CLIFDEN FARMHOUSE
Hospital Road,
Clifden, Co Galway

Tel: 095-21263	Fax: -
Open: 1st April - 30th October	

No Rooms:	4	Triple:	–
Twin/Double:	4	Family:	–
Single:		En suite:	2

B&B: £17	€21.59	HBW ES:	-	S.Supp: £20 €25.39	Dinner:	-
B&B ES: £19	€24.13	3 day HB:	-	CSP: -	High Tea:	-
HBW: -		3 day HB ES:	-			

Modern farmhouse situated on open farm in peaceful surroundings.
5 minutes walk from Clifden with spectacular view of 12 Bens and overlooking Clifden town.
Great centre for touring Connemara and only a walk away from traditional night time entertainment.
Tea/coffee on arrival.

CLIFDEN 2 km   Galway GY7

Michael & Kathleen Conneely
FAUL HOUSE
Ballyconneely Road, Clifden,
Connemara, Co Galway

Tel: 095-21239	Fax: 095-21998
Open: 15th March - 1st November	

No Rooms:	6	Triple:	3
Twin/Double:	1	Family:	2
Single:		En suite:	6

`EC`

B&B:	-	HBW ES:	-	S.Supp: -	Dinner:	-
B&B ES: £20/21	€25.39/26.68	3 day HB:	-	CSP: 10%	High Tea:	-
HBW: -		3 day HB ES:	-			

Relax at "Faul House" set in spacious gardens overlooking sea, amidst farm animals,
Connemara ponies and wildlife. Tranquil location 1km from Clifden off Ballyconneely Rd. Turn right at Connemara
Pottery and proceed for 1 km. Recommended in Le Guide du Routard Ireland. Home baking, breakfast menu and turf
fires. All rooms are complete with tea/coffee making facilities and hairdryers. 5mins walk to sea. AA Listed. QQQQ.

CLIFDEN 1 km   Galway GY9

Mrs May Mannion
CARRAIG A RÓN
Beach Road
Clifden, Co Galway

Tel: 095-21193/21062	Fax: 095-21621
Open: 15th March - 31st October	

No Rooms:	4	Triple:	–
Twin/Double:	2	Family:	2
Single:		En suite:	4

OBA
`AE`
`AM`
`V`
`EC`

B&B:	-	HBW ES:	-	S.Supp: £6.50 €8.25	Dinner:	-
B&B ES: £19/20	€24.13/25.39	3 day HB:	-	CSP: 33.3%	High Tea:	-
HBW: -		3 day HB ES:	-			

Bright comfortable house on water front. Mature gardens. Glorious sea views.
Quiet peaceful location. 1km from town, 500m from safe, sandy beach. Boat club, horse riding, golf, water
sports, hillwalking adjacent. Home baking a speciality. Warm hospitality. Friendly advice and local information
freely offered. Garden for visitors use. Car Parking. Central Heating. Email: marieb@eircom.net

---

CLIFDEN 5 km   Galway GY10

John & Kathy Mullen
ARDMORE HOUSE
Sky Road, Clifden,
Connemara, Co Galway

Tel: 095-21221	Fax: 095-21100
Open: 1st April - 1st October	

No Rooms:	6	Triple:	1
Twin/Double:	4	Family:	1
Single:	-	En suite:	6

B&B:	-	HBW ES: £220	€286	S.Supp: -	Dinner: £16	€20.23
B&B ES: £19/21	€24.13/26.67	3 day HB:	-	CSP: -	High Tea:	-
HBW: -		3 day HB ES:	-			

Spacious farmhouse, set on the edge of the Atlantic ocean, amid beautiful scenery. 5 km
west of Clifden, signposted on the Sky Road. Recommended in the 'B&B Guide to Ireland' & 'Inside Ireland'. All rooms have
television, tea/coffee making facilities & hairdryers. Home baking, fresh seafood, breakfast menu. Turf fires, quiet location.
Scenic walk to to the sea for guests. AAQQQQ Email: info@ardmore-house.com. Website: www.ardmore-house.com

CLONBUR 1 km | Galway GY14

Mrs Ann Lambe
BALLYKINE HOUSE
Clonbur
Co Galway

Tel: 092-46150		Fax: 092-46150	
Open: 1st April – 1st November			
No Rooms:	5	Triple:	--
Twin/Double:	4	Family:	1
Single:		En suite:	4

B&B:	-	-	HBW ES:	-	S.Supp:£6.50 €8.25	Dinner: -
B&B ES: £19	€24.13	3 day HB:	-	CSP: 35%	High Tea:-
HBW:		3 day HB ES: -			

⊠ S 🐾 ⛱ ♪ ♨ ♻

Fine country residence in beautiful woodlands, between Lough Mask and Lough Corrib. Entrance signposted off Cong/Clonbur R345 road. Ideal location for peaceful holiday. Guided forest walks from house. Close to Ashford Castle. Ideal centre for touring Connemara. Angling on Lough Mask and Lough Corrib. Restaurants within walking distance of house. Email: ballykine@eircom.net

---

EYRECOURT 3 km | Galway GY15

Mrs Josephine Lynch
LYNCH'S FARMHOUSE
Mayour
Eyrecourt, Co Galway

Tel: 0905-75156		Fax: –	
Open: 1st January – 31st December			
No Rooms:	3	Triple:	1
Twin/Double:	2	Family:	–
Single:		En suite:	

B&B: £17	€21.59	HBW ES:	-	S.Supp: -	Dinner: £14 €17.77
B&B ES: -		3 day HB: £80	€101.59	CSP: 20%	High Tea:£8 €10.15
HBW: £170	€215.86	3 day HB ES: -			

✗ ⊠ 🐾 S ⛱ ♪ ▶ ☑

Spacious dormer bungalow situated 2 miles east of Eyrecourt on Meelick Road and 1 mile from River Shannon for game and coarse angling. Golf, pet farm, fishing, pitch & putt, bog rail tours nearby. French spoken. Convenient to Clonfert, Clonmacnoise, Birr & Portumna Castles. Excellent standards of comfort, food, service and genuine hospitality.

GALWAY 12 km | Galway GY16

Scott-Furey Family
CORRIB VIEW FARM
Annaghdown
Co Galway

Tel: 091-791114		Fax: –	OBA
Open: 15th April –15th September			
No Rooms:	4	Triple:	1
Twin/Double:	3	Family:	-
Single:		En suite:	3

B&B: £20	€25.39	HBW ES:	-	S.Supp: £7 €8.89	Dinner: -
B&B ES: £22	€27.93	3 day HB:	-	CSP: 25%	High Tea:-
HBW:		3 day HB ES: -			

⛱ ⛴ 🖥 🔌 ♨ ⚘ S

Superb 19th century award winning farmhouse, renowned for comfort, breakfast menu, home baking in peaceful setting near Lough Corrib. Ideal for touring Connemara, Clifden. Trips to Aran Islands arranged. 3 km off Galway- Headford- Castlebar N84 road. Signposted at Cloonboo Cross near Regans Bar/Restaurant. Galway City 10 mins. Email: mscottfurey@hotmail.com

---

GORT 2 km | Galway GY47

Collins Family
EALAMAR
'Coole', Gort,
Co. Galway.

Tel: 091-631572		Fax: 091-631572	AM V
Open: 1st May - 31st Sept			
No Rooms:	4	Triple:	-
Twin/Double:	3	Family:	1
Single:		En suite:	3

B&B: £17	€21.58	HBW ES:	-	S.Supp: £7 €8.88	Dinner: -
B&B ES: £19	€24.13	3 day HB:	-	CSP: 50%	High Tea:-
HBW:		3 day HB ES: -			

S ⛱ 🔌 ☕ 👓 ▶ ☑ ⊘ TV

Comfortable, cosy family run B&B situated in tranquil setting on entrance to 'Coole National Park and Nature reserve' - former estate of Lady Agusta Gregory. W.B. Yeat's Thoorballylee nearby. Ideal base for touring 'The Burren'', Cliffs of Moher', Galway City, Connemara and Aran Islands. Medieval banquets in nearby Dunguaire Castle. Fishing and sandy beaches 10 mins. Email: pmcoll@indigo.ie

---

GORT 3 km　　　　Galway GY17

Patrick & Helen Diviney
LOUGH CUTRA FARMHOUSE
Gort,
Co Galway

Tel: 091-631385　Mobile: 086-2850306
Open: 1st May – 30th September

No Rooms:	5	Triple:	-
Twin/Double:	3	Family:	1
Single:	1	En suite:	2

AE AM V EC

B&B:	£17	€21.58	HBW ES:	-	-	S.Supp: £6.50 €8.25	Dinner: £16 €20.32
B&B ES:	£19	€24.13	3 day HB:	-	-	CSP: 50%	High Tea:£8 €10.16
HBW:	-	-	3 day HB ES:	-			

Large dormer style house on sheep and cattle farm. 45 mins from Shannon and Galway. 200 metres off N18 at entrance to Castle. 3 km south of Gort. Ideal base for touring Burren, Cliffs of Moher and Connemara. Coole Park nearby. Golfing, fishing, horse riding locally. Groups, families welcome. Email: LOUGHCUTRAFARMHOUSE@HOTMAIL.COM

GORT　　　　Galway GY18

Olive Kilroy
GLENBRACK LODGE,
Gort,
Co. Galway

Tel: 091-632042　　Fax: 091-632042
Open: 1st January - 31st December

No Rooms:	4	Triple:	2
Twin/Double:	1	Family:	1
Single:	-	En suite:	4

B&B:	-	-	HBW ES:	-	-	S.Supp: £6.50 €8.25	Dinner: -	-
B&B ES:	£20	€25.39	3 day HB:	-	-	CSP: 25%	High Tea:-	-
HBW:	-	-	3 day HB ES:	-			

Modern spacious family run farmhouse panoramic views of "The Burren" and "Sliabh Aughty". Ideally situated for touring The Burren, Connemara, Galway City and Aran Islands. Coole Park, Thoor Ballylee and Kilmacduagh Monastery. 18 hole golf course, fishing and riding nearby. Gort is a Heritage town known as "The home of the stranger". Glenbrack lodge is home from home to the stranger.

GORT 6 km　　　　Galway GY19

Mrs Bridie Nolan
CORKER HOUSE
Corker
Gort, Co Galway

Tel: 091-631369　　Fax: –
Open: 1st April – 31st October

No Rooms:	4	Triple:	–
Twin/Double:	3	Family:	–
Single:	1	En suite:	3

AE

B&B:	£17	€21.58	HBW ES:	-	-	S.Supp: £6.50 €8.25	Dinner: -	-
B&B ES:	£19	€24.13	3 day HB:	-	-	CSP: 20%	High Tea:-	-
HBW:	-	-	3 day HB ES:	£90	€115		

Spacious farmhouse in quiet rural setting. Turn left 4km north of Gort on N18. Visit Kiltartan Gregory Museum, Thoor Ballylea home of W.B. Yeats, Coole Park and Kilmacduagh Round Tower. Ideal base for touring the Burren, Cliffs of Moher, Connemara and the Aran Islands. Medieval banquets in Dunguaire Castle. New 18 hole golf course in Gort. Garden for visitors use. Internet access available to guests. Email: corkerhouse@eircom.net

---

HEADFORD 5 km　　　　Galway GY20

Matt & Kathleen Cunningham
& Family
HAZEL HOUSE
Mausrevagh, Headford, Co Galway

Tel: 091-791204　　Fax: 091-791204
Open: 1st April – 1st October

OBA

No Rooms:	5	Triple:	-
Twin/Double:	4	Family:	1
Single:	–	En suite:	3

B&B:	£17.50	€22.22	HBW ES:	-	-	S.Supp: £7 €8.88	Dinner: £16.50 €20.95
B&B ES:	£19.50	€24.76	3 day HB:	-	-	CSP: 25%	High Tea:-
HBW:	-	-	3 day HB ES:	-			

National Award winning farmhouse, in peaceful surroundings, 1km off Galway-Castlebar N84 Road. 20 minutes from Galway City. Ideal for touring Connemara and Mayo. Recommended by Beth Bryant, Gault Millau, Amblinn Travel, Karen Browne & other travel writers. Lawn tennis court. Delicious home baking. Tea & scones on arrival. Email: hazelhouse@esatclear.ie

KINVARA 3 km — Galway GY22

Mrs Brenda McTigue
CLAREVIEW HOUSE
Kinvara,
Co Galway

Tel: 091-637170 Fax: 091-637170
Open: 1st March – 1st November OBA

No Rooms:	5	Triple:	2
Twin/Double:	2	Family:	1
Single:	–	En suite:	5

B&B:	-	-	HBW ES:	-	S.Supp: £6.50 €8.25	Dinner: £15	€19.05
B&B ES: £20	€25.39		3 day HB:	-.	CSP: 25%	High Tea:-	
HBW:			3 day HB ES: -				

Spacious farmhouse in rural setting 3 km east of Kinvara, 4 km west of N18 at Ardrahan. Recommended by O'Sullivan B/B Guide, 'Le Guide du Routard'. Medieval banquets at nearby Dunguaire Castle. Convenient to beach and restaurants. Ideal base for touring the Burren, Cliffs of Moher and Connemara.

KINVARA 3 km — Galway GY23

Mrs Bernadette Silke
FORT VIEW HOUSE
Lisheeninane
Kinvara, Co Galway

Tel: 091-637147 Fax: 091-637757
Open: 1st February – 31st October OBA

No Rooms:	6	Triple:	1
Twin/Double:	2	Family:	2
Single:	1	En suite:	6

B&B:	-	-	HBW ES:	-	S.Supp: £6.50 €8.25	Dinner: -	-
B&B ES: £19	€24.13		3 day HB:	-	CSP: 20%	High Tea:-	-
HBW:	-		3 day HB ES: -				

Luxury farmhouse with approved horse riding centre. Capacity for 16 people. TV, tea/coffee facilities and en-suite in all rooms. Walking trails to archaeological sites. Banquets nightly at nearby Dunguaire castle. Ideal base for touring Burren, Cliffs of Moher and Connemara. Beach 3km. Signposted from Dunguaire Castle. Email: fortviewhousebandb@eircom.net

KINVARA 4 km — Galway GY21

BURREN VIEW
O'Connor Family
Doorus
Kinvara, Co Galway

Tel: 091-637142 Fax: 0905-44474
Open: Easter – 30th October

No Rooms:	5	Triple:	1	V
Twin/Double:	4	Family:	-	
Single:	-	En suite:	2	

B&B:	£17	€21.58	HBW ES:	-	S.Supp: £6.50 €8.25	Dinner: -	-
B&B ES: £19	€24.13		3 day HB:	-	CSP: 25%	High Tea: £9	€11.42
HBW:	-		3 day HB ES: -				

Beautifully situated on peninsula, facing unique Burren hills, off N67 road, Kinvara - Ballyvaughan. Serene, unpolluted environment, rich in archaeological, historical and botanical interest. Birdwatching, walking, fishing, golfing. Swimming at local blue flag beach. Local produce, pub (300 yards). Medieval banquets 3 miles. Coole Park 10 miles. Ailwee Caves 10 miles.

LEENANE 0.4 km — Galway GY25

Miss Fiona King
KILLARY HOUSE
Leenane
Co Galway

Tel: 095-42254 Fax: –
Open: All year except Christmas

No Rooms:	6	Triple:	–
Twin/Double:	5	Family:	1
Single:	–	En suite:	4

B&B:	£17	€21.59	HBW ES:	-	S.Supp: £7 €8.89	Dinner: £15	€19.05
B&B ES: £20	€25.39		3 day HB:	-	CSP: -	High Tea:-	
HBW:	-		3 day HB ES: -				

Award winning farmhouse overlooking Killary Harbour on N59 and "Western Way". Ideally located for fishing, touring and hillwalking on the Maamturk and Sheeffry mountains. Only 400m from Leenane pubs and restaurants. Sea cruise on "The Connamare Lady" 2 miles away or pony trekking locally. "Scubadive West" 12 miles away. T.V. Lounge

LEENANE 8 km — Galway GY26

Mrs Josephine O'Neill
GLEN VALLEY HOUSE & STABLES
Glencroff, Leenane,
Connemara, Co Galway

Tel: 095-42269 Fax: 095-42365
Open: 1st March – 30th October *OBA*

No Rooms:	4	Triple:	–
Twin/Double:	4	Family:	–
Single:	–	En suite:	3

B&B	£18	€22.86	HBW ES:	-	-	S.Supp: £10 €12.70	Dinner: -	-
B&B ES:	£20	€25.39	3 day HB:	-	-	CSP: 20%	High Tea:-	
HBW:	-	-	3 day HB ES:	-	-			

Award winning farmhouse and stables, standing in a secluded valley. Glen Valley House offers select riding holidays in the wild & beautiful Connemara. An ideal base for horse lovers or walking enthusiast. 'Western Way' walkway running through our farm. Beaches, National Park nearby. Breeders of Connemara ponies. Recommended by Frommer Guide. Email: gvhouse@yahoo.com

---

MAUM 4 km — Galway GY27

Mrs Breege Gavin
LECKAVREA VIEW HOUSE
Maam (Maum)
Co Galway

Tel: 092-48040 Fax: 092-48040
Open: 2nd January – 20th December *OBA*

No Rooms:	6	Triple:	1
Twin/Double:	3	Family:	1
Single:		En suite:	5

B&B	£17	€21.58	HBW ES:	-	-	S.Supp: -	-	Dinner: £15 €19.04
B&B ES:	£19	€24.13	3 day HB:	-	-	CSP: 25%	High Tea:-	-
HBW:	-	-	3 day HB ES:	-	-			

Lakeside farmhouse in picturesque surroundings overlooking Castle Kirk (Grace O'Malley's castle). Boat trips to castle. Fishing, own boats, engines, gillies available. Groups welcome. Children's playground. Recommended by Frommers Le Guide du Routarde and other travel writers. Local amenities: mountain climbing, walks, horse riding, golf, pitch and putt.

MOYCULLEN 4 km — Galway GY30

Tim & Kathleen Griffin
ROCKFIELD HOUSE
Newtown
Moycullen, Co Galway

Tel: 091-555586 Fax: -
Open: 1st April – 31st October

No Rooms:	4	Triple:	1
Twin/Double:	2	Family:	1
Single:	-	En suite:	3

B&B	£18	€22.85	HBW ES:	-	-	S.Supp: £10 €12.70	Dinner: -	-
B&B ES:	£20	€25.39	3 day HB:	-	-	CSP: 25%	High Tea:-	-
HBW:	-	-	3 day HB ES:	-	-			

Spacious, farmhouse where the Griffin family have farmed for four generations. Farmhouse situated on N59, 2 miles west of Moycullen Village and 15 minutes drive from Galway City. Convenient for visiting the Aran Islands, touring Connemara, the Burren and the Cliffs of Moher. Non-smoking house. Email: rockfieldhouse@oceanfree.net

---

MOYCULLEN 5 km — Galway GY29

Michael & Máire Canney
PORTARRA LODGE
Tullykyne
Moycullen, Co Galway

Tel: 091-555051 Fax: 091-555052
Open: 1st March – 1st December *OBA*

AM
V
EC

No Rooms:	5	Triple:	–
Twin/Double:	5	Family:	–
Single:	–	En suite:	5

B&B	-	-	HBW ES:	£260/277 €330/352	S.Supp: £10 €12.70	Dinner: £19.25 €24.44
B&B ES:	£22.50/25 €28.57/31.74	3 day HB:	-	-	CSP: 20%	High Tea: £5 €6.35
HBW:	-	-	3 day HB ES:	£115/123 €146/156		

A modern farmhouse, beside Lough Corrib. 5 km from Moycullen. Private shoreline with boats, engines and expert gillies for hire. Ideally located for both game and coarse angling. Excellent accommodation. Timber floors with log/turf fires. Modern fire alarm system. Irish/French spoken. Email: portarralodge@eircom.net Website: www.portarralodge.com

ORANMORE 2 km | Galway GY31

Mrs Mary Cannon
CARTROON FARM
Galway Coast Road
Oranmore, Co Galway

Tel: 091-794345　　Fax: –
Open: Easter – 1st November

No Rooms:	4	Triple:	1
Twin/Double:	2	Family:	1
Single:	–	En suite:	4

				HBW ES:	-	S.Supp: £7 €8.89	Dinner: £16 €20.32
B&B:	£18	€22.86		3 day HB:	-	CSP: 50%	High Tea:£8 €10.16
B&B ES:	£20	€25.39		3 day HB ES:£220	€279		
HBW:	-						

Spacious farmhouse in scenic surroundings overlooking Galway Bay. Situated 1 mile West of Oranmore along Oranmore-Galway City Coast Rd (N6 & N18) and 4.5 miles east of Galway City. Ideal base for touring Connemara, Burren and Cliffs of Moher. Galway City and Airport 7 mins drive. Galway Bay Golf and Country Club 5 mins. Horse riding, fishing, sailing, walking locally. Pony kept. French and Spanish spoken. Email: cartroonfarmhouse@eircom.net

---

ORANMORE 4 km | Galway GY32

Mrs Sal Cannon
CANKELLA FARMHOUSE
Tonroe, Oranmore,
Co Galway

Tel: 091-794281　　Fax: –
Open: 1st May – 1st November

No Rooms:	5	Triple:	–
Twin/Double:	5	Family:	
Single:		En suite:	3

				HBW ES:	-	S.Supp: £6.50 €8.25	Dinner: £16.50 €20.95
B&B:	£18	€22.86		3 day HB:	-	CSP: 25%	High Tea:-
B&B ES:	£20	€25.39		3 day HB ES:	-		
HBW:	-						

Bright comfortable farmhouse in excellent location on N18 road between Oranmore and Clarenbridge. Ideal base for touring The Burren, Cliffs of Moher and Connemara. Galway Bay Golf and Country Club 5 mins. Galway City 15 mins. Car parking. Swimming pool, leisure complex, TV lounge for guests, French spoken.

OUGHTERARD 1 km | Galway GY36

Pat & Mary Rattigan
WELLFIELD
Oughterard
Co Galway

Tel: 091-552356　　Fax: 091-552918
Open: 1st March – 31st October

No Rooms:	6	Triple:	–
Twin/Double:	6	Family:	
Single:	-	En suite:	4

				HBW ES:	-	S.Supp: £6.50 €8.25	Dinner: -
B&B:	£17	€21.58		3 day HB:	-	CSP: 10%	High Tea:-
B&B ES:	£19	€24.13		3 day HB ES:	-		
HBW:	-						

Attractive old farmhouse in tranquil rural setting with mixed farming. Enjoy a warm welcome with home baking and turf fires. Along the main N59 1 km from Oughterard which offers fishing, golf and lake trips. Ideal base to explore the delights of Connemara.

OUGHTERARD 3 km | Galway GY35

Ethel and Rita Lee
CORRIB VIEW FARMHOUSE
Oughterard, Connemara
Co Galway

Tel: 091-552345　　Fax: 091-552880
Open: 1st February - 30th November

No Rooms:	6	Triple:	1
Twin/Double:	3	Family:	2
Single:	–	En suite:	6

AM V EC

			HBW ES:	-	S.Supp: £6.50 €8.25	Dinner: -
B&B:	-	-	3 day HB:	-	CSP:	High Tea:-
B&B ES:	£20/24	€25.39/30.47	3 day HB ES:	-		
HBW:	-	-				

Charming old Georgian style farmhouse set in peaceful surroundings with a commanding view of Lough Corrib. 3km east of Oughterard, turn off N59 at sign post for Oughterard golf course. Boats, engines, boatmen available on request. Private all weather tennis court. 18 hole golf course, pitch and putt and Aughnanure castle within walking distance. Email: corribvw@gofree.indigo.ie

OUGHTERARD 3 km — Galway GY48

Michael and Maria Healy
CORRIB WAVE FARM GUESTHOUSE
Portcarron, Oughterard
Connemara, Co. Galway

Tel: 091-552147   Fax: 091-552736
Open: All Year - Except Christmas

No Rooms:	10	Triple:	–
Twin/Double:	8	Family:	2
Single:		En suite:	10

OBA

B&B:	-	-	HBW ES:	£240/260	€304/330	S.Supp: £8	€10.16	Dinner: £15	€19.05
B&B ES: £22.50/25	€28.5/31.7	3 day HB:			CSP: 25%		High Tea:-	
HBW:	-	-	3 day HB ES: £110/117.5	€139/149				

Corrib Wave Guesthouse 3 Star. The home of Michael and Maria Healy and family. Panoramic lakeside setting. Beautiful bedrooms. Superb home cooking. Warm welcome. Peace and quietness. Turf fire. Angling specialists. Boats. Engines. Boatmen for hire. Lakeshore and farm walks. Colour brochure on request. Off season groups specially catered for. Email: CWH@GOFREE.indigo.ie

Vouchers Not Accepted

OUGHTERARD 5 km — Galway GY34

Mrs Mildred Joyce
BROOKVILLE
Glengola
Oughterard, Co Galway

Tel: 091-552163   Fax: –
Open: 1st May – 30th September

No Rooms:	3	Triple:	–
Twin/Double:	2	Family:	–
Single:		En suite:	–

B&B:	£17	€21.58	HBW ES:	-	-	S.Supp: £6.50	€8.25	Dinner: £15	€19.05
B&B ES: -	-		3 day HB:	£90	€114.28	CSP: 20%		High Tea:£10	€12.70
HBW:	£190	€241.25	3 day HB ES: -						

Comfortable farm bungalow centrally situated between Oughterard and Maam Cross off the N59 road. Home baking, open turf fires. Ideal touring location centre for Connemara. Peaceful location. Mountain walks, golfing, pony trekking, coarse and game angling locally. Mixed farming.

VOUCHERS ACCEPTED

RECESS 1 km — Galway GY38

Terry & Rosie Joyce
GLENDALOUGH HOUSE
Recess
Connemara, Co Galway

Tel: 095-34669   Fax: –
Open: Mid May – Mid September

No Rooms:	5	Triple:	1
Twin/Double:	3	Family:	1
Single:		En suite:	3

B&B:	£17	€21.58	HBW ES:	-	-	S.Supp: £6.50	€8.25	Dinner: -	
B&B ES: £19	€24.13		3 day HB:	-	-	CSP: 20%		High Tea:-	
HBW:	-	-	3 day HB ES: -						

Modern spacious bungalow in a very peaceful location. An ideal base for touring. Overlooking Glendalough Lake and the Twelve Pins. It has its own 18 hole pitch & putt. 1km from Recess off N59. Recommended in the Guide du Routard. Tea/coffee making facilities in all rooms. Beef and sheep farm with oak wood walks. Email: rosiej@eircom.net website: connemara.net/glendaloughhouse.

VOUCHERS ACCEPTED

ROUNDSTONE 3 km — Galway GY39

Mrs Ellie Conneely
ATLANTIC VIEW HOUSE
Errisbeg
Roundstone, Co Galway

Tel: 095-35849   Fax: –
Open: 15th May – 30th September

No Rooms:	3	Triple:	–
Twin/Double:	2	Family:	1
Single:	–	En suite:	–

EC

B&B:	£17	€21.58	HBW ES:	-	-	S.Supp: £7	€8.88	Dinner: -	
B&B ES: -	-		3 day HB:	-	-	CSP: 20%		High Tea:-	
HBW:	-	-	3 day HB ES: -						

Modern farm bungalow on elevated site overlooking Gurteen and Dogs Bay beaches. 500 yards from sea, at rear Errisbeg mountain. Located 50 yards off main R341, off N59 road. 2 miles from Roundstone. Ideal for walking and mountain climbing, sea and lake fishing, wind surfing, golf and pony trekking 10km. Email: -ellieconneely@hotmail.com

VOUCHERS ACCEPTED

SPIDDAL 1.5 km — Galway GY40

Nancy Hopkins Naughton
CLOCH NA SCITH
THATCHED COTTAGE
Kellough, Spiddal, Co Galway

Tel: 091-553364   Fax: 091-553890
Open: 17th March–31st December   *OBA*

No Rooms:	3	Triple:	1
Twin/Double:	–	Family:	2
Single:		En suite:	3

B&B:		HBW ES:	-	-	S.Supp: -		Dinner: £20 €25.39
B&B ES: £20/22	€25.39/27.93	3 day HB:	-	-	CSP: -		High Tea:-
HBW:		3 day HB ES:	-	-			

"Guide du Routard", "Guide Dillard" and "Frommels Guide" recommended. Featured on TV "Unusual holidays in Ireland". Original 18th century standards overlooking Galway Bay, Burren, Aran Islands. Breadbaking demonstration cooked in pot oven over turf fire daily. Bread served with tea or coffee on arrival for guests. Email: thatch@eircom.net Website: www.thatchcottage.com

SPIDDAL 2 km — Galway GY41

Mrs Mary Naughton
COISE NA COILLE
Shanavooneen
Spiddal, Co Galway

Tel: 091-553352   Fax: –
Open: March – November   *OBA*

No Rooms:	4	Triple:	-
Twin/Double:	3	Family:	1
Single:		En suite:	2

B&B:	£18.50	€23.49	HBW ES:	-	-	S.Supp: £6.50 €8.25	Dinner:	-
B&B ES: £20	€25.39		3 day HB:	-	-	CSP: 25%	High Tea:-
HBW:	-		3 day HB ES:	-	-		

Modern farmhouse with views of Galway Bay. Situated near a river and a wood. Sandy beaches within walking distance. Ideal for touring Connemara and the west. First turn right immediately after Spiddal village, proceed for 2km. Tea/coffee on arrival. Open turf fire, home baking.

SPIDDAL — Galway GY42

Mrs Mairéad Neachtain
TEARMANN
Baile an t-Sagairt
Spiddal, Co Galway

Tel: 091-553216   Fax: –
Open: 1st April – 31st October

No Rooms:	4	Triple:	–
Twin/Double:	4	Family:	–
Single:		En suite:	2

B&B:	£18.50	€23.49	HBW ES:	-	-	S.Supp: £6.50 €8.25	Dinner:	-
B&B ES: £20	€25.39		3 day HB:	-	-	CSP: 25%	High Tea:-
HBW:	-		3 day HB ES:	-	-		

Modern farmhouse with view of Galway Bay, Clare Hills and the Aran Islands. 200 metres off L100 Coast road, east of Spiddal village in quiet rural surroundings. Ideally located for touring Connemara, Aran Islands and The Burren. Sandy beaches within walking distance. Canoeing and sea angling available. Gaeilge teanga an tí seo.

TUAM 3 km — Galway GY45

Mrs Esther Mannion
GARDENFIELD HOUSE
Tuam,
Co Galway

Tel: 093-24865   Fax: 093-24865
Open: 1st January - 31st December

No Rooms:	3	Triple:	–
Twin/Double:	2	Family:	1
Single:		En suite:	3

AM V EC

B&B:	£18	€22.85	HBW ES: £220	€279.34	S.Supp: £6.50 €8.25	Dinner: £17 €21.58
B&B ES: £20	€25.39		3 day HB: £80	€101.58	CSP: 50%	High Tea:£9 €11.43
HBW: £200	€253.95		3 day HB ES:£100	€126.97		

Michael our children and I invite you to visit us this year. Gardenfield House was built in 1860 and is set in an idyllic landscape. We offers you a quiet retreat with gourmet food, open fires, a warm welcome. We also have two award winning apartments. National winners in AIB Tourist Awards.

TUAM 9 km   Galway GY44

The Fahy Family
WENSLEYDALE FARMHOUSE
Cummer
Tuam, Co Galway

Tel: 093-41467   Fax: 093-41467
Open: 15th March – 1st November

No Rooms:	5	Triple:	1
Twin/Double:	3	Family:	1
Single:	–	En suite:	4

B&B:	£17	€21.58	HBW ES:	-	-	S.Supp:	£9	€11.43	Dinner:	£14	€17.78
B&B ES:	£19	€24.13	3 day HB:	-	-	CSP:	50%		High Tea:	£9	€11.43
HBW:			3 day HB ES:	£90	€114.30						

Newly restored Farmhouse on Galway-Tuam N17 road, 22km from Galway, 9km from Tuam. 60 acre working farm with cows, cattle, horses and pony. Guests may walk through farm on farm road. Play station & games for children. Ideally situated for touring Connemara, Mayo, The Burren & visiting Knock Shrine. Tea & scones on arrival. Fishing locally. Hairdryers & electric blankets. Turf fires. Email: wensleydale@emerge.ie

TUAM 10 km   Galway GY43

Mrs Mary Birmingham
ST ANN'S
Milltown
Tuam, Co Galway

Tel: 093-51337   Fax: –
Open: 1st April – 31st October

OBA
EC

No Rooms:	3	Triple:	1
Twin/Double:	1	Family:	1
Single:	–	En suite:	3

B&B:	-	-	HBW ES:	-	-	S.Supp:	£6.50	€8.25	Dinner:	-	-
B&B ES:	£19/20	€24.13/25.40	3 day HB:	-	-	CSP:	50%		High Tea:	-	-
HBW:	-	-	3 day HB ES:	£105/115	€133/146						

Friendly family run old style farmhouse in peaceful wooded rural surroundings directly off N17 from Galway to Sligo. Tennis, fishing, golf locally. Ideal base for touring Connemara, Achill and Mayo. Knock Shrine 15 miles. Mixed farm. Extra large bedrooms. Tea/coffee facilities and hairdryers in all rooms. Email: st_annes_bb@hotmail.com

To reach any of our farmhouses on the worldwide web, why not look up the award winning **Irish Tourist Board Internet site** http://www.ireland.travel.ie/farmhouses or the **Irish Farmhouse Holidays Internet site** at http://www.irishfarmholidays.com and view the full range of details available on each of our premises.

Ireland and the Environment

Ireland is a beautiful country. Research has shown that people come to Ireland to meet the friendly local people and enjoy our unspoiled natural landscape. We try as much as we can to keep our country clean and 'green', and we appreciate your co-operation in this matter.

We love to share this beauty with as many people as we can. Therefore it is all in our interests to maintain and enhance the natural splendour that Ireland is lucky enough to enjoy. Respect for natural amenities is essential in order to sustain this beautiful, unspoiled environment. By leaving the places we visit tidy we can all do our bit to help, thus ensuring that future generations will come to visit a naturally green Ireland too.

Kerry

Sculptured by the ice-age and influenced by the waters of the Gulf Stream, Kerry is steeped in ancient history. It boasts a wealth of pre-historic buildings and monuments, many of them in remarkably well preserved condition. The region claims some of the most breathtaking scenery in Ireland including the Killarney lakes and the stunning landscapes of the Beara and Dingle peninsulas. Kerry is also famous for its world-famous golf courses.

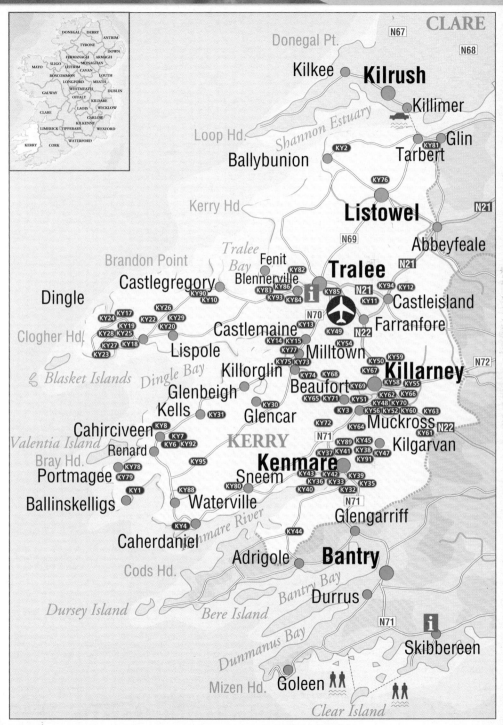

BALLINSKELLIGS | Kerry KY1

Jackie & Mary Sugrue
ISLAND VIEW
Ballinskelligs
Co Kerry

Tel: 066-9479128   Fax: –
Open: 1st April – 1st November

No Rooms:	4	Triple:	–	EC
Twin/Double:	3	Family:	–	
Single:	1	En suite:	3	

B&B:	£17	€ 21.58	HBW ES:	-	-	S.Supp: £6.50	€ 8.25	Dinner: £12	€ 15.24
B&B ES: £19		€ 24.13	3 day HB:	-	-	CSP: -		High Tea: £9	€ 11.40
HBW:	-	-	3 day HB ES:	-					

Enjoy a peaceful stay, 10 km off N70 Ring of Kerry, on Skellig Ring, overlooking Ballinskelligs bay. 0.5 km from EC Blue Flag Beach. Skellig Rock Trips daily. Golf, horse riding, diving, pitch & putt, fishing nearby. Home baking. Breakfast menu. Email: msugrue@esatclear.ie

---

BALLYBUNION 2 km | Kerry KY2

Mrs Eileen Walsh
THE COUNTRY HAVEN
Asdee Tarbert Road
Ballybunion, Co Kerry

Tel: 068-27103   Fax: 068-27822
Open: Easter– 31st October

No Rooms:	5	Triple:	–
Twin/Double:	5	Family:	–
Single:	–	En suite:	5

B&B:	-	-	HBW ES:	-	-	S.Supp: £6.50	€ 8.25	Dinner: -	-
B&B ES: £20/25		€ 25.39/31.74	3 day HB:	-	-	CSP: 50%		High Tea: -	
HBW:	-	-	3 day HB ES:	-					

Discerning travellers perfect choice near Ireland's most prestigious golf course. Justly famed for splendid accommodation with its own private putting green, driving range and hard tennis court, overlooking Atlantic. Rooms with seaview, hair dryers and satellite TV. Also honeymoon suite. 10% green fees reduction. Clubs and racquets for hire on premises. Convenient Tarbert Ferry and Shannon. Recommended in 'Le Guide du Routard'. Email: eileenwalsh@eircom.net Website: http://homepage.tinet.ie/~eileenwalsh

---

CAHERDANIEL 8 km | Kerry KY4

Mrs Nancy Moran
MORAN'S FARMHOUSE
Bunavalla
Caherdaniel, Co Kerry

Tel: 066-9475208   Fax: –
Open: 1st February – 30th November

No Rooms:	4	Triple:	-	EC
Twin/Double:	3	Family:	1	
Single:	-	En suite:	4	

B&B:	-	-	HBW ES:	-	-	S.Supp: £10	€ 12.97	Dinner: £17	€ 21.58
B&B ES: £19		€ 24.13	3 day HB:	-	-	CSP: 40%		High Tea: £12	€ 15.24
HBW:	-	-	3 day HB ES: £108		€ 137.13				

Dormer bungalow with spectacular view overlooking Derrnane Harbour and the Atlantic. This location is situated 4 miles from Caherdaniel between Coomakiste Pass and the sea. Fishing, boating, yachting, walking, diving and wind surfing facilities nearby. Golf at Waterville (6 miles). Sandy beaches. Trips to Skelligs. Dairy farm. Email:nancymoran@eircom.net

---

CAHIRCIVEEN 5 km | Kerry KY6

Mrs Mae McCrohan
MCCROHAN'S SEA FRONT
FARMHOUSE
Renard South, Cahirciveen, Co Kerry

Tel: 066-9472357   Fax: –
Open: 1st May – 15th September

No Rooms:	4	Triple:	–
Twin/Double:	4	Family:	–
Single:	–	En suite:	4

B&B:	£17	€ 21.58	HBW ES:	-	-	S.Supp: £6.50	€ 8.25	Dinner: £15	€ 19.05
B&B ES: £19		€ 24.13	3 day HB:	-	-	CSP: 50%		High Tea: £10	€ 12.70
HBW:	-	-	3 day HB ES: £100		€ 126.97				

Traditional style farmhouse on dairy and beef farm overlooking Valentia Island 2 km off Ring of Kerry N70 road on Waterville side. Mountain scenery peaceful atmosphere with leisurely walks through farm to private sea shore. Tea/coffee facilities. Trips to Skellig island arranged 'Le Guide du Routard Ireland' recommended. Email: mccrohanm@eircom.net

CAHIRCIVEEN 8 km — Kerry KY92

Mrs Catherine Morris
FÁILTE FARMHOUSE
Derrymore, Cahirciveen
Co Kerry

Tel: 066-9472425 Fax: -
Open: 1st April - 31st October

OBA

No Rooms:	3	Triple: —
Twin/Double:	3	Family: —
Single:	—	En suite: 3

B&B:	-	-	HBW ES:	-	-	S.Supp: £6.50 €8.25	Dinner: £15 €19.05
B&B ES: £19	€24.13		3 day HB:	-	-	CSP:	High Tea:- -
HBW:	-	-	3 day HB ES: £100	€126.97			

Luxury farmhouse situated on large farm nestled between the mountains and sea. Close to Ring of Kerry. Adjacent to Kerry Way, hill walking and walks through native bogland on own farm. Horse riding, sandy beaches, fishing, golf, boat trips to Skelligs, diving and sea sports nearby. Many local archaeological sites. Email: failtefarm@mail.com

---

CAHIRCIVEEN 2 km — Kerry KY7

Mrs Claire O'Donoghue
OCEAN VIEW FARMHOUSE
Renard Rd, Cahirciveen,
Ring of Kerry, Co Kerry

Tel: 066-9472261 Fax: 066-9472261
Open: 3rd January — 19th December

No Rooms:	6	Triple: 1
Twin/Double:	4	Family: 1
Single:	—	En suite: 6

B&B:	-	-	HBW ES:			S.Supp: £6.50 €8.25	Dinner: - -
B&B ES: £19	€24.13		3 day HB:			CSP: Under 12's	High Tea:- -
HBW:	-	-	3 day HB ES: -			25% Reduced	

Luxury farmhouse overlooking Cahirciveen Bay within walking distance of town, offering 6 en suite bedrooms, tastefully decorated and all with spectacular sea and mountain views. Peat/wood fires. Tea/coffee facilities. Recommended by Rough Guide. Leisure activities available nearby. Valentia Car Ferry, Skellig Rock Ferry within walking distance. AA QQQ.

CAHIRCIVEEN 1.5 km — Kerry KY8

Mrs Kathleen O'Sullivan
THE FINAL FURLONG
FARMHOUSE & RIDING STABLES
Cahirciveen, Co Kerry

Tel: 066-9473300 Fax: 066-9472810
Open: 1st March - 1st November

OBA
AM
V
EC
AE

No Rooms:	4	Triple: —
Twin/Double:	3	Family: 1
Single:	-	En suite: 4

B&B: £17	€21.58	HBW ES:	-	-	S.Supp: £6.50 €8.25	Dinner: £16 €20.32
B&B ES: £19	€24.13	3 day HB:	-	-	CSP: 20%	High Tea:- -
HBW:	-	3 day HB ES: £99	€125.70			

Beautifully situated by the water yet just 1.5 km from Cahirciveen town on Ring of Kerry. Our farm combines suckler cows, sport horses & approved riding stables - wonderful beach gallops! Golf, sea-angling, lake fishing, walking, Skellig Rock trips arranged. Seafood served. Special offers available. Rough Guide & Dillard/Causin recommended. Email: finalfurlong@eircom.net Website: www.finalfurlong.rural-biznet.com

---

CASTLEGREGORY 6 km — Kerry KY90

Mercedes O'Connor
KILCUMMIN HOUSE
Kilcummin, Castlegreory
Co Kerry

Tel: 066-7139152 Fax: -
Open: April - October

OBA
V

No Rooms:	3	Triple: 2
Twin/Double:	1	Family: —
Single:	—	En suite: 3

B&B: £18	€22.58	HBW ES: £225	€285.75	S.Supp: £6.50 €8.25	Dinner: £15 €19.05
B&B ES: £20	€25.90	3 day HB:	-	CSP: 50%	High Tea:- -
HBW:	-	3 day HB ES: £110	€139.70		

This farm house set in peaceful scenic surroundings on the Dingle Peninsula overlooking Kilcummin Beach. Home cooking our speciality.

CASTLEISLAND 8 km — Kerry KY94

Marie L. Hickey
BALLINATTIN B&B
Ballinattin, Knocknagoshel,
Tralee, Co. Kerry

Tel: 068-46456 Fax: -
Open: All Year OBA

	No Rooms: 3	Triple: –
	Twin/Double: 2	Family: 1
	Single: –	En suite: 3

				S.Supp: -	Dinner: -	-
B&B:	-	HBW ES:	-			
B&B ES: £20 €25.40	3 day HB:	-	CSP: -	High Tea: -	
HBW:	-	3 day HB ES:	-			

Delightful Georgian Farmhouse on hilltop setting. Active dairy and beef farming. Charming river and farm walks, home baking a speciality. Located on N21. Central for touring Kerry. 1hr from Shannon, 20 mins from Ballybunion golf and beach. Rooms En Suite and luxury jacuzzi.

VOUCHERS ACCEPTED

CASTLEISLAND 3 km — Kerry KY11

O'Mahony Family
BEECH GROVE FARM
Camp Road
Castleisland, Co Kerry

Tel: 066-7141217 Fax: 066-7142877
Open: Easter – 30th September OBA

V AM AE

	No Rooms: 4	Triple: 2
	Twin/Double: 2	Family: –
	Single: –	En suite: 4

				S.Supp: £7 €8.89	Dinner: -	-
B&B:	-	HBW ES:	-			
B&B ES: £20/22.50 €25.39/28.57	3 day HB:	-	CSP: 25%	High Tea: -	
HBW:	-	3 day HB ES: -				

Fourth generation family farm, in peaceful setting approached by mature beech lined avenue. Signposted off N21 & N23. Complementary refreshments on arrival. Central for Killarney, Ring of Kerry and Dingle Peninsula. 2 mile nature trail. Excellent restaurants nearby. Agri Tourism awards. Dillard and Causin recommended. Featured in "Wish you were here". Irish spoken.

VOUCHERS ACCEPTED

CASTLEISLAND 0.5 km — Kerry KY12

Mrs Ann Prendiville
BAWN FARM HOUSE
Crag Caves Road
Castleisland, Co Kerry

Tel: 066-7142104 Fax: –
Open: All year - Except Christmas

	No Rooms: 3	Triple: –
	Twin/Double: 3	Family: –
	Single: –	En suite: 3

				S.Supp: £7 €8.89	Dinner: £13 €16.51
B&B:	-	HBW ES:	-		
B&B ES: £19 €24.13	3 day HB:	-	CSP: 50%	High Tea: -
HBW:	-	3 day HB ES: £100 €126.98		

Attractive modern house set on a dairy farm with a river running through it. Enjoy warm hospitality and a very high standard of accommodation. Charming rural setting situated 0.5 km from Castleisland on the Crag Cave Road. (5 minutes walk from Caves). Ideal base for touring Ring of Kerry, Killarney and Dingle. Kerry airport five miles. Tea/coffee facilities.

VOUCHERS ACCEPTED

CASTLEMAINE 1 km — Kerry KY13

Mrs Phena Buckley
'TOM & EILEENS'
Castlemaine
Co Kerry

Tel: 066-9767373 Fax: 066-9767373
Open: 1st May – 1st October

V AM AE

	No Rooms: 5	Triple: –
	Twin/Double: 5	Family: –
	Single: –	En suite: 5

				S.Supp: £6.50 €8.25	Dinner: -	-
B&B:	-	HBW ES:	-			
B&B ES: £19 €24.13	3 day HB:	-	CSP: 50%	High Tea: -	
HBW:	-	3 day HB ES: -				

A traditional Irish welcome from this award winning old style farmhouse nestling under Sliabh Mish Mountains. Situated 1 km from Castlemaine off N70 Tralee Road in centre of Kerry and ideal for touring Tralee, Killarney, Dingle and Ring of Kerry. All activities locally. River flows through this suckling herd and horse farm. Tea making facilities and electric blankets. Recommended 'Le Guide du Routard'. Cúpan tae on arrival. Email: phenab@gofree.indigo.ie

VOUCHERS ACCEPTED

CASTLEMAINE 1 km | Kerry KY14

Mary & The Murphy Family
MURPHY'S FARMHOUSE
Boolteens, Castlemaine
Co Kerry

Tel: 066-9767337	Fax: 066-9767839

Open: All year except December 24th, 25th

No Rooms:	14	Triple:	–
Twin/Double:	12	Family:	
Single:	2	En suite:	14

AM V EC

B&B:	-	-	HBW ES:	£220	€ 279.34	S.Supp:	£6.50	€ 8.25	Dinner: £15 € 19.04
B&B ES:	£19/20	€ 24.13/25.39	3 day HB:	£87	€ 110.47	CSP:	50%		High Tea:£10 € 12.60
HBW:	£184	€ 233.63	3 day HB ES:	£100	€ 126.97				

Traditional comfortable farmhouse on dairy farm, 300 yards off Dingle Road at Boolteens, Inch Beach and Kerry Airport. 4 miles Central for touring Dingle, Tralee, Killarney and Ring of Kerry. Golfing and Walking holidays arranged. Tea/coffee facilities, Murphy's Bar 300 yds. Email: murphyfarmhouse@eircom.net

VOUCHERS ACCEPTED

CASTLEMAINE 2 km | Kerry KY15

Kitty Nagle
PALMGROVE
Ardcanaught,
Castlemaine, Co Kerry

Tel: 066-9767170	Fax: –

Open: 1st April – 15th October

No Rooms:	4	Triple:	–
Twin/Double:	4	Family:	
Single:	–	En suite:	2

AM V EC

B&B:	£17/18	€ 21.58/22.86	HBW ES:	£220	€ 279.34	S.Supp:	£6.50	€ 8.25	Dinner: £15 € 19.04
B&B ES:	£19/20	€ 24.13/25.39	3 day HB:	-	-	CSP:	50%		High Tea:£10 € 12.69
HBW:	£210	€ 267.28	3 day HB ES:	£100	€ 126.97				

Gateway to Ring of Kerry and Dingle Peninsula two storey farmhouse in peaceful surroundings 1 km off the main Dingle Road. Central for touring Dingle, Tralee and Killarney. Inch beach 7 miles, Farranfore Airport 8 miles. Golf, mountain walks, cycling, pony trekking nearby. Experience life on a family-run mixed farm. Home baking with refreshments served on arrival. Visitors may bring own wine.

VOUCHERS ACCEPTED

DINGLE | Kerry KY17

Jimmy Bruic
COILL NA RÓIS
Bally Ganeen, Feohanagh,
Dingle, Co. Kerry

Tel: 066-9155475 / 9155198	Fax: 066-9155233

Open: March to October

No Rooms:	4	Triple:	-
Twin/Double:	4	Family:	
Single:	-	En suite:	4

AM V

B&B:	-	-	HBW ES:	-	-	S.Supp:	£6.50	€ 8.25	Dinner: £20 € 25.39
B&B ES:	£21/25	€ 26.67/31.75	3 day HB:	-	-	CSP:	50%		High Tea:-
HBW:			3 day HB ES:	-					

Nestled at the foot of Mount Brandon amid the tranquil waters of Dingle Bay, lies this cosy little hideaway. Contemporary and spacious guest rooms. Jacuzzi, steam rooms and body showers. Eclectic breakfast menu includes Irish, American and Continental. Nearby activities abound, traditional music and dancing nightly in local pubs. Email: coillnarois@eircom.net

VOUCHERS ACCEPTED

DINGLE 6 km | Kerry KY18

Mrs Brenda Connor
TRANTS LEAP
Clahane, Ventry
Dingle, Co Kerry

Tel: 066-9159844	Fax: –

Open: 12th April– 1st October

No Rooms:	4	Triple:	–
Twin/Double:	2	Family:	2
Single:	–	En suite:	4

B&B:	-	-	HBW ES:	-	-	S.Supp:	£6.50 € 8.25	Dinner: -
B&B ES:	£20	€ 25.39	3 day HB:	-	-	CSP:	25%	High Tea: -
HBW:			3 day HB ES:	-				

Modern farmhouse situated in peaceful surroundings overlooking Ventry Harbour, just off main Dingle Slea Head road. Fine view of beach and ocean. Mixed farm, fresh farm produce, home baking. 1 km from shop, post office, restaurants, pub and beach. Wind, surfing, angling, pony riding nearby. Golf (9 km). Email: trants@iol.ie Website: www.dinglewest.com

VOUCHERS ACCEPTED

DINGLE 4 km

Kerry KY19

John Joe & Anne Curran
BRÓIGÍN
Knockavrogeen East
Dingle, Co Kerry

Tel: 066-9151292   Fax: 066-9151292
Open: 1st January to 31st December

No Rooms:	5	Triple:	–
Twin/Double:	3	Family:	1
Single:	1	En suite:	4

B&B:	£17/19	€21.58/24.13	HBW ES:	-	-	S.Supp: £6.50	€8.25	Dinner: -	-
B&B ES:	£19/21	€24.13/26.15	3 day HB:	-	-	CSP:	33%	High Tea:-	-
HBW:	-	-	3 day HB ES:	-	-				

A warm family welcome awaits you at Bróigín, peacefully located with the majestic Brandon
Mountains in the background. 1 km off Ballyferiter Road. TV Lounge, open fire, tea/coffee facilities, hairdryers etc.
Archaeological tours, walks, golf and pony trekking locally. Rent-a-bike and tennis court on premises. After Dingle, over
Milltown Bridge and next two rights. Le Guide Du Routard, Brittany Ferries recommended. 3 days B&B ES £53.

DINGLE 5 km

Kerry KY20

Mrs Mary Devane
DEVANE'S FARMHOUSE
Lisdargan
Lispole, Co Kerry

Tel: 066-9151418   Fax: –
Open: 1st April – 1st November

No Rooms:	4	Triple:	1
Twin/Double:	3	Family:	–
Single:	–	En suite:	3

B&B:	£17	€21.58	HBW ES:	-	-	S.Supp: £6.50	€8.25	Dinner: £15	€19.05
B&B ES:	£19	€24.13	3 day HB:	-	-	CSP:	25%	High Tea:£11	€13.97
HBW:	-	-	3 day HB ES:£220	€279.40					

Two storey family run farmhouse nestling at the foot of mountains with
beautiful view of Dingle Bay, located off the Tralee Road 5 km from Dingle in peaceful area along
the Dingle Way, mountain climbing, fishing, golfing and pony riding nearby. Beaches 10 minutes drive.
All home baking and home made jams. Garden for guests use, carparking.

DINGLE 1 km

Kerry KY22

Mrs Patricia Devane
HAZELBROOK
Milltown, Dingle
Co Kerry

Tel: 066-9151589   Fax: –
Open: 1st April – 1st November

No Rooms:	4	Triple:	–
Twin/Double:	3	Family:	1
Single:	–	En suite:	4

B&B:	-	-	HBW ES:	-	-	S.Supp: £10	€12.69	Dinner: -
B&B ES:	£20	€25.39	3 day HB:	-	-	CSP:	33%	High Tea:-
HBW:	-	-	3 day HB ES:-	-			

Well situated modern house with magnificent views of harbour and mountains,
1 km west of Dingle on Cuas Road (signposted at Milltown roundabout). Peaceful location. Milltown River
flows through farm. Recommended in 'Inside Ireland.' Clock radios, hairdryers, tea/coffee facilities.
Delicious home baking. Breakfast menu. Ideal location for walkers and cyclists.

DINGLE 10 km

Kerry KY23

Mrs Joan Garvey
GARVEY'S FARMHOUSE
Kilvicadownig, Ventry
Dingle, Tralee, Co Kerry

Tel: 066-9159914   Fax: 066-9159921
Open: 1st March – 1st November

No Rooms:	5	Triple:	–
Twin/Double:	4	Family:	1
Single:	–	En suite:	4

B&B:	£18	€22.86	HBW ES:	-	-	S.Supp: £10	€12.70	Dinner: £17	€21.59
B&B ES:	£20-21	€25.39-26.66	3 day HB:	-	-	CSP:	25%	High Tea:£12	€15.24
HBW:	-	-	3 day HB ES:£110	€139.68					

Welcome to our home on family run working dairy and sheep farm. 3 km
west of Ventry on the Dingle-Slea Head Road, past Pub Paudi O'Shea, opposite Celtic Museum.
Wonderful view of Ventry Harbour at foot of Mount Eagle on the Dingle Way walk. Blue Flag beach
Windsurfing and sailing in vicinity. Complimentary refreshments. 'Le Guide du Routard' recommended.

DINGLE 14 km

Kerry KY10

Mrs Catherine Griffin
GRIFFINS TIP TOP
Country Farmhouse,
Goulane, Conor Pass Road,
Castlegregory, Dingle, Co Kerry

Tel: 066-7139147   Fax: 066-7139147
Open: 1st March – 1st November

No Rooms:	6	Triple:	2
Twin/Double:	2	Family:	1
Single:	1	En suite:	4

AM / V / EC / BC

B&B:	£19.50	€24.75	HBW ES:	-	-	S.Supp: £6.50 €8.25	Dinner: -	-
B&B ES:	£20/25	€31.75/25.40	3 day HB:	-	-	CSP: 25%	High Tea: -	-
HBW:	-	-	3 day HB ES:	-				

A warm welome awaits you at Griffins Tip Top two storey farmhouse on the beautiful Dingle
Peninsula. Fronted by safe sandy beaches. As a background a varied range of mountains. Far from the "Madding Crowd". Tralee 19 miles. AA
QQ and Frommer recommended. Sea angling, one of the best fishing grounds in Europe. Ideal for the ornithologist, landscape artist. Sheep
farm. Golf, surfing, hang gliding. Kite flying on the beach nearby. Multi channel TV in lounge. Email: griffin'stiptopfarmhouse@eircom.net

VOUCHERS ACCEPTED

DINGLE 11 km

Kerry KY24

The Hurley Family
AN DOONEEN
Kilcooley, Ballydavid
Dingle, Co Kerry

Tel: 066-9155112   Fax: 066-9155112
Open: Easter – 1st October

No Rooms:	4	Triple:	—
Twin/Double:	4	Family:	—
Single:	—	En suite:	3

EC

B&B:	£17	€21.58	HBW ES:	-	-	S.Supp: £6.50 €8.25	Dinner: -	-
B&B ES:	£19	€24.13	3 day HB:	-	-	CSP: 50%	High Tea: -	-
HBW:	-	-	3 day HB ES:	-				

Comfortable spacious farmhouse located on the Dingle Peninsula, 11 km
west of Dingle. Rugged coastal scenery and sandy beaches close by. 10 km from Blasket Islands.
Ideal location for quiet holiday. Sea fishing, golf, mountain climbing and places of archaeological
interest. Located on the Dingle Way Walk. AA recommended. Email: thehurleyfarmhouse@hotmail.com

VOUCHERS ACCEPTED

DINGLE 2km

Kerry KY25

Kathleen Lynch
KILLFOUNTAIN FARM
Killfountain
Dingle, Co. Kerry

Tel: 066-9151389   Fax: -
Open: March - November

No Rooms:	6	Triple:	1
Twin/Double:	2	Family:	3
Single:	1	En suite:	5

OBA / V

B&B:	-	-	HBW ES:	-	-	S.Supp: £6.50 €8.25	Dinner: -	-
B&B ES:	£19	€24.13	3 day HB:	-	-	CSP: 25%	High Tea: -	-
HBW:	-	-	3 day HB ES:	-				

Beautiful tranquil location, 2km west of Dingle off the Ballyferriter Road (R559).
Private garden, private parking, home baking, tea/coffee on arrival. Convenient to golf,
fishing, beaches, tennis, horse riding, pitch and putt 1km, archaeological tours, angling and "The Dingle Way" walking
trail. Le Guide de Routard recommended. Families welcome. Working Dairy Farm. 6 bedrooms (5 en-suite)

VOUCHERS ACCEPTED

DINGLE 10 km

Kerry KY26

Mrs Veronica Maunsell
LOCH AN DÚIN
Ballyhoneen, Conor Pass Road
Cloghane, Co Kerry

Tel: 066-7138163   Fax: —
Open: 1st April – 15th October

No Rooms:	3	Triple:	—
Twin/Double:	3	Family:	—
Single:	—	En suite:	2

AM / V / EC

B&B:	£17	€21.59	HBW ES:	-	-	S.Supp: -	Dinner: -	
B&B ES:	£19	€24.13	3 day HB:	-	-	CSP: 50%	High Tea: -	
HBW:	-	-	3 day HB ES:	-				

Modern family home situated on Conor Pass Road, (R560) with panoramic
views of Mt. Brandon & Bay. Sheep Farm. Beaches, fishing, watersports and archaeological sites nearby.
Located close to Dingle Way Walk. Cloghane Village 4km. Breakfast menu. A warm welcome awaits you.
3 day B&B ES £57. Email: lochanduin@eircom.net Website: www.kerry-insight.com/lochanduin/

VOUCHERS ACCEPTED

DINGLE 8 km — Kerry KY27

Bríd & Ted Moriarty
MORIARTY'S FARMHOUSE
Rahanane, Ventry
Tralee, Co Kerry

Tel: 066-9159037 Fax: 066-9159037
Open: 1st January – 31st December

No Rooms:	6	Triple:	–
Twin/Double:	4	Family:	2
Single:	–	En suite:	6

AM V EC

B&B:	-	-	HBW ES:	£245	€ 311.09	S.Supp: £10	€ 12.70	Dinner: £16 € 20.32
B&B ES: £20	€ 25.39		3 day HB:	-	-	CSP:	£16 € 20.32	High Tea:£12 € 15.24
HBW:	-	-	3 day HB ES:	£105	€ 133.32			

Welcome to our family run home overlooking Ventry Harbour, 8 km west of Dingle just off Dingle-Slea Head Road. Signposted at Ventry Church. All rooms en suite with sea view, tv, tea facilities, clock radio, electric blankets and hairdryer. Tea scones on arrival. Blue Flag beach, spectacular walks off Dingle-Way Walk. Historical sites nearby. Breakfast menu. 3 day B&B ES £57 Email: mrty@eircom.net Website: www.dinglevacation.com

VOUCHERS ACCEPTED

DINGLE 8 km — Kerry KY28

Mrs Ailene Murphy
ÁRD AN CHÁISLEAN
Rathanane Castle,
Ventry, Dingle, Co Kerry

Tel: 066-9159846 Fax: 066-9159127
Open: All year round

OBA

No Rooms:	5	Triple:	–
Twin/Double:	4	Family:	1
Single:	–	En suite:	5

AM V EC

B&B:	-	-	HBW ES:	£210	€ 266.64	S.Supp: £7	€ 8.89	Dinner: £16 € 20.32
B&B ES: £20	€ 25.39		3 day HB:	-	-	CSP:	25%	High Tea:£12 € 15.12
HBW:	-	-	3 day HB ES:	£105	€ 133.32			

Enjoy the peace and tranquility of life on an Irish dairy farm overlooking Ventry harbour on the grounds of a 16th century castle and ringfort. Excellent home cooking. Tea and scones on arrival. 10 min drive from Dingle. Take Slea Head drive road. Second turn right and second left after Ventry village. 1km from shops, pubs, restaurant. Blue flag beach. Horseriding, windsurfing, hillwalking. Golf nearby. Email: murphysfarmhouse@tinet.ie

VOUCHERS ACCEPTED

DINGLE 4 km — Kerry KY29

Catherine O'Dowd
O'DOWD'S FARMHOUSE
Knockavrogeen
Dingle, Co Kerry

Tel: 066-9151307 Fax: –
Open: May to 15th September

EC

No Rooms:	5	Triple:	1
Twin/Double:	2	Family:	1
Single:	1	En suite:	5

B&B:	-	-	HBW ES:	-	-	S.Supp: £6.50 € 8.25	Dinner: - -
B&B ES: £19	€ 24.13		3 day HB:	-	-	CSP: -	High Tea: -
HBW:	-	-	3 day HB ES:	-	-		

Modern farm bungalow located 4 km west of Dingle on Ballyferriter Road. Tennis court (green). Covered swimming pool, mini golf all on premises for guest's use. Breakfast menu, tea/coffee making facilities in bedrooms. Comfortable, warm and relaxing. 5 minutes drive from beach and Dingle restaurants. Signposted at O'Dowd's B&B.

VOUCHERS ACCEPTED

GLENBEIGH 11 km — Kerry KY31

Marion O'Grady
GLENVILLE FARMHOUSE
Gleesk
Kells, Co Kerry

Tel: 066-9477625 Fax: 066-9477625
Open: 1st April – 30th October

No Rooms:	3	Triple:	1
Twin/Double:	2	Family:	1
Single:	–	En suite:	3

AM V EC AE

B&B:	-	-	HBW ES:	-	-	S.Supp: £6.50 € 8.25	Dinner: -
B&B ES: £20	€ 25.39		3 day HB:	-	-	CSP: 33%	High Tea:-
HBW:	-	-	3 day HB ES:	-	-		

Welcome to Glenville Farmhouse on Ring of Kerry route N70, between Glenbeigh and Cahirciveen. Panoramic views of Dingle Bay, Brandon Mountains and Rossbeigh beach. Mixed farming. Hill walking on own farm. Adjacent to Kerry Way. Great fishing in Kells bay, also safe sandy beach. Fishing trips and trips to Skellig Rock arranged. Golf courses and restaurants nearby. Traditional Irish pub, music and dance next door. TV lounge. Car parking. Garden for visitors use. Email: eogrady@esatclear.ie

VOUCHERS ACCEPTED

GLENCAR | Kerry KY30

Mrs Breda Breen
BLACKSTONES HOUSE
Glencar
Co Kerry

Tel: 066-9760164		Fax: 066-9760164	
Open: 1st April – 31st October			OBA
No Rooms: 6		Triple: -	AE V
Twin/Double: 6		Family: -	
Single: –		En suite: 6	

B&B:	-	-	HBW ES:	-	S.Supp: £6.50 €8.25	Dinner: £15 €19.05
B&B ES: £20	€25.39		3 day HB:	-	CSP: 33%	High Tea: -
HBW:	-		3 day HB ES:	-		

Spacious farmhouse. Scenically situated beside Blackstones Bridge, Lickeen Wood. Over-looking the Caragh River. All rooms with picturesque views of the river, Blackstones Falls, McGillicuddy Reeks, fishing, shooting, mountaineering, walking, hillwalking, forest walks. On Kerry Way walking route. Golf courses 12 km. Ideal base for touring Ring of Kerry. Award Winner 1995. Home baking. Highly commended Boston Globe., Country Walking magazine, Guide de Routard. Email: blstones@iol.ie

VOUCHERS ACCEPTED

KENMARE 1.5 km | Kerry KY32

Mrs Joan Brown
THE NOOK
Muxnaw
Kenmare, Co Kerry

Tel: 064-41196		Fax: –	
Open: 17th March – 31st October			
No Rooms: 4		Triple: –	EC
Twin/Double: 3		Family: 1	
Single: –		En suite: 4	

B&B:	-	-	HBW ES:	-	S.Supp: £6.50 €8.25	Dinner: - -
B&B ES: £20-22	€25.39-27.93		3 day HB:	-	CSP: 30%	High Tea: -
HBW:	-		3 day HB ES:	-		

Family run farmhouse. Beautiful view of Caha Mountains. Situated 1.5 km from Kenmare just off N71 Glengarriff Road. Set in peaceful surroundings with large garden. Tea making facilities, breakfast menu. Golf, fishing, horse riding locally. 'Guide du Routard' listed.

VOUCHERS ACCEPTED

KENMARE 2.5 km | Kerry KY33

Mrs Patricia Dignam
GLENDARRAGH
Kenmare
Co Kerry

Tel: 064-41436		Fax: 064-41956	
Open: 1st June – 1st October			
No Rooms: 6		Triple: 1	V
Twin/Double: 3		Family: 1	EC
Single: 1		En suite: 4	

B&B: £20	€25.39		HBW ES:	-	S.Supp:	Dinner: - -
B&B ES: £21.50/25	€27.3/31.75		3 day HB:	-	CSP: 50%	High Tea: -
HBW:	-		3 day HB ES:	-		

Tastefully furnished warm friendly home in quiet location – 2 km from Kenmare off R571. Panoramic views from farm. Idyllic base for walking and wild life enthusiasts. Bridge evenings arranged. Multi-channel TV in all rooms. Tea making facilities. Also sauna and sunbed. Extra large superior beds. Breakfast menu. Highly recommended by 'Which' and many publications. Mobile: 087 - 2791999.

VOUCHERS ACCEPTED

KENMARE 3 km | Kerry KY89

Gaine Family
GAINE'S COUNTRY HOUSE
Two-Mile-Bridge, Killarney Rd.,
Kenmare, Co. Kerry.

Tel: 064-42476		Fax: –	
Open: 12th April – 31st October			
No Rooms: 3		Triple: 1	
Twin/Double: 1		Family: 1	
Single: –		En suite: 3	

B&B:	-	-	HBW ES:	-	S.Supp: £6.50 €8.25	Dinner: - -
B&B ES: £19.00	€24.13		3 day HB:	-	CSP: 25%	High Tea: -
HBW:	-		3 day HB ES: £100	€126.97		

Picturesque mountain setting on N71 Kenmare / Killarney rd., Gaine's Farmhouse is set on 137 acres of mountian farmland, suckler herd. Kenmare 3km. Ideal base for walking /touring Cork, Kerry peninsula. Complementary tea, coffee, home baking. Beautiful bedrooms. Extensive breakfast menu. Guest lounge with tea, coffee facilities. Email: gainescountryhouse@eircom.net

VOUCHERS ACCEPTED

KENMARE 4 km — Kerry KY35

Mrs Mary Downing
GREEN ISLE
Glengarriffe Road
Kenmare, Co Kerry

Tel: 064-41087 Fax: –
Open: 1st May – 30th September

No Rooms:	4	Triple:	–
Twin/Double:	2	Family:	2
Single:	–	En suite:	3

B&B:	£17	€21.58	HBW ES:	-	-	S.Supp: £6.50	€8.25	Dinner: £15	€19.05
B&B ES:	£19	€24.13	3 day HB:	-	-	CSP:	-	High Tea:£12	€15.24
HBW:	-	-	3 day HB ES: £60	€76.18					

Attractive farm home situated 4 km from Kenmare town on Kenmare-Glengarriff road. Relaxing atmosphere, log fires in lounge. Nice walks, River Sheen flows through farm. Flower garden. Friendly donkey for children. Home baking, fresh farm produce. Ideally located for touring Cork, Glengarriff, Beara, Ring of Kerry. Sea 4 km.

KENMARE 6 km — Kerry KY36

Mrs Mary Falvey
BAYVIEW FARM
Templenoe
Kenmare, Co Kerry

Tel: 064-41383 Fax: 064-41383
Open: Easter – October 31st

No Rooms:	6	Triple:	3
Twin/Double:	2	Family:	-
Single:	1	En suite:	4

V / AM / EC

B&B:	£17	€21.58	HBW ES:	£220	€279.34	S.Supp: £6.50	€8.25	Dinner: £15	€19.50
B&B ES:	£19	€24.13	3 day HB:	-	-	CSP: 25%		High Tea:-	-
HBW:	£200	€254.39	3 day HB ES: £110	€139.67					

Old style farmhouse on 100 acres overlooking Kenmare Bay. 6 km from Kenmare on Sneem Ring of Kerry road N70. Home cooking a speciality. Ideal situation for mountain climbing and touring. 18 hole golf course next - Ideal for river lake and deep sea fishing. Tea/coffee in all bedrooms.

KENMARE 3 km — Kerry KY37

John and Maureen Harris
CARHOOMEENGAR FARMHOUSE
Carhoomeengar East
Kenmare, Co Kerry

Tel: 064-41987 Fax: -
Open: 1st April - 30th September

OBA

No Rooms:	3	Triple:	–
Twin/Double:	3	Family:	–
Single:	–	En suite:	3

B&B:	-	-	HBW ES:	£218	€277	S.Supp: £6.50	€8.25	Dinner: £15	€19.05
B&B ES:	£19/20	€24.13/25.39	3 day HB:	-	-	CSP: 33%		High Tea:£10	€12.70
HBW:	-	-	3 day HB ES: £96	€122					

Tastefully restored old style farmhouse abounding with antiques set in 120 acres with panoramic views over Kenmare Bay and surrounding mountains. Ideal for walking, climbing, fishing, golf, touring Ring of Kerry/Beara. Extensive breakfast menu. Spacious warm comfortable rooms. Suckler herd and rare breeds of poultry. Just off N71 Kenmare/Killarney Road.

KENMARE 1 km — Kerry KY38

Mrs Thérèse Hayes
CEANN MARA
Killowen, Kenmare
Co Kerry

Tel: 064-41220 Fax: 064-41220
Open: 1st June – 15th September

No Rooms:	4	Triple:	–
Twin/Double:	4	Family:	–
Single:	–	En suite:	3

B&B:	£20	€25.40	HBW ES:	-	-	S.Supp: £7	€8.89	Dinner: £16	€20.32
B&B ES:	£22	€27.90	3 day HB:	-	-	CSP:	-	High Tea:£12	€14.72
HBW:	-	-	3 day HB ES: -	-					

An award winning home, 1 km from Kenmare on R569 (Cork Road). Ceann Mara overlooks Kenmare estuary with private access to shore. It has a large garden with interesting plants. Vegetarians welcome. Log fire. Private parking. - Galtee breakfast awards - "Ireland's 300 Best B&Bs." "Special places to stay." "Which" Recommended. Email: ceann.mara@eircom.net

KENMARE 4 km Kerry KY39

Lovett Family
WHITE HEATHER FARM
Glengarriff Road
Kenmare, Co Kerry

Tel: 064-41550   Fax: 064-42475
Open: 15th April – 30th September

No Rooms:	5	Triple:	1
Twin/Double:	1	Family:	2
Single:	1	En suite:	4

V EC

B&B:	£18	€ 22.85	HBW ES:	£220	€ 279.34	S.Supp: £7	€ 8.89	Dinner: £15	€ 19.05
B&B ES: £20		€ 25.39	3 day HB:	-	-	CSP: 25%		High Tea: £8	€ 10.16
HBW: £200		€ 253.95	3 day HB ES: -						

Family farm 4km on Kenmare-Glengariff N71 road. Easy to find. We are at the head ✗ ✿ S 🔥 ⊗ 🐾 U TV
of Beara Peninsula and Ring of Kerry. Convenient quiet location. Mixed farm with many animals. Spectacular
mountain views. Ideal base for walking, touring and fishing on river Sheen which flows through farm. Cab arranged.
Orthopaedic beds, T.V., hairdryers. Tea/coffee making facilities on request. 'Le Guide de Routard' recommended.

VOUCHERS ACCEPTED

KENMARE 1 km   Kerry KY40

Mrs Anne Maybury
TARA FARM
O'Sullivan–Maybury's Tara Farm
Tubrid, Kenmare, Co Kerry

Tel: 064-41272   Fax: 064-41377
Open: 10th March – 15th November

No Rooms:	6	Triple:	3
Twin/Double:	2	Family:	1
Single:	-	En suite:	6

V AM AE

B&B:	-		HBW ES:	£240	€ 304.74	S.Supp: -	-
B&B ES: £20/23	€ 25.35/29.20	3 day HB:	-	-	CSP: 33%	Dinner: £15	€ 19.05
HBW: -	-	3 day HB ES: £110	€ 139.67			High Tea: £12	€ 15.24

Tara Farm superbly situated overlooking Kenmare Bay with river and   TV 🖥 S 🐾 🔥 ⊡ U 🎵
private shore on farmlands. Luxury, spacious, warm, comfortable accommodation. Bedrooms with
patios/balconies with sea/mountain views. 1km from Kenmare. Signposted off Ring of Kerry N70
and Killarney N71 roads. Seafood specialty. Breakfast menu. Email: tarafarm@eircom.net

VOUCHERS ACCEPTED

KENMARE 1.5 km   Kerry KY91

Mrs. McCarthy
KILLOWEN HOUSE
Killowen, Kenmare
Co Kerry

Tel: 064-41415   Fax: 064-42200
Open: 1st May - 1st October

No Rooms:	3	Triple:	–
Twin/Double:	2	Family:	–
Single:	1	En suite:	2

V

B&B:	£17	€ 21.58	HBW ES:	£220	€ 279.34	S.Supp: £7	€ 8.89	Dinner: £14.50	€ 18.41
B&B ES: £19		€ 24.13	3 day HB:	-	-	CSP: 25%		High Tea: -	-
HBW: -	-	3 day HB ES: -							

A warm welcome awaits when visiting Killowen House, set in 105 acres including   ✿ S 🔥 🐶 ⊡ 🎣 🐾 ✓
bird and wildlife reserve, fishing and 1/2 mile of private shoreline. Historic ruins of castle, panoramic views of
Roughty Estuary, Sheen Falls and mountains. In-house beautician on request, cookery demonstrations,
French/German spoken. Situated less than 1.5km from Kenmare on R569. Email: shellfis@indigo.ie

VOUCHERS ACCEPTED

KENMARE 1 km   Kerry KY41

Mrs Thérèse O'Shea
CÉOL NA HABHANN
Killarney Road
Kenmare, Co Kerry

Tel: 064-41498   Fax: –
Open: 1st February – 10th November

No Rooms:	5	Triple:	1
Twin/Double:	3	Family:	1
Single:	–	En suite:	4

OBA EC

B&B:	£18/19	€ 22.85/24.13	HBW ES:	-	-	S.Supp: £6.50	€ 8.25 Dinner: -
B&B ES: £19/21		€ 24.13/26.66	3 day HB:	-	-	CSP: 33.3%	High Tea: £9
HBW: -			3 day HB ES: -				€ 11.43

O'Sheas farm home is situated in a tranquil area of glorious settings, off N71 Killarney ✗ ✿ S 🔥 ⊡ 🐾 B D TV
- ring of Kerry rd., approx 1km from Kenmare town. Close to Kerry Way. Ring fort on dairy farm. Spacious rooms
all with T.V. Tea and coffee facilities and hairdryers. Families welcome. Travel writers recommended. Golf, fishing,
water sports, hill walking and mountain climbing. Traditional music locally. Email: osheasfarmhouse@eircom.net

VOUCHERS ACCEPTED

KENMARE 1 km — Kerry KY42

O'Sullivan Family Farm
GORTAMULLEN HOUSE
Gortamullen
Kenmare, Co Kerry

Tel: 064-41216 Fax: –
Open: 1st May – 1st October

No Rooms:	4	Triple:	1
Twin/Double:	3	Family:	–
Single:	–	En suite:	4

EC

B&B:	-	HBW ES:	-	S.Supp:	-	Dinner:	-
B&B ES: £19	€24.13	3 day HB:	-	CSP:	-	High Tea:	-
HBW:	-	3 day HB ES:	-				

Large two storey residence on working dairy farm with commanding views of mountains and of the town. Situated 1 km from Kenmare town off the Ring of Kerry N70 and Killarney N71 roads. Boat/fishing, golf, horse riding available locally.

VOUCHERS ACCEPTED

KENMARE 1 km — Guesthouse — Kerry KY43

Mrs Mary Patricia O'Sullivan
SEA SHORE
Tubrid, Kenmare
Co Kerry

Tel: 064-41270 Fax: 064-41270
Open: 1st Feburary – 15th November

No Rooms:	6	Triple:	2
Twin/Double:	4	Family:	–
Single:	-	En suite:	6

OBA

AM
V
EC

B&B:	-	HBW ES:	-	S.Supp: £10	€12.97	Dinner:	-
B&B ES: £27.50/35.00	€35/44.50	3 day HB:	-	CSP: 50%		High Tea:	-
HBW:	-	3 day HB ES:	-				

Grade A, 3 Star Guesthouse, 4 Diamond AA Selected, blissfully quiet, 1 mile from town. Spacious bedrooms overlooking Kenmare Bay, king beds DD phones, wheelchair friendly. Recommended by Le Guide du Routard, Los Angeles Times. Signposted 300m from Kenmare on Killarney Road at junction N70/N71. Email:seashore@eircom.net Website: http://seashorefarm.homepage.com

Vouchers Not Accepted

KENMARE / BEARA 20 km — Kerry KY44

Mrs Sheila O'Sullivan
MOUNTAIN VIEW
Healy Pass Road, Lauragh
Kenmare, Co Kerry

Tel: 064-83143 Fax: –
Open: Easter – 15th October

No Rooms:	3	Triple:	1
Twin/Double:	2	Family:	–
Single:	-	En suite:	2

OBA

B&B: £17	€21.58	HBW ES: £200	€253.88	S.Supp: £6.50 €8.25	Dinner: £13/14 €16.5/17.8		
B&B ES: £19	€24.13	3 day HB:	-	CSP: 50%	High Tea:	-	
HBW:	-	3 day HB ES:	-				

Relax at Mountain View amongst farm animals and wildlife. Superbly situated on the beautiful Beara Peninsula. Excellent home cooking and baking. Fresh local seafood daily. Visitors welcome to bring own wine. Web access, spectacular walks, maps provided. Email: mountainview@eircom.net

VOUCHERS ACCEPTED

KENMARE 7 km — Kerry KY45

Randles Family
DOIRE FARM
Upper Clontoo
Kilgarvan, Co Kerry

Tel: 064-85312 Fax: –
Open: 1st April – 31st October

No Rooms:	3	Triple:	–
Twin/Double:	3	Family:	–
Single:	-	En suite:	1

B&B: £17	€21.58	HBW ES:	-	S.Supp: £6.50 €8.25	Dinner: £15	€19.04	
B&B ES: £19	€24.13	3 day HB:	-	CSP: 25%	High Tea: £10	€12.70	
HBW:	-	3 day HB ES:	-				

You are assured of a warm welcome to our farmhouse as you are greeted with tea/coffee and home baking. Situated on the Kenmare/Cork R569 road, overlooking the picturesque Roughty Valley in peaceful surroundings, convenient to Ring of Kerry and West Cork. Fishing free to guests. Horse riding, watersports, tennis and walks locally. Email: doirefarm@eircom.net

VOUCHERS ACCEPTED

KILGARVAN 0.5 km

The Traynor Family
RIVERSIDE FARM
Kilgarvan
Killarney, Co Kerry

Tel: 064-85487		Fax: –	
Open: 1st April– 30th October			
No Rooms:	4	Triple:	2
Twin/Double:	2	Family:	–
Single:	–	En suite:	1

B&B:	£17	€21.58	HBW ES:	-	S.Supp:£6.50 €8.25	Dinner: -	-
B&B ES: £19		€24.13	3 day HB:	-	CSP: -	High Tea: -	
HBW: -			3 day HB ES: -				

Three storey period house dating 1815 on main Kenmare-Cork road. Overlooking Roughty River with large mature gardens. Fishing free to guests. Home baking, fresh wild salmon. Pony trekking arranged. Shooting, golf, sea fishing in the area. Ideal centre for touring the Ring of Kerry, Killarney, Dingle Peninsula. Large car park. Gault et Millau recommended. Central heating.

KILLARNEY 3 km

Mrs Marie Beazley
CARRIGLEA HOUSE
Muckross Road
Killarney Co Kerry

Tel: 064-31116		Fax: 064-37693	
Open: 1st April - 1st November			
No Rooms:	8	Triple:	2
Twin/Double:	6	Family:	-
Single:	-	En suite:	8

AM
V
EC

B&B:	-	-	HBW ES:	-	S.Supp: £8 €10.15	Dinner: -	-
B&B ES: £20/21		€25.49/26.66	3 day HB:	-	CSP: -	High Tea: -	
HBW: -			3 day HB ES: -				

150 year old Victorian manor house with unrivalled situation overlooking lakes and mountains. Located adjacent to National Park, lakes and walking trails. Luxury accommodation, spacious en-suite rooms decorated in old world style, with TV and hairdryer, tea making facilities on request. Frommer guide, Lonely Planet recommended. Email: carriglea@oceanfree.net

KILLARNEY 10 km

Burke Family
GRANGE GROVE FARM
Firies, Killarney
Co Kerry

Tel: 066-9764372		Fax: –	
Open: Easter – 31st October			
No Rooms:	6	Triple:	1
Twin/Double:	2	Family:	2
Single:	1	En suite:	5

EC

B&B:	£17	€21.58	HBW ES:	-	S.Supp: -	Dinner: £15	€19.05
B&B ES: £19		€24.13	3 day HB:	-	CSP: 30%	High Tea: -	
HBW: -			3 day HB ES: -				

Comfortable 18th century farmhouse. Mixed farm on 100 acres on Ring of Kerry L561 road, 2 miles north east of Castlemaine, 3 miles west of Farranfore Airport. Horses, ponies and 'Tiny Tears' pony for riding (free on farm). Slides, tree house, swings for children. Basketball, snooker available. Beaches (15 miles). Good fishing nearby. Email: grangegrovefarm@eircom.net

KILLARNEY 4 km

Mrs Sheila Fitzgerald
CASA CASILA
Tralee Road
Killarney, Co Kerry

Tel: 064-32687		Fax: –	
Open: 17th March – 1st November			
No Rooms:	3	Triple:	1
Twin/Double:	1	Family:	-
Single:	-	En suite:	3

B&B:	£17	€21.58	HBW ES:	-	S.Supp: £6.50 €8.25	Dinner: -	-
B&B ES: £19		€24.13	3 day HB:	-	CSP: -	High Tea: -	
HBW: -			3 day HB ES: -				

Charming country house with magnificent views of Killarney's mountains and valleys on the N22 Tralee-Limerick Road. 5 minutes drive from Killarney. All rooms en suite with TV, clock radios, tea/coffee making facilities and hair dryers. Tea and scones on arrival. Early breakfast. Low season rates available.

KILLARNEY 8 km | Kerry KY51

Joan Galvin
POT OF GOLD
Beaufort Village
Killarney, Co Kerry

Tel: 064-44194   Fax: 064-44194
Open: 1st April - October 31st

No Rooms:	6	Triple:	-
Twin/Double:	5	Family:	-
Single:	1	En suite:	4

B&B:	£17	€21.58	HBW ES:	-	-	S.Supp: £6.50 €8.25	Dinner: -	-
B&B ES:	£19	€24.13	3 day HB:	-		CSP: -	High Tea: -
HBW:	-	-	3 day HB ES: -				

Modern bungalow with beautiful view of Gap of Dunloe and
McGillycuddy's Reeks in Beaufort village. Fishing on River Laune which flows through farm. Donkey
for children. Private TV and reading lounge available for visitors. Golf 3 km, sea 18km, Killarney 8
km. Dairy and sheep farm. Choice of restaurant in village.

KILLARNEY 5.5 km | Kerry KY52

Joy Family
FOREST HAVEN
Loughitane Road
Muckross, Killarney, Co Kerry

Tel: 064-33757   Fax: –
Open: March – October

No Rooms:	6	Triple:	–
Twin/Double:	5	Family:	1
Single:	–	En suite:	5

EC

B&B:	£17	€21.58	HBW ES:	-	-	S.Supp: -	-	Dinner: -	-
B&B ES:	£19	€24.13	3 day HB:	-		CSP: -	High Tea: -
HBW:	-	-	3 day HB ES: -				

Hillside bungalow situated in peaceful surroundings with magnificent view
of Killarney's Lakes and Mountains. Ideal location for walking or cycling holiday as we are situated
1 km from National Park, 5.5 km from Killarney. Home cooking and tourist information available.
Tours arranged.

KILLARNEY 10 km | Kerry KY54

Mrs Mary Kearney
GAP VIEW FARM
Firies, Killarney
Co Kerry

Tel: 066-9764378   Fax: –
Open: 20th April – 30th September

No Rooms:	6	Triple:	2
Twin/Double:	3	Family:	1
Single:	–	En suite:	6

EC

B&B:	-	-	HBW ES:	-	-	S.Supp: £6.50 €8.25	Dinner: -	-
B&B ES:	£19	€24.13	3 day HB:	-		CSP: 25%	High Tea: -
HBW:	-	-	3 day HB ES: -				

18th century farmhouse with panoramic vista of Gap of Dunloe and Kerry
mountains. An ideal base for touring the Ring of Kerry, Dingle Peninsula and exploring Killarney. 10 km
from Killarney off N22 road. We offer the visitor an experience on a dairy, tillage and sheep farm.
Frommers Guide and Gault Millau recommended. Visitors may bring own wine. Golf course 10 km.

KILLARNEY 6 km | Kerry KY55

Mrs Margaret Kissane
BEECHGROVE
Knockeragh
Killarney, Co Kerry

Tel: 064-33292   Fax: 064-33292
Open: 1st May - 1st October

No Rooms:	3	Triple:	1
Twin/Double:	2	Family:	–
Single:	–	En suite:	2

B&B:	£17	€21.59	HBW ES:	-	-	S.Supp: £6.50 €8.25	Dinner: -	-
B&B ES:	£19	€24.13	3 day HB:	-		CSP: 40%	High Tea: -
HBW:	-	-	3 day HB ES: -				

Modern farm bungalow in quiet panoramic location just 6km from
Killarney Town with its many amenities. Fishing, golf, hill walking, National Park. Ideal touring base
for Ring of Kerry and Dingle Peninsula trips. Comfortable lounge for guests with peat fire. Friendly
family atmosphere and a warm welcome assured. Email: beechgrove@eircom.net

KILLARNEY 5.5 km   Kerry KY56

Looney Family
KILTRASNA FARMHOUSE
Loughquittane Road
Muckross, Killarney, Co Kerry

Tel: 064-31643   Fax: 064-39775
Open: 1st May – Mid October

No Rooms:	6	Triple:	2
Twin/Double:	3	Family:	-
Single:	1	En suite:	6

B&B:	-	HBW ES:	-	S.Supp:	-	Dinner:	-
B&B ES: £19	€ 24.13	3 day HB:	-	CSP:	50%	High Tea:	-
HBW:	-	3 day HB ES:	-				

Situated in the heart of Muckross lakeland district with magnificent views of Torc and Mangerton mountains. 2km from National Park and Torc Waterfall. Ideal base for touring the "Kerry Way". Bike hire available, leisure complex nearby. Kiltrasna offers good food in a friendly atmosphere. Recommended by Le Guide du Routarde. Farranmore airport 10 miles. Excellent restaurants nearby. Golf and pony trekking locally. Organised walking trips.

VOUCHERS ACCEPTED

KILLARNEY 2 km   Farm Guesthouse   Kerry KY58

Mr Michael Moynihan
FOREST VIEW
Cork Road
Killarney, Co Kerry

Tel: 064-33971   Fax: 064-37620
Open: 1st April – 31st October

No Rooms:	10	Triple:	1
Twin/Double:	7	Family:	1
Single:	1	En suite:	10

V / AM

B&B:	-	HBW ES:	-	S.Supp: £6.50	€ 8.25	Dinner:	-
B&B ES: £19	€ 24.13	3 day HB:	-	CSP:	50%	High Tea:	-
HBW:	-	3 day HB ES:	-				

Large modern comfortable farmhouse, 2 km from Killarney on the main N22 Killarney-Cork Road. Ideal holiday base. Forest walks and river fishing nearby. Golf and horse riding close by. Peat fires and TV lounge. Friendly and relaxed atmosphere. Complimentary refreshments. Dry stock farm.

VOUCHERS ACCEPTED

KILLARNEY 5 km   Kerry KY59

O'Connor Family
GLEBE FARMHOUSE
Tralee Road (off)
Killarney, Co Kerry

Tel: 064-32179   Fax: 064-32039
Open: 1st February – 20th December

No Rooms:	6	Triple:	–
Twin/Double:	3	Family:	2
Single:	1	En suite:	4

V / AM

B&B:	£17	€ 21.58	HBW ES:	£202	€ 256.49	S.Supp: £6.50	€ 8.25	Dinner: £13	€ 16.51
B&B ES:	£19	€ 24.13	3 day HB:	£80	€ 101.58	CSP:	50%	High Tea: £8	€ 10.16
HBW:	£178	€ 226.01	3 day HB ES: £86		€ 109.20				

Comfortable farmhouse, peacefully set overlooking Killarney's mountains. Situated 1km off Tralee N22 road, 5kms from Killarney. Animals and pony rides for children. Vintage museum. Central for Ring of Kerry and Dingle Peninsula. Low season rates. Fishing nearby. Friendly atmosphere and warm welcome assured. Good food and home baking. Tea/Coffee facilities. T.V. & hairdryer in rooms. Email: glebefarmhouse@eircom.net

VOUCHERS ACCEPTED

KILLARNEY 8 km   Kerry KY60

Sheila O'Donoghue & Family
VALLEY VIEW FARMHOUSE
Gortdromakerry, Muckross
Killarney, Co Kerry

Tel: 064-31206   Fax: 064-31206
Open: 1st May – 1st October

No Rooms:	5	Triple:	–
Twin/Double:	4	Family:	–
Single:	1	En suite:	4

AM / V

B&B:	£17	€ 21.59	HBW ES:	-	S.Supp:	-	Dinner:	-
B&B ES:	£19	€ 24.13	3 day HB:	-	CSP:	-	High Tea:	-
HBW:	-	3 day HB ES:	-				

Two storey farmhouse on 70 acre mixed farm on the shore of Lough Guitane situated 4 km off N71 and 5km off N22, 8 km from Killarney. Ideal location for outdoor pursuit activities. Ponies and jaunting car for hire. Bus tours arranged. Recommended 'Le Guide du Routard.' Credit cards accepted. Email: valleyview1@eircom.net

VOUCHERS ACCEPTED

KILLARNEY 17 km   Kerry KY61

Mrs Eileen O'Donoghue
WOODGROVE FARMHOUSE
Glenflesk
Killarney, Co Kerry

Tel: 064-53010   Fax: –
Open: 1st April – 1st November   EC

	No Rooms:	3	Triple:	–
	Twin/Double:	3	Family:	–
	Single:	–	En suite:	3

B&B:	£19	€24.13	HBW ES:	-	-	S.Supp: £6.50 €8.25	Dinner: £12 €15.24
B&B ES:	£19	€24.13	3 day HB:	-	-	CSP: 20%	High Tea: £10 €12.97
HBW:	-	-	3 day HB ES:	£100	€126.98		

18th century, 4th generation farm cottage at the foot of Crohane Mountains in the River Flesk Valley. Killarney is 15km, 1 mile off N22 Killarney-Cork Road. Quiet and peaceful. Home cooking. Fresh produce. Tea making facilities on request, hairdryers. Warm welcome assured. Email: woodgrv@gofree.indigo.ie

---

KILLARNEY 3 km   Kerry KY62

Mrs Margaret O'Donoghue
SUNRISE VILLA
Mill Road
Killarney, Co Kerry

Tel: 064-32159   Fax: 064–32159
Open: 1st May – 1st October   V AM EC

	No Rooms:	4	Triple:	–
	Twin/Double:	4	Family:	–
	Single:	–	En suite:	4

B&B:	-	-	HBW ES:	-	-	S.Supp: £7 €8.89	Dinner: - -
B&B ES:	£19	€24.13	3 day HB:	-	-	CSP: 25%	High Tea: -
HBW:	-	-	3 day HB ES:	-			

Modern two storey farmhouse in quiet scenic surroundings situated 3 km from Killarney. Accessible from both N22 and N71 at Gleneagle Hotel. TV in all bedrooms. Convenient to Muckross House Abbey and Lakes of Killarney. Email: sunrisevilla@tinet.ie Website: www.kerryweb.ie/destination/kerry/killarney/sunrise.html

---

KILLARNEY 14 km   Kerry KY63

Mrs Sheila O'Donoghue
SALMON LEAP
Inch, Glenflesk
Killarney, Co Kerry

Tel: 064-53005/53118 Fax: 064-53005
Open: 1st February – 30th November

	No Rooms:	6	Triple:	1
	Twin/Double:	5	Family:	–
	Single:	–	En suite:	6

B&B:	-	-	HBW ES:	£220	€279.34	S.Supp: £6.50 €8.25	Dinner: £14 €17.78
B&B ES:	£19	€24.13	3 day HB:	-	-	CSP: 20%	High Tea: £10.50 €13.33
HBW:	-	-	3 day HB ES:	£96	€121.89		

Over 200 year old farmhouse in scenic setting on N22 road 9 miles east of Killarney. Beef farming. Angling, golfing and walking nearby. Of great archaeological interest, farm contains early christian burial ground dating from 800-1500 AD. Home baking and dinners by candlelight. Visitors welcome to bring own wine. Dogs welcome. This is an ideal base for touring the south west of Ireland. Email: salmleap@gofree.indigo.ie

---

KILLARNEY 3.5 km   Kerry KY64

Mrs Maureen O'Donovan
MUCKROSS RIDING STABLES
Mangerton Road, Muckross
Killarney, Co Kerry

Tel: 064-32238   Fax: –
Open: 1st March – 15th November

	No Rooms:	6	Triple:	-
	Twin/Double:	4	Family:	2
	Single:	-	En suite:	5

B&B:	£17	€21.58	HBW ES:	£230	€292.1	S.Supp: £7 €8.90	Dinner: £14.50 €18.41
B&B ES:	£19/20	€24.20/25.4	3 day HB:	-	-	CSP: 50%	High Tea: - -
HBW:	-	-	3 day HB ES:	-			

Farmhouse set in peaceful valley. Large warm comfortable rooms with panoramic view of mountains, oak forest with red deer, walkers paradise for people not interested in riding. Short walk to Muckross House and Killarney Lakes. Approved stables. Jaunting cars for hire. 3.5 km south of Killarney, 0.5 km off Ring of Kerry Road. All rooms with orthopaedic beds. Peat fires. Recommended 'Le Guide du Routard'. AA listed ♦♦♦ email: muckross_stables_bandb75@yahoo.ie

KILLARNEY 17.5 km — Kerry KY65

John & Eileen O'Shea
FARMSTEAD LODGE
Shanara Cross, Kilgobnet
Beaufort, Killarney, Co Kerry

Tel: 066-9761968   Fax: 066-9761968
Open: 1st April – 1st November

No Rooms:	4	Triple:	1
Twin/Double:	3	Family:	–
Single:	–	En suite:	1

B&B:	£17	€21.58	HBW ES:	£190	€241.25	S.Supp: £6.50 €8.25	Dinner: £14.50 €18.41
B&B ES:	£19	€24.13	3 day HB:	£87	€110.47	CSP: 50%	High Tea: £10 €12.70
HBW:	£184	€233.63	3 day HB ES:	£90	€114.28		

Dairy farm nested at the foot of Ireland's highest mountains. Perfect base for touring Ring of Kerry, Dingle, Killarney and Gap of Dunloe. Choice of golf courses, fishing, horse riding, mountain climbing and peaceful walks locally. Beach 30 minutes drive, restaurants, pubs, 10 minutes. Large garden, picnic area, barbecue, swings for kids, Irish music/dance by family. TV lounge. Tours arranged. Complimentary refreshments

VOUCHERS ACCEPTED

KILLARNEY 5 km — Kerry KY66

Mrs Alice O'Sullivan
RIVER VALLEY FARMHOUSE
Minish, Cork Road
Killarney, Co Kerry

Tel: 064-32411   Fax: 064-37909
Open: 1st March – 15th November

No Rooms:	6	Triple:	2
Twin/Double:	2	Family:	1
Single:	1	En suite:	6

AE / AM / V / EC

B&B:	-	-	HBW ES:	£215	€273.05	S.Supp: £7.50 €9.52	Dinner: £14 €17.78
B&B ES:	£19	€24.13	3 day HB:	-		CSP: 25%	High Tea: £10 €12.70
HBW:	-	-	3 day HB ES:	£96	€121.89		

200 year old farmhouse with modern facilities. 5 km from Killarney, 0.5 km off N22 Killarney-Cork Road. Suitable touring base for. Fishing, golfing, nature walks, music in area. Orthopaedic beds, tea facilities and TV in bedrooms. 'Le Guide du Routard' recommended. Warm welcome assured. Email: rivervalleyfarmhouse@eircom.net Website: rivervalleyfarmhouse.eircom.net

VOUCHERS ACCEPTED

KILLARNEY 1 km — Kerry KY67

Donie & Noreen O'Sullivan
KILLARNEY RIDING STABLES
Ballydowney
Killarney, Co Kerry

Tel: 064-31686   Fax: 064-34119
Open: 1st March – 20th December

No Rooms:	4	Triple:	–
Twin/Double:	4	Family:	–
Single:	–	En suite:	4

AE / DC / AM / V / EC

B&B:	-	-	HBW ES:	-	S.Supp: £10 €12.70	Dinner: -	-
B&B ES:	£22	€27.93	3 day HB:	-	CSP: -	High Tea: -	
HBW:	-	-	3 day HB ES:	-			

Modern farmhouse beside Killarney National Park, lakes and golf courses. Located 1 km west of Killarney on the Ring of Kerry Road (N72). Approved stables with riding for 1, 2 or 3 hours in National Park. 4 & 6 day Killarney Reeks Trail. Email: Killarney Reek Trail. Email: krs@eircom.net

VOUCHERS ACCEPTED

KILLARNEY 10km — Kerry KY68

Eileen O'Sullivan
LAUNE LODGE
Kilbonane, Beaufort,
Killarney, Co. Kerry.

Tel: 064-44238   Fax: -
Open: 1st March – 31st October

No Rooms:	4	Triple:	2
Twin/Double:	2	Family:	-
Single:	-	En suite:	4

V / AM / AE

B&B:	-	-	HBW ES:	-	S.Supp: £7.00 €8.89	Dinner: -	-
B&B ES:	£19	€24.13	3 day HB:	-	CSP: 20%	High Tea: -	-
HBW:	-	-	3 day HB ES:	-			

Luxurious new house purpose built with our guests in mind. Enjoy the spectacular view which overlooks the River Laune and MacGillycuddy's Reeks. Private fishing free to our guests. Located on the Ring of Kerry (N72). Ideal base for touring all Kerry. You are welcome!

VOUCHERS ACCEPTED

KILLARNEY 8 km — Kerry KY69

John & Mary Anne O'Sullivan
KYLIE FARMHOUSE
Pallas, Beaufort,
Killarney, Co Kerry

Tel: 064-44197   Fax: –
Open: 1st March – 31st October

No Rooms:	3	Triple:	–
Twin/Double:	3	Family:	
Single:	–	En suite:	2

V

B&B:	£18	€22.86	HBW ES:	-	S.Supp: £7	€8.89 Dinner: -	-
B&B ES:	£20	€25.39	3 day HB:	-	CSP: 25%	High Tea:-	
HBW:	-		3 day HB ES:	-			

Comfortable family bungalow on 50 acre dairy farm. Enjoys an enviable position overlooking Killarney Lakes, McGillycuddy Reeks, Dunloe, River Laune. 8 km west of Killarney, 0.5 km off N72. Good home baking, fowl, bees, vintage machinery, pony etc. Mobile phone no.: 087-8257182. Email: o_sullivanjohn@hotmail.com

KILLARNEY 5 km — Kerry KY70

Mrs Noreen O'Sullivan
LÍOS NA MANACH
Off Mill Road, Muckross
Killarney, Co Kerry

Tel: 064-31283   Fax: –
Open: 15th January – 15th December

No Rooms:	6	Triple:	1
Twin/Double:	2	Family:	
Single:	1	En suite:	2

AM V EC

B&B:	£17	€21.58	HBW ES:	£215	€273.99	S.Supp: £6.50 €8.25	Dinner: £14 €17.78
B&B ES:	£19	€24.13	3 day HB:	-		CSP: 25%	High Tea: -
HBW:	£200	€253.95	3 day HB ES:	£96	€121.89		

Quiet and secluded family run farmhouse. 5km from Killarney and 5 km from Muckross National Park. Accessible from both N22 & N71 Road at Glen Eagle Hotel. Scenic nature walks and private fishing on River Flesk which flows by farm. Orthopaedic beds. Home baking, peat fires, cows to beef farm. Email: liosnamanach@eircom.net

KILLARNEY 9 km — Farm Guesthouse — Kerry KY71

Noel & Eileen Spillane
INVERARAY
Coolmagort, Beaufort,
Killarney, Co Kerry

Tel: 064-44224   Fax: 064-44775
Open: 10st March – 1st November

No Rooms:	10	Triple:	3
Twin/Double:	4	Family:	2
Single:	1	En suite:	9

EC

B&B:	-	-	HBW ES:	£220/240 €279.3/304.7	S.Supp: £6.50 €8.25	Dinner: £13 €16.51
B&B ES:	£19/24	€24.13/30.47	3 day HB:	-	CSP: 33.3%	High Tea:-
HBW:	-	-	3 day HB ES:	£95/105 €120.6/133.3		

Luxury house, view of lakes and Gap of Dunloe, 9 km west of Killarney, 1 km off N72 left over Laune Bridge at "Shop". Free private trout and salmon fishing on river Laune. Horse riding, golf, singing pubs, playroom, playground and pony for children. Seafood. Tea room. Direct Dial phones, Satellite TV. Guide de Routard '2000. Email: inver@indigo.ie

KILLARNEY 10 km — Kerry KY3

Mrs Mary Sweeney
THE INVICTA
Tomies, Beaufort
Killarney, Co Kerry

Tel: 064-44207   Fax: 064-44207
Open: 1st April – 31st October

No Rooms:	4	Triple:	1
Twin/Double:	2	Family:	1
Single:	–	En suite:	4

AM V EC AE

B&B:	-	-	HBW ES:	-	S.Supp: £6.50 €8.25	Dinner: -	-
B&B ES:	£19	€24.13	3 day HB:	-	CSP: 25%	High Tea:-	-
HBW:	-	-	3 day HB ES:	-			

Charming home overlooking Killarney's Lakes. Fishing for salmon and trout, boats available. Enjoy the walks of Gap of Dunloe, Tomies woods and Carrauntoohill. Golfers have a choice of 9 and 18 hole courses. Take N72 from Killarney, after 3 miles, take left for Gap of Dunloe, signposted at next junction.

KILLARNEY 28 km   Kerry KY72

Mary R. Tangney
HILLCREST FARMHOUSE
Gearahmeen, Black Valley
Killarney, Co Kerry

Tel: 064-34702		Fax: 064-34702
Open: 1st March – 1st November		*OBA*

		AM
No Rooms:	5	Triple:	—
Twin/Double:	5	Family:	—
Single:		En suite:	5

OBA / AM / V

		HBW ES:	-	-	S.Supp: £6.50 €8.25	Dinner: £15 €19.05
B&B:	-	-				
B&B ES: £20	€25.39	3 day HB:	-	-	CSP: 25%	High Tea: -	-
HBW:	-	-	3 day HB ES: -			

Traditional style farmhouse scenically situated midst Killarney's lake and mountain district. Signposted at Molls Gap on N71 Ring of Kerry road. 100 metres off Kerry Way walking route. 5 minutes walk to national park and Upper Lake. Boating, fishing, pony riding, mountain climbing, nature walks locally. No Dogs. Drying room available. Home baking. Recommended le Guide de Routard and many walking books.

KILLORGLIN 3 km   Kerry KY73

Mrs Mary Foley
DROMIN FARMHOUSE
Killorglin, Miltown Post
Office, Co Kerry

Tel: 066-9761867		Fax: –
Open: 1st April – 31st October		

		AM / V / EC
No Rooms:	4	Triple:	1
Twin/Double:	2	Family:	1
Single:	—	En suite:	3

		HBW ES:	-	-	S.Supp: £6.50 €8.25	Dinner: £16.50 €20.95
B&B: £17/19	€21.59/24.13	3 day HB:	-	-	CSP: Negot.	High Tea: -
B&B ES: £19/20	€24.13/25.39	3 day HB ES: £105	€133.32			
HBW:	-	-				

Welcome to our home - a real working dairy and sheep farm with goat and rabbit. Perfect base between Killorglin & Milltown. Signposted on the N70 one mile from Killorglin. Panoramic mountain views including Ireland's highest mountain. Home baking. TV lounge, peat fires. Orthopaedic beds. Can bring own wine. Special rate for 3 or more nights off season. Tea & home made scones on arrival. AAQQQ Approved. Email: drominfarmhouse@yahoo.com

---

KILLORGLIN 4 km   Kerry KY74

The Johnston Family
DUNGEEL FARMHOUSE
Killorglin
Co Kerry

Tel: 066-9761456		Fax: –
Open: May 1st – September 30th		

		V
No Rooms:	4	Triple:	—
Twin/Double:	3	Family:	1
Single:		En suite:	4

		HBW ES:	-	-	S.Supp: £6.50 €8.25	Dinner: -
B&B:	-	-				
B&B ES: £19/20	€24.13/25.39	3 day HB:	-	-	CSP: 25%	High Tea: -
HBW:	-	-	3 day HB ES: -			

Spacious 300 year old, 6th generation home on 100 acre dairy and sheep farm, overlooking McGillycuddy Reeks and Gap of Dunloe on N72, Killarney to Killorglin road. Gateway to Ring of Kerry and Dingle. Killorglin 4 km. Killarney 10 km. Choice of restaurants, golf and house riding nearby. Warm welcome and good food.

KILLORGLIN 3.5 km   Kerry KY75

Joe & Dorothea Stephens
HILLVIEW FARMHOUSE
Milltown P.O.
Co Kerry

Tel: 066-9767117		Fax: 066-9767910
Open: 1st March – 31st October		*OBA*

		AM / V / EC / AE
No Rooms:	4	Triple:	1
Twin/Double:	2	Family:	1
Single:	—	En suite:	4

		HBW ES: £250	€317.43	S.Supp: £6.50 €8.25	Dinner: £16.50 €20.95
B&B:	-	-			
B&B ES: £19/20	€24.13/25.39	3 day HB:	-	-	CSP: 25%	High Tea: -
HBW:	-	-	3 day HB ES: £105	€133.32		

A warm welcome awaits you at this 5th generation family run working dairy/ sheep farm, overlooking Slieve Mish mountain, on the N70 between Killorglin/Milltown. Recommended by Australian and French journalists. Golf, fishing 1 km. Beaches, walking, mountain climbing, pony trekking nearby. Airport 10 km. Reputation for good food. Complimentary refreshments. Email: dstephens@eircom.net

LISTOWEL 1 km — Kerry KY76

Mrs J Groarke
BURNTWOOD HOUSE
Listowel
Co Kerry

Tel: 068-21516/21724 Fax: 068-21017
Open: Easter – 1st November

AM
V

	No Rooms:	6	Triple:	1
	Twin/Double:	3	Family:	2
	Single:	–	En suite:	4

B&B:	£17	€21.58	HBW ES:	-	-	S.Supp: £6.50	€8.25	Dinner:	-	-
B&B ES:	£19	€24.13	3 day HB:	-	-	CSP:	10%	High Tea:	-	
HBW:			3 day HB ES:	-						

200 year old Georgian residence, set in a tree lined avenue, 1 km from Listowel on Ballylongford Road. 15 km from Tarbert car ferry. Shannon Airport 1.5 hour drive, Ballybunnion golf course 15 km. Tea/coffee making facilities. Frommers Guide recommended. Reduction for Continental Breakfast. Credit Cards accepted.

MILTOWN 1 km — Kerry KY77

Mrs Gret Leane
KILBURN HOUSE
Miltown
Killarney, Co Kerry

Tel: 066-9767364 Fax: 066-9767364
Open: 2nd January - 20th December

V
AM

	No Rooms:	4	Triple:	–
	Twin/Double:	3	Family:	1
	Single:	–	En suite:	4

B&B:			HBW ES:	£250	€317.43	S.Supp: £6.50	€8.25	Dinner:	£16	€20.32
B&B ES:	£22.5/25	€28.57/31.74	3 day HB:	-	-	CSP:	50%	High Tea:	£10	€12.70
HBW:			3 day HB ES:	£110	€139.67					

Luxury Georgian Farmhouse, listed in "Houses of Kerry" on dairy / sheep farm, on the N70 between Killorglin & Miltown. Nestled between Kilderry Wood and banks of River Maine with commanding views of Dingle Peninsula. Central base for touring. May bring own wine. Relax and unwind by open fires and enjoy the ambience and hospitality of country life that awaits you. Email: kilburnhouse@eircom.net

PORTMAGEE 5 km — Kerry KY78

Mrs Kathleen Lynch
HARBOUR GROVE
Aghadda
Portmagee, Co Kerry

Tel: 066-9477116 Fax: 066-9477172
Open: 1st April – 1st November

OBA
V
AM

	No Rooms:	3	Triple:	–
	Twin/Double:	2	Family:	1
	Single:	–	En suite:	3

B&B:	-	-	HBW ES:	£220	€279.34	S.Supp: £7	€8.89	Dinner:	£12	€15.24
B&B ES:	£19	€24.13	3 day HB:	-	-	CSP:	50%	High Tea:	£8	€10.16
HBW:	-	-	3 day HB ES:	£85	€107.93					

Friendly, homely farmhouse, on Skellig Ring, 6km off Ring of Kerry N70, 60 metres from private foreshore. Breathtaking views, mountain, sea, island. Peaceful location, grove of mature trees. Spacious bathrooms en-suite. Skelligs Centre/boats 4km. Blue flag beach 10km. Golf, fishing, horseriding, walking, boats, etc. , arranged by Kathleen. Mobile: 087-2239933

PORTMAGEE 3 km — Kerry KY79

Mrs Mairead Lynch
HARBOUR LIGHTS
Kilkeaveragh
Portmagee, Co Kerry

Tel: 066-9477172 Fax: 066-9477172
Open: 1st March – 30th October

AM
V
EC

	No Rooms:	3	Triple:	–
	Twin/Double:	2	Family:	1
	Single:	–	En suite:	3

B&B:	-	-	HBW ES:	£200	€253.95	S.Supp: £6.50	€8.25	Dinner:	£12	€15.24
B&B ES:	£19	€24.13	3 day HB:	-	-	CSP:	50%	High Tea:	£8	€10.16
HBW:	-	-	3 day HB ES:	£86	€109.20					

6.5 km off Ring of Kerry, situated between the mountains and the sea Harbour Lights is 40 metres from the seashore. Enjoy the relaxed atmosphere of our home and the wonderful views of Valentia and Harbour from the bedroom, sittingroom windows. Extensive breakfast menu. Diving. Skellig interpretative. Portmagee is the departure point for Skellig boats. Email: harbourlights@eircom.net

SNEEM 1 km   Kerry KY80

Mrs Mary Teahan
DERRY EAST FARMHOUSE
Sneem
Killarney, Co Kerry

Tel: 064-45193   Fax: 064-45193
Open: 1st April – 1st October

No Rooms:	4	Triple:	–
Twin/Double:	3	Family:	1
Single:	–	En suite:	3

B&B:	-	-	HBW ES:	£235	€298.39	S.Supp: £10	€12.70	Dinner: £16	€20.32
B&B ES: £20	€25.39		3 day HB:	-		CSP:	25%	High Tea:£12	€15.24
HBW:	-	-	3 day HB ES: £100	€126.95					

Spacious, comfortable family run farmhouse. Quiet, scenic area 200 metres off Ring of Kerry, N70. 500 meters from "Kerry Way" walking route. Spectacular mountain views, relaxing farm and river walks. Private tennis and fishing. Area for botanists. Home baking, turf fires in lounge. AIB Award. Organised demonsration on turf cutting. Email: teahans@eircom.net

---

TARBERT 1 km   Kerry KY81

Thomas & Mary Dillane
DILLANES FARMHOUSE
Doonard, Listowel Road
Tarbert, Co Kerry

Tel: 068-36242   Fax: 068-36242
Open: Easter – 1st October

No Rooms:	4	Triple:	-
Twin/Double:	2	Family:	1
Single:	-	En suite:	3

B&B: £18	€22.86	HBW ES:	-	S.Supp: £6.50	€8.25	Dinner:	-	-
B&B ES: £19	€24.13	3 day HB:	-	CSP:	£10	High Tea:	-	-
HBW:	-	3 day HB ES:	-					

Comfortable modernised farmhouse. Quiet elevated site back from Tarbert-Listowel Road. House overlooks farmland views of River Shannon. 5 mins to car ferry across Shannon. Good restaurants nearby. Golf 15 minutes. Traditional music on request. Woodland walk 5 minutes. Beaches 15 mins. Ideal base for touring Kerry, Limerick & Clare. Cheaper rate for three day stay. Email: dillanesfarmhouse@eircom.net

---

TRALEE 4 km   Kerry KY93

Mrs. Catherine Dwyer
TONEVANE HOUSE
Tonevane, Blennerville,
Tralee, Co. Kerry

Tel: 066-7128241   Fax: 066-7128241
Open: 1st May - 30th September

No Rooms:	3	Triple:	–
Twin/Double:	3	Family:	–
Single:	–	En suite:	2

V
AM

B&B: £17	€21.58	HBW ES:	-	S.Supp: £6.50	€8.25	Dinner:	-
B&B ES: £19	€24.13	3 day HB:	-	CSP:	25%	High Tea:	-
HBW:	-	3 day HB ES:	-				

Spacious dormer bungalow on a working sheep farm, set in quiet scenic countryside. Signposted on the N86, 1.5km from Blennerville Windmill. Tea/coffee on arrival. Relax in our sun lounge and enjoy the picturesque mountain setting. Breakfast choice. Adjacent to Tralee Town Centre and Aqua Dome. Ideal location for touring Dingle Peninsula.

TRALEE 4 km (R558)   Kerry KY82

Mrs Maureen Foley
THE FARMHOUSE
Knockanish Spa
Tralee, Co Kerry

Tel: 066-7122036   Fax: 066-7122036
Open: 1st April – 1st December

OBA
AM
V

No Rooms:	5	Triple:	2
Twin/Double:	1	Family:	–
Single:	2	En suite:	2

B&B: £17	€21.58	HBW ES:	-	S.Supp: £6.50	€8.25	Dinner:	-	-
B&B ES: £19	€24.13	3 day HB:	-	CSP:	20%	High Tea:	-	-
HBW:	-	3 day HB ES: £100	€126.97					

Traditional farmhouse on mixed working farm off Fenit Road. Commanding excellent view of Tralee Bay and Slieve Mish Mountains. 2.5 miles north of Tralee. Quiet location. Gateway to Dingle Peninsula, Ring of Kerry and Killarney. Excellent restaurants, traditional music, golfing, sea angling, horse riding, hill walking, sandy beaches, steam train, medieval centre, sea zoo, aqua centre nearby. Email: farmhouse@oceanfree.net

TRALEE 7 km   Kerry KY83

Mrs Bridget Keane
CURRAHEEN HOUSE
Curraheen
Tralee, Co Kerry

Tel: 066-7121717   Fax: 066-7128362
Open: 1st February – 30th November

No Rooms:	4	Triple:	1
Twin/Double:	3	Family:	–
Single:	–	En suite:	4

AM V EC

B&B:	-	HBW ES:	-	S.Supp: £6.50 €8.25	Dinner:	-	
B&B ES: £19	€24.13	3 day HB:	-	CSP: 25%	High Tea:	-	
HBW:	-	3 day HB ES:	-				

Traditional style farmhouse, overlooking Tralee Bay. Situated between mountains and sea along Tralee-Dingle Road. 7 km from Tralee. Frommers Guide recommended. Dingle Way walking route nearby. Ideal touring centre. Golfing, fishing, pony trekking locally. Sandy beaches 4 km. Bar and Restaurant on grounds. Email: curraheenhouse@mail.com

TRALEE 2 km   Kerry KY84

Ann & Hanna Kerins
HEATHERVILLE FARM
Blennerville
Tralee, Co Kerry

Tel: 066-7121054   Fax: 066-7121054
Open: 1st March – 31st October

No Rooms:	6	Triple:	–
Twin/Double:	4	Family:	2
Single:	–	En suite:	6

AM V

B&B:	-	HBW ES:	-	S.Supp: £6.50 €8.25	Dinner:	-	
B&B ES: £20/25	€25.39/31.74	3 day HB:	-	CSP: 25%	High Tea:	-	
HBW:	-	3 day HB ES:	-				

Experience real comfort and quality at our spacious farmhouse in peaceful scenic surroundings off N86 at Blennerville. A magical, timeless haven of peace awaits you as you stroll through our landscaped gardens. Rooms with direct dial telephone, hairdryers, electric blankets. Breakfast menu. A A ♦ ♦ ♦ ♦ Stay at Heatherville…Experience an Experience. 3 Days B&B ES £55.50/70 - €70.50/87.50 Email: heatherville@eircom.net

TRALEE 3 km   Kerry KY85

Mrs Maureen O'Connor
MOUNT PROSPECT
Caherbreagh
Tralee, Co Kerry

Tel: 066-7122672   Fax: –
Open: Mid. May – October

No Rooms:	4	Triple:	–
Twin/Double:	4	Family:	–
Single:	–	En suite:	3

B&B:	£17	€21.58	HBW ES:	-	S.Supp: £6.50 €8.25	Dinner:	-
B&B ES: £19	€24.13	3 day HB:	-	CSP: 25%	High Tea:	-
HBW:	-	3 day HB ES:	-			

Modern family run farmhouse . Accessible from N21 and N22 road. (2 miles from Tralee/Killarney road). Magnificent view of Slieve Mish mountains in scenic surroundings. Working dairy farm. Ideal location for touring. Convenient to local amenities, golfing, aquadome, Siamsa Tíre, Museum etc. Excellent hotels and restaurants nearby. Complimentary tea/coffee served on arrival.

TRALEE 2 km   Kerry KY86

Mrs Peggy O'Shea
BLEACH FARMHOUSE
Blenerville
Tralee, Co Kerry

Tel: 066-7121785   Fax: 066-7121785
Open: 1st February – 31st October

OBA

No Rooms:	5	Triple:	1
Twin/Double:	4	Family:	-
Single:	–	En suite:	5

AM V EC

B&B:	-	HBW ES:	-	S.Supp: £6.50 €8.25	Dinner:	-	
B&B ES: £20/21	€25.39/26.66	3 day HB:	-	CSP: 25%	High Tea:	-	
HBW:	-	3 day HB ES:	-				

Traditional homely farmhouse, picturesque setting, start of Dingle Way Walk on N86. Home baking, breakfast menu, TV lounge, tea making facilities. Excellent restaurants, folk theatre, aquadome and steam-train. 3 days B&B £55. Christmas and New Year breaks.

WATERVILLE 5 km

Mrs Margaret Curran
SEA VIEW
Toor, Waterville
Co Kerry

Tel: 066-9474297   Fax: –
Open: February - November

No Rooms:	3	Triple:	–
Twin/Double:	2	Family:	1
Single:	–	En suite:	3

EC

B&B:	-	HBW ES:	-	S.Supp: £6.50 €8.25	Dinner: -	-
B&B ES: £19	€24.13	3 day HB:	-	CSP: 25%	High Tea:-	-
HBW:		3 day HB ES:-				

Modern bungalow overlooking picturesque Ballinskelligs Bay and Atlantic.
Mountains at rear of house. Fishing, golf, horse riding, cycling. Ideal base for walking and cycling
trips. Skellig boat trips arranged. Brittany Ferries and 'Le Guide du Routard' recommended.
Complimentary tea/coffee. Email: jfcurran@eircom.net

VOUCHERS ACCEPTED

WATERVILLE 14 km

The Hallissey Family
OISIN
Gortatlga, Mastergeehy
Waterville, Co Kerry

Tel: 066-9474479   Fax: –
Open: 1st March - 31th October

No Rooms:	3	Triple:	–
Twin/Double:	2	Family:	1
Single:	–	En suite:	2

OBA
AM
V
EC

B&B:	£17	€21.51	HBW ES:	£196	€248.87	S.Supp: £6.50 €8.25	Dinner: £12.50 €15.87
B&B ES: £19	€24.13	3 day HB:	£81	€102.85	CSP: 50%	High Tea: £9	€11.43
HBW: £152	€231.09	3 day HB ES: £87	€110.47			

Modern bungalow in beautiful scenic area of Kerry. Ideal base for walking.
Close to "Kerry Way". Mountain climbing, cycling, fishing, horse riding. Home baking. Traditional
music in house. A warm, friendly welcome is guaranteed.

VOUCHERS ACCEPTED

BANKING AND CURRENCY

The unit of currency is the Irish Pound (IR£). Most banks are normally open from

Monday to Friday 10.00h to 16.00h. Many banks stay open

until 17.00h one day of the week. Check locally.

Banks are closed at Weekends and Public Holidays.

Kildare

Kildare's fertile plains make it an ideal place to visit for anyone with an interest in gardening or horticulture. There are many famous houses and gardens to visit including the Japanese Gardens and the stunning Palladian mansion of Castletown House. The county is the headquarters of the Irish bloodstock industry and the National Stud and the Curragh Racecourse are both located there.

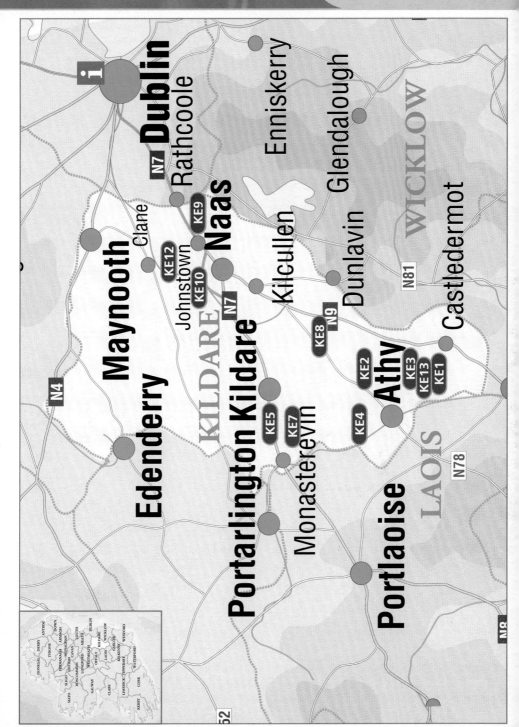

ATHY 3 km | Kildare KE1

Marion & Liam Dunne
BRAY HOUSE
Athy,
Co Kildare

Tel: 0507-31052/31759 Fax: 0507-31052
Open: All Year

No Rooms:	4	Triple:	–
Twin/Double:	1	Family:	2
Single:	1	En suite:	3

OBA

B&B:	£17	€21.58	HBW ES:	-	S.Supp: -	Dinner: -	-
B&B ES:	£19	€24.13	3 day HB:	-	CSP: 50%	High Tea: £12 €15.24
HBW:			3 day HB ES: -				

A two storey 19th century farmhouse with modern decor, located on a tillage and cattle farm. High quality breakfast with a menu to suit all tastes. Special facilities for children. Guests are free to explore the farm and walk through the garden at leisure. One hour from airport and ferryports. French and fluent German spoken.

ATHY 5 km | Kildare KE2

Anne & Noel Flood
ARDSCULL FARMHOUSE
Dublin Road (N78)
Athy, Co Kildare

Tel: 0507-26188 Fax: 0507-26188
Open: 1st March – 30th November

No Rooms:	3	Triple:	-
Twin/Double:	2	Family:	-
Single:	1	En suite:	3

B&B:	£17	€21.59	HBW ES:	-	S.Supp: £6.50 €8.25	Dinner: £14 €17.78
B&B ES:	£19/20	€24.13/25.39	3 day HB:	-	CSP: -	High Tea: £8 €10.15
HBW:	-		3 day HB ES: £93	€118.09			

On Dublin's doorstep, Anne and Noel invite you to their home at this prestigious location on the N78, 15 km from Kilcullen towards Athy, 45 mins from Dublin. Close to Curragh, Punchestown Races, National Stud, K and Japanese Gardens. Ideal touring base for Dublin, Wicklow, Kilkenny, bright restful home, turf fire in guest sitting room. Welcome tray on arrival.

ATHY 9 km | Kildare KE3

Mary & Vincent Gorman
BALLINDRUM FARM
Ballindrum
Athy, Co Kildare

Tel: 0507-26294 Fax: 0507-26294
Open: 1st March – 24th October

No Rooms:	6	Triple:	–
Twin/Double:	5	Family:	1
Single:		En suite:	6

AM
V
EC

B&B:	-	-	HBW ES:	-	S.Supp: £6.50 €8.25	Dinner: £13 €16.51
B&B ES:	£20	€25.39	3 day HB:	-	CSP: £10 €12.7	High Tea: £10 €12.70
HBW:	-		3 day HB ES: £95	€120.63			

National Agri-Tourism Award. National Award of Excellence. National Farm Family Award. Bright spacious house in an area of rural beauty. Guided farm tours. Touring base for Dublin, Kilkenny, Wicklow. Home baking and homemade jams on arrival. Dinner Monday, Tuesday, Wednesday. Email: ballindrumfarm@eircom.net

---

ATHY 5 km | Kildare KE4

Mary & Raymond Pelin
MOATE LODGE
Off Dublin Road
Athy, Co Kildare

Tel: 0507-26137 Fax: 0507-26109
Open: 1st January – 31st December

No Rooms:	4	Triple:	-
Twin/Double:	4	Family:	-
Single:	-	En suite:	3

AM
V
EC

B&B:	£17	€21.58	HBW ES:	£220	€279.34	S.Supp: £6.50 €8.25	Dinner: £13 €16.51
B&B ES:	£19	€24.13	3 day HB:	£85	€107.93	CSP: 50%	High Tea: £9 €11.43
HBW:	£205	€260.30	3 day HB ES: £90	€114.28			

Moate Lodge is an 18th century Georgian house of unrivalled charm and character. Log fires, home baking. Complimentary tea/coffee and scones during stay. Ideal touring centre for south east. Only 1 hr to all car ferries. Signposted off the N78 at the Norman Moate. Mary and Raymond Pelin and family look forward to welcoming you to their home.

KILDARE 4 km — Kildare KE5

Mrs Elizabeth Fitzpatrick
CASTLEVIEW FARMHOUSE
Lackaghmore
Kildare, Co Kildare

Tel: 045-521816   Fax: 045-521816
Open: 1st March – 1st December
OBA *AM* *V* *EC*

No Rooms:	3	Triple:	-
Twin/Double:	2	Family:	1
Single:	-	En suite:	2

B&B:	£17/20.50	€21.58/26	HBW ES:	-	-	
B&B ES:	£19/22.50	€24.13/29	3 day HB:	-	-	
HBW:	-	-	3 day HB ES:	-	

S.Supp:	£7	€8.89	Dinner: -
CSP:	25%		High Tea: -

Liz and Ned invite you to experience life and relaxation on their working dairy farm in exquisitely tranquil and historic surroundings. Le Guide du Routard recommended. Well signposted. 4 km from Kildare Town. Turn right off N7 between Kildare and Monasterevin. 10 minutes drive to National Stud, Japanese Gardens, Curragh, Punchestown, Naas Racecourse. 40 minutes Dublin. Welcome Tray. Tea / coffee facilities. Email: castleviewfarmhouse@oceanfree.net

---

KILLCULLEN 7 km — Kildare KE8

Frances and Seán Doyle
ASH LANE FARM
Ballyshannon, Tippeenan,
Kilcullen, Co Kildare

Tel: 045-485486   Fax: 045-485486
Open: 15th February - 30th November
EC *V* *AM*

No Rooms:	3	Triple:	-
Twin/Double:	3	Family:	-
Single:	-	En suite:	3

B&B:	-	-	HBW ES:	-	-	
B&B ES:	£19	€24.13	3 day HB:	-	-	
HBW:	-	-	3 day HB ES:	-	

S.Supp:	£6.50	€8.25	Dinner: -
CSP:	50%		High Tea: -

Ash Lane Farm is situated in the heart of beautiful, green, fertile countryside. It is a modern, one storey house with landscaped gardens for you to enjoy. We are within 20 km of all three race courses, Naas, Punchestown and the Curragh. 40 mins drive on M9 motorway from Dublin, take N78 for Athy, after 8 km turn left. Our home is yours. Mobile: 087-234 7526

MONASTEREVIN 3 km — Kildare KE7

Mrs Marie McGuinness
CLONCARLIN HOUSE
Monasterevin
Co Kildare

Tel: 045-525722   Fax: -
Open: 1st February – 1st December
OBA

No Rooms:	6	Triple:	-
Twin/Double:	4	Family:	1
Single:	-	En suite:	2

B&B:	£17/20	€21.59/25.39	HBW ES:	-	-	
B&B ES:	£19/22	€24.13/27.93	3 day HB:	-	-	
HBW:	-	-	3 day HB ES:	-	

S.Supp:	£8	€10.16	Dinner: -
CSP:	25%		High Tea: -

Spacious 18th century family run period farmhouse of character on 180 acres of sheep and beef farm. Situated on elevated site in pleasant, peaceful surroundings. Barrow River and Grand Canal for fishing. Horse riding stables 6 km. 15 minutes drive from National Stud, Japanese Gardens. 1 Hour from Airport and Ferryports.

MOONE 5 km — Kildare KE13

The Coyle Family
PILL LODGE FARMHOUSE
Belan, Moone
Athy, Co Kildare

Tel: 0507-24147   Fax: -
Open: 1st January - 31st December

No Rooms:	3	Triple:	-
Twin/Double:	1	Family:	1
Single:	-	En suite:	1

B&B:	£17/20	€21.58/25.39	HBW ES:	-	-	
B&B ES:	£20/23	€25.39/29.20	3 day HB:	-	-	
HBW:	-	-	3 day HB ES:	-	

S.Supp:	-	-	Dinner: -
CSP:	-		High Tea: -

Two-storey farmhouse, 2500 sq. feet. Six bedrooms, built in 1979 on 156 acres. Farm guided walk of dairy and tillage farm. Home baking, complimentary tea/coffee and scones with home made jam on arrival. Plenty of parking around house. Located on quiet country road, 1 hour drive from Dublin airport.

Vouchers Not Accepted

NAAS 8 km

Kildare KE9

Mrs Margaret Gillespie
SPRINGFIELD
Rathmore, Naas
Co Kildare

Tel: 045-862116   Fax: -
Open: 20th April – 20th October *OBA*

No Rooms:	3
Twin/Double:	2
Single:	-

Triple:	1
Family:	-
En suite:	-

B&B	£18	€ 22.86	HBW ES:	-	-	S.Supp: £6.50 € 8.25 Dinner: - -
B&B ES: -			3 day HB:			CSP: 25% High Tea: -
HBW: -			3 day HB ES: -			

Farmhouse with mature gardens in quiet scenic countryside on Dublin doorstep, off the N7 at Rathcoole or N81 north of Blessington. Ideal for touring Dublin, Glendalough, Russborough, National Stud and Japanese Gardens. Horse riding, golf. Punchestown, Naas and Curragh race courses nearby. Dublin tours arranged from Rathcoole. Tea making facilities and hairdryers in bedrooms.

NAAS 6 km

Kildare KE10

Mrs Joan McLoughlin
SETANTA FARMHOUSE
Caragh, Mondello Road
Naas, Co Kildare

Tel: 045-876481   Fax: –
Open: 1st March – 31st October

No Rooms:	5
Twin/Double:	1
Single:	2

Triple:	1
Family:	1
En suite:	3

B&B:	£20	€ 25.39	HBW ES:	-	-	S.Supp: - - Dinner: -
B&B ES: £20		€ 25.39	3 day HB:	-	-	CSP: - High Tea: -
HBW: -			3 day HB ES: -			

Working Farm. Centrally located for N7 and N4 (both routes connect with M50 by-pass for airport). Regular bus service Naas/Dublin. Discount for Dublin Bus Tour. Children over seven only. Email: setantafarmhouse@eircom.net

---

NAAS 8 km

Kildare KE12

John & Kathleen Phelan
SILVERSPRING HOUSE
Firmount, Clane, Naas
Co Kildare

Tel: 045-868481   Fax: 045-892246
Open: 1st January – 15th December *OBA* **AM V**

No Rooms:	4
Twin/Double:	1
Single:	-

Triple:	1
Family:	2
En suite:	4

B&B:	-	-	HBW ES:	-	-	S.Supp: - - Dinner: -
B&B ES: £25		€ 31.74	3 day HB:	-	-	CSP: - High Tea: -
HBW: -			3 day HB ES: -			

Farmhouse in peaceful, rural setting, secluded gardens. Clane 1.5 km, Prosperous 1.5 km, Sallins 4 km, Naas 8 km. 30 mins from Dublin by road, 20 mins Rapid Rail. Elegant bedrooms with TVs. Central to all attractions including 10 golf courses. Ideal touring base. AA Selected. Tea making facilities. K Club nearby. Electric blankets. Aga-cooked breakfast. 1/2 hourly bus service to Dublin. Health and Leisure centre in village. Email: silverspring@hotmail.com

Vouchers Not Accepted

ARRIVAL TIMES / LATE ARRIVALS

Rooms are normally held until 6pm

If your arrival time is later than 6pm please confirm this with

the Farmhouse or telephone if you are delayed or wish to arrive later

Kilkenny

Famous for its magnificent castle and world
famous design centre, Kilkenny has many
attractions for the visitor. The medieval city is
a paradise for shoppers and sightseers. Every
year the city plays host to the Kilkenny Arts
Week and the Cat Laughs Festival. Boasting
Jerpoint Abbey and the ancient town of Kells,
Kilkenny can justly claim to be the medieval
capital of Ireland.

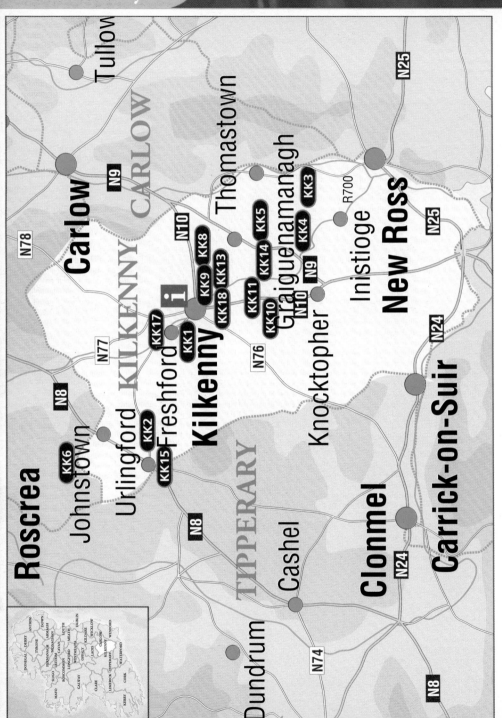

BENNETSBRIDGE 1 km   Kilkenny KK18

The Quane Family
LINFIELD
Rathclough, Bennetsbridge
Co Kilkenny

Tel: 056-27839   Fax: 056-27839
Open: 1st June - 31st August

No Rooms:	3	Triple:	–
Twin/Double:	2	Family:	1
Single:	–	En suite:	3

V EC

B&B:	-	HBW ES:	-	S.Supp: €7 €8.89		Dinner:	-
B&B ES: €25	€31.74	3 day HB:	-	CSP: 20%		High Tea: -
HBW:	-	3 day HB ES:	-			

Spacious and comfortable Georgian style country house. Walking distance from restaurants/crafts in Bennetsbridge. Five 18-hole golf courses within 12 miles. Fishing, canoeing, walking, equestrian activities close by. Five miles from medieval city of Kilkenny. 3 day B&B ES £70 €88.89 **Vouchers Not Accepted** Located 1 mile off R700 Kilkenny Rosslare road. 1 Mile N10. Email: linfield@eircom.net

FRESHFORD 0.5 km   Kilkenny KK17

Mrs K. Cahill
MOATE FARM B&B
Kilkenny Road, Freshford
Co Kilkenny

Tel: 056-32283   Fax: -
Open: January – 1st December

 OBA AM V EC

No Rooms:	4	Triple:	–
Twin/Double:	4	Family:	–
Single:	–	En suite:	4

B&B:	-	HBW ES:	-	S.Supp: €7.00 €9.52	Dinner:	-
B&B ES: €23	€29.20	3 day HB:	-	CSP: -	High Tea: €8	€10.15
HBW:	-	3 day HB ES:	-		

A warm welcome awaits you at our family run farmhouse on working farm situated on the main Kilkenny to Cashel Road, 8.5 miles from the lovely city of Kilkenny, 5mins walk to Freshford village.

VOUCHERS ACCEPTED

FRESHFORD 7 km   Kilkenny KK1

Mrs Lil Kellaghan
CRADÓG
Tubrid, Woodsgift
Co Kilkenny

Tel: 056-35224   Fax: –
Open: 27th December – 23rd December

 OBA

No Rooms:	4	Triple:	1
Twin/Double:	3	Family:	–
Single:	–	En suite:	4

B&B:	-	HBW ES: £185	€234.90	S.Supp: €6.50 €8.25	Dinner: £12	€15.23
B&B ES: £19	€24.13	3 day HB: £75	€95.23	CSP: 20%	High Tea: £8	€10.15
HBW:	-	3 day HB ES: £82	€104.11		

A warm welcome in quiet countryside. Beautiful views and historic sites. Ideal touring base for Kilkenny/Cashel area. Horse riding and brown trout fishing within driving distance, 7 km. Situated 7 km off the Dublin-Cork N8 or 2 km off Kilkenny-Cashel R693. Complimentary tea on arrival. Email: kellaghan@unison.ie

VOUCHERS ACCEPTED

FRESHFORD 6 km   Kilkenny KK2

Mrs Gretta Power
THE BUNGALOW FARMHOUSE
Clomantagh, Woodsgift
Co Kilkenny

Tel: 056-35215   Fax: 056-35215
Open: 5th January – 20th December

OBA

No Rooms:	4	Triple:	-
Twin/Double:	1	Family:	3
Single:	-	En suite:	4

B&B:	-	HBW ES:	-	S.Supp: €6.50 €8.25	Dinner: £12.50	€15.87
B&B ES: £19	€24.13	3 day HB:	-	CSP: 25%	High Tea: £8	€10.16
HBW:	-	3 day HB ES: £90	€114.30		

Modern bungalow on a beef and sheep farm set in beautiful quiet scenic countryside just off the main Kilkenny-Urlingford-Cashel R693 road. 6 km from Urlingford. Ideal base for touring Kilkenny, Cashel & Thurles. Families very welcome. Many sporting amenities nearby. Mobile: 087-2456016

VOUCHERS ACCEPTED

GRAIGUENAMANAGH 4 km Kilkenny KK3

McCabe Family
BRANDON VIEW
Ballyogan, Graiguenamanagh
Co Kilkenny

Tel: 0503-24191 Fax: 0503-24451
Open: 1st February – 30th September

No Rooms:	3	Triple:	–
Twin/Double:	3	Family:	–
Single:		En suite:	3

B&B:	–	–	HBW ES:	–	–	S.Supp: £6.50 €8.25	Dinner: £18 €22.85
B&B ES: £19	€24.13	3 day HB:	–	–	CSP: –	High Tea:£12 €15.23
HBW:	–	–	3 day HB ES:£110	€139.67		

Attractive farm residence built before 1740. Recommended in travel guides for good food and high class accommodation. Large garden overlooking own coarse fishing lake at the foot of Brandon Hill. Free coarse fishing to residents. Angling, golf and walking in the area. Signposted walking on the farm. A warm welcome assured. Signposted on the Graiguenamanagh-New Ross Road.

VOUCHERS ACCEPTED

INISTIOGE 5 km Kilkenny KK4

Mrs Nellie Cassin
GROVE FARM HOUSE
Ballycocksuist, Inistioge
Co Kilkenny

Tel: 056-58467 Fax: –
Open: Easter – 31st October

OBA
AM
V
EC

No Rooms:	4	Triple:	–
Twin/Double:	3	Family:	1
Single:	–	En suite:	3

B&B: £17	€20.95	HBW ES:	–	–	S.Supp: £6.50 €8.25	Dinner: –
B&B ES: £19	€23.49	3 day HB:	–	–	CSP: –	High Tea: –
HBW:	–	–	3 day BB ES: £54	€68.57		

200 year old Georgian country house set in mature gardens with breathtaking views of scenic countryside. Family home for generations. South Leinster Way passes through farm. Signposted between Thomastown and Inistioge on the R700. Convenient to Kilkenny and the South East. 1 hour from Rosslare. 7 nights B&B for £115, 3 nights B&B for £54. Email: grovefarmhse@unison.ie

VOUCHERS ACCEPTED

INISTIOGE/THOMASTOWN 4 km Kilkenny KK5

Mrs Breda Thomas
BALLYDUFF HOUSE
Ballyduff, Thomastown
Co Kilkenny

Tel: 056-58488 Fax: –
Open: 31st March – 1st November

OBA

No Rooms:	3	Triple:	1
Twin/Double:	2	Family:	–
Single:	–	En suite:	3

B&B: £25	€31.75	HBW ES:	–	–	S.Supp: £6.50 €8.25	Dinner: –
B&B ES: £25	€31.75	3 day HB:	–	–	CSP: –	High Tea: –
HBW:	–	–	3 day HB ES: –			

18th century manor house situated in its original grounds. Overlooking the River Nore. This charming location offers very private and period surroundings as well as salmon and trout fishing. A full 18 hole Golf Course at Mount Juliet, 5 miles drive. Also hunting, riding, quad track, canoeing can be arranged with notice. Film location for 'Circle of Friends' and 'Where the Sun is Rising'. Many beautiful walks on the estate. Email: ballyd@gofree.indigo.ie

Vouchers Not Accepted

JOHNSTOWN 7 km Kilkenny KK6

The Delaney Family
BAYSWELL HOUSE
Crosspatrick
Johnstown, Co Kilkenny

Tel: 056-31168 Fax: 056-31168
Open: 1st May–1st October

No Rooms:	3	Triple:	–
Twin/Double:	2	Family:	1
Single:	–	En suite:	3

B&B:	–	–	HBW ES:	–	–	S.Supp: £6.50 €8.25	Dinner: –
B&B ES: £20	€25.39	3 day HB:	–	–	CSP: 25%	High Tea: –
HBW:	–	–	3 day HB ES: –			

Elegant Georgian country house. Dairy farm. 500 metre tree lined avenue, walled garden containing historic holy well. Antiques, ornate ceilings. Tea making facilities. 5 minutes from N8 at Johnstown. Signposted on N502 (Templemore Road). 30 minutes Kilkenny and Cashel. 1.5 hours from Rosslare and Dublin Airport Welcoming refreshments. Email: bayswellhouse@ireland.com Website: gofree.indigo.ie/~bayswell

VOUCHERS ACCEPTED

KILKENNY 5 km
Kilkenny KK8

Rita O'Brien
HILLVIEW
Sheestown
Kilkenny

Tel: 056-27230   Fax: –
Open: 1st March – 1st December

No Rooms:	4	Triple:	–
Twin/Double:	4	Family:	–
Single:		En suite:	2

EC

B&B:	£17	€21.58	HBW ES:	-	S.Supp: £7	€8.89	Dinner: -	-
B&B ES:	£19	€24.13	3 day HB:	-	CSP:	-	High Tea: -	-
HBW:	-		3 day HB ES:	-				

Comfortable farmhouse situated in tranquil scenic area on beef and cereal farm. Located 5 km south of Kilkenny Medieval city on main R700-Kilkenny-Rosslare Road. Ideal touring base. Horse riding, flying, tennis, golf. Mt Juliet Golf Course nearby. Dunmore Caves close by. Accommodation includes guest lounge, antique furniture and orthopaedic beds.

VOUCHERS ACCEPTED

KILKENNY 1 km
Kilkenny KK9

Kitty and Dan Stallard
DANVILLE HOUSE
New Ross Road
Kilkenny

Tel: 056-21512   Fax: 056-21512
Open: 15th March – 1st November

No Rooms:	5	Triple:	2
Twin/Double:	2	Family:	1
Single:	–	En suite:	4

B&B:	£18	€22.85	HBW ES:	-	S.Supp: £10	€12.70	Dinner: -	-
B&B ES:	£20	€25.39	3 day HB:	-	CSP:	10%	High Tea: -	-
HBW:	-		3 day HB ES:	-				

200 year old Georgian house set in peaceful location among mature trees. Situated 1 km from Kilkenny City. Entrance is 0.2 km past roundabout on R700 road to New Ross. Relaxed atmosphere, maintained old garden with croquet on lawn and walled kitchen garden. Fishing, golf and horse riding nearby. Galtee Award winner. Email: treecc@iol.ie

VOUCHERS ACCEPTED

KNOCKTOPHER 3 km
Kilkenny KK10

Mrs Brid Cummins
FLOODHALL HOUSE
Knocktopher
Co Kilkenny

Tel: 056-68652   Fax: –
Open: 1st April – 1st November

No Rooms:	4	Triple:	–
Twin/Double:	4	Family:	–
Single:	–	En suite:	4

OBA

B&B:	-		HBW ES:	-	S.Supp: £6.50	€8.25	Dinner: -	-
B&B ES:	£19	€24.13	3 day HB:	-	CSP:	50%	High Tea: -	-
HBW:	-		3 day HB ES:	-				

Spacious 18th century residence on family run mixed farm. 400 metres off Kilkenny-Waterford N10 road. 16 km from medieval City of Kilkenny. Waterford 20 minutes, Rosslare 1 hour, Mount Juliet Golf Course, 1 mile. Historical sites, fishing, tennis and horse riding locally. Ideal base for touring south east.

VOUCHERS ACCEPTED

THOMASTOWN 5 km
Kilkenny KK11

Mrs Mary Fitzgerald
OLDTOWN FARMHOUSE
Stoneyford, Thomastown,
Co Kilkenny

Tel: 056-28224   Fax: 056-28481
Open: 31st December – 14th December

No Rooms:	4	Triple:	–
Twin/Double:	3	Family:	–
Single:	1	En suite:	3

OBA
AM
V
EC

B&B:	£17	€21.58	HBW ES:	-	S.Supp: £6.50	€8.25	Dinner: -	-
B&B ES:	£19	€24.13	3 day HB:	-	CSP:	50%	High Tea: -	-
HBW:	-		3 day HB ES:	-				

Comfortable and friendly farmhouse with a scenic view on a working farm with ancient ring fort and propagation nursery. 0.3 km off the Waterford-Kilkenny N10, 3 km off the N9, 10 minutes Kilkenny, 20 minutes Waterford, Kells, Thomastown and Jerpoint Abbey, 5 minutes. Mount Juliet Golf Course 0.5 km. Historic sites fishing, horse riding locally. Ideal touring base. Rosslare 1 hour. Email: pfitz@iol.ie

VOUCHERS ACCEPTED

THOMASTOWN 5 km — Kilkenny KK13

Mrs Mary O'Connell
KNOCKANORE
Thomastown
Co Kilkenny

Tel: 056-24125 Fax: 056-54505
Open: 1st April – 1st October OBA

No Rooms:	3	Triple:	–
Twin/Double:	2	Family:	1
Single:	–	En suite:	2

B&B:	£18	€22.85	HBW ES:	-	-	S.Supp: £7.00 €8.88	Dinner:	-	-
B&B ES:	£20	€25.39	3 day HB:	-	-	CSP:	50%	High Tea:	-
HBW:	-	-	3 day HB ES:	-				

Knockanore Farmhouse is situated on a working dairyfarm in the valley of the River Nore. Convenient to Jerpoint Abbey, Kells, Kilkenny and Mount Juliet. Private fishing available to guests on farm. Situated 1.5 km off R700 Kilkenny/Rosslare Road. Signposted half-way between Thomastown and Bennettsbridge. Email: knockanorebandb@eircom.net

---

THOMASTOWN 3 km — Kilkenny KK14

Rita & Joseph Teesdale
BELMORE
Jerpoint Church
Thomastown, Co Kilkenny

Tel: 056-24228 Fax: –
Open: 29th December – 22nd December

No Rooms:	3	Triple:	–
Twin/Double:	3	Family:	–
Single:	–	En suite:	3

B&B:	-	-	HBW ES:	-	-	S.Supp: £6.50 €8.25	Dinner:	-	-
B&B ES:	£20/25	€25.39/31.74	3 day HB:	-	-	CSP:	-	High Tea:	-
HBW:	-	-	3 day HB ES:	-				

A warm welcome is assured in this charming period house on family run mixed farm, with beautiful views of River Nore valley. Just off N9 road near Jerpoint Abbey and adjacent to Mount Juliet Golf course. Fishing available to guests. Many other attractions locally.

URLINGFORD 1 km — Kilkenny KK15

Mrs Eileen Joyce
SPRINGVIEW HOUSE
Urlingford
Co Kilkenny

Tel: 056-31243 Fax: –
Open: 1st April – 1st November

No Rooms:	3	Triple:	3
Twin/Double:	–	Family:	–
Single:	–	En suite:	2

B&B:	£18	€22	HBW ES:	-	-	S.Supp: £6.50 €8.25	Dinner:	-	-
B&B ES:	£20	€25	3 day HB:	-	-	CSP:	-	High Tea:	-
HBW:	-	-	3 day HB ES:	-				

Fine early 19th century residence, retaining the characteristics of the period. Signposted off main Dublin-Cork N8 road at Urlingford. Entrance is 600 metres from Urlingford on R693 road to Kilkenny. Mixed enterprise farm. Ideal base for touring. Convenient to Cashel & Kilkenny. Fishing & golf within driving distance.

HOW TO DIAL IRELAND FROM ABROAD

| Country Access Code ++ | + | Country Code ++ | + | Area Code | + | Local Number |

Example (to Call Dublin, Ireland) Telephone:
01 (Dublin Area Code) + Local Number 1234567
Dial: Access Code **+ 353 + 1 + 1234567**

Example (to Call Galway, Ireland) Telephone:
091 (Galway Area Code) + Local Number 1234567
Dial: Access Code **+ 353 + 91 + 1234567**

Laois

Laois is a county of contradictions, mixing as it does a fondness for festivals with many reminders of the contemplative history of the region. The county has an array of pre-historic monuments and a large number of country houses famous for their architecture and gardens. Visitors can experience the Gaelic games of hurling and football as well as the more international attractions of fishing, shooting and golf. The heritage town of Abbeyleix is well worth a visit.

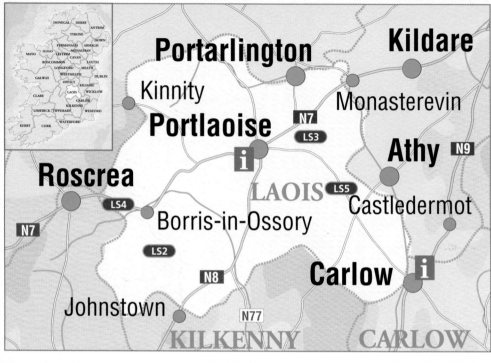

Map of Laois, Midlands East showing:
Portarlington, Kildare, Kinnity, Monasterevin, Portlaoise, N7, LS3, Athy, N9, Roscrea, LS4, LAOIS, LS5, Castledermot, Borris-in-Ossory, LS2, N7, N8, Carlow, Johnstown, N77, KILKENNY, CARLOW

BORRIS-IN-OSSORY 8 km | Laois LS2

Mrs Moira Phelan
CASTLETOWN HOUSE
Donaghmore,
Co Laois

Tel: 0505-46415		Fax: 0505-46788
Open: 1st March – 1st November		OBA
No Rooms: 4	Triple:	1
Twin/Double: 2	Family:	1
Single: -	En suite:	4

AM V EC

B&B:	-	-	HBW ES:	-	-	S.Supp:	-	Dinner:	-	-
B&B ES:	£19	€24.13	3 day HB:	-	-	CSP:	35%	High Tea:	-	-
HBW:	-	-	3 day HB ES:	-						

Beautifully restored early 19th century family home on working farm.
Remains of Norman Castle on land. Agri-Tourism Award winner 1990, 1996 & 1997. Recommended
by Brittany Ferries, Dillard/Causin and Frommers. Golf, fishing and Workhouse Museum locally. 1km
off R435 at Donaghmore village. Complimentary tea. Email: castletown@eircom.net

VOUCHERS ACCEPTED

PORTLAOISE 8 km | Laois LS3

Mrs Breda Mulhall
WOODGROVE FARM
Emo, Portlaoise
Co Laois

Tel: 0502-26324		Fax: -
Open: 1st April – 1st November		OBA
No Rooms: 3	Triple:	-
Twin/Double: 2	Family:	1
Single: -	En suite:	2

V

B&B:	£18	€22.86	HBW ES:	-	-	S.Supp:	£6.50 €8.25	Dinner:	-	-
B&B ES:	£20	€25.39	3 day HB:	-	-	CSP:	-	High Tea:	-	-
HBW:	-	-	3 day HB ES:	-						

A warm welcome in a quiet farmhouse with beautiful, landscaped gardens.
1 km from N7, 8 km from Portlaoise. 1 hour's drive to Dublin. 20 minutes drive to National Stud and
Japanese Gardens. 3 km Emo Court House & Gardens. Complimentary tea and scones on arrival.
'Irish Times' recommended. Open off season by arrangement. Email: woodgrovefarm@oceanfree.net

VOUCHERS ACCEPTED

ROSCREA 5 km

Laois LS4

Mrs Carole England
BALLAGHMORE HOUSE
Ballaghmore, Borris-in-Ossory
Co Laois

Tel: 0505-21366		Fax: –						OBA
Open: 1st January – 31st December								V AM
No Rooms:	4	Triple:	–					
Twin/Double:	3	Family:	1					
Single:	–	En suite:	4					

B&B:	-	-	HBW ES:	£189	€240	S.Supp: £6.50 €8.25	Dinner: £15	€19
B&B ES: £19-22	€24.13-27.93	3 day HB:	-	-	CSP:	High Tea: £8	€10.15
HBW:	-	-	3 day HB ES: £81	€103			

Spacious farmhouse on working farm, situated on N7 Dublin–Limerick Road ☕ 🍴 ⚓ 🅿️ 🐕 TV
halfway between Borris-in-Ossory and Roscrea (Heritage Town). Dublin 1.5 hours, Limerick 1.25 hours.
Activity holidays a specialty, packages including golfing, fishing, trail riding, hill walking & cycling. Private
lake for coarse fishing, excellent carp, tench & pike. Email: ballaghmorehse@eircom.net

STRADBALLY 4 km

Laois LS5

Pat & Caroline Farrell
TULLAMOY HOUSE
Tullamoy, Stradbally
Co Laois

Tel: 0507-27111		Fax: –			
Open: 1st January – 20th December					OBA
No Rooms:	4	Triple:	–		
Twin/Double:	2	Family:	2		
Single:	–	En suite:	4		

B&B:	-	-	HBW ES:	£250	€317.39	S.Supp: £6.50 €8.25	Dinner: £17	€21.58
B&B ES: £22	€27.93	3 day HB:	-	-	CSP: 50%	High Tea: -	-
HBW:	-	-	3 day HB ES: £115	€146.00			

Tullamoy house is a 19th century stone built house set in mature
gardens. The rooms are large with high ceilings and open fires. It is within easy reach of the
Curragh race course, numerous golf courses, swimming pools, riding schools and fishing areas.
Located 4kms south of Stradbally, just off the N80. Email: tullamoy@indigo.ie

---

HOW TO DIAL IRELAND FROM ABROAD
Country Access Code + Country Code
+ Area Code + Local Code
Example (to call Galway, Ireland)
Dial: Access Code + 353 + 91 + 12345

SO TELEFONIERT MAN VOM AUSLAND NACH IRLAND
Auslandsvorwahl + Ländercode + Vorwahl + Rufnummer
Beispiel (um Galway, Irland anzurufen)
Wählen Sie: Auslandsvorwahl +353 + 91 + 12345

COMMENT APPELER L'IRLANDE DE L'ÉTRANGER
Code d'accès à l'étranger + Code du pays + Code régional + Numéro local
Par exemple (pour appeler Galway, en Irlande)
Composez :
Code d'accès à l'étranger + 353 + 91 + 123456

HOE U IERLAND VANUIT HET BUITENLAND KUNT BELLEN
Internationaal toegangsnummer + Land toegangsnummer + Netnummer + Abonneenummer
Om bijvoorbeeld Galway in Ierland te bellen:
Kies: internationaal toegangsnummer + 353 + 91 + 12345

CÓMO LLAMAR A IRLANDA DESDE EL EXTRANJERO
Código de acceso del país
+ código del país + código del área + número local
Ejemplo (para llamar a Galway, Irlanda)
Marque: Código de acceso + 353 + 91 + 12345

COME TELEFONARE IN IRLANDA DALL'ESTERO
Codice Accesso Paese + Codice Paese + Codice Area + Numero Locale
Esempio (per chiamare Galway, Irlanda)
Digitare: Codice di Accesso + 353 + 92 + 12345

Leitrim

With a mixture of plains and hills, and plenty
for the eye to take in, Leitrim is ideal cycling
country. The county is divided by Lough
Allen, which is just one of the locations
where you can fish for wild trout and salmon
in pure waters. The county's principal town,
Carrick-on-Shannon is a centre for boating
and cruising on the Shannon river.

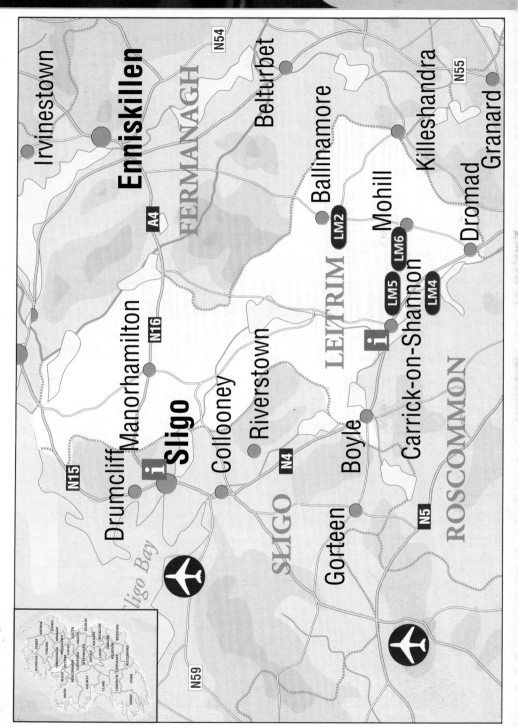

BALLINAMORE 4 km — Leitrim LM2

Mrs Teresa Kennedy
GLENVIEW
Aughoo, Ballinamore
Co Leitrim

Tel: 078-44157   Fax: 078-44814
Open: All year round

No Rooms:	6	Triple:	1
Twin/Double:	5	Family:	-
Single:	-	En suite:	6

AM V

B&B:	£25/£30	€ 31.74/38.09	HBW ES:	-	-	S.Supp: £10	€ 12.70	Dinner: £15	€ 19.05
B&B ES:	-	-	3 day HB:	£115	€ 146.02	CSP:		High Tea:-	
HBW:	£220	€ 279.34	3 day HB ES:	-	-				

Glenview House, 2 miles south of Ballinamore, is a holiday haven. 500m from the Shannon-Erne Waterway with its boating, canoeing, fishing and tranquil canal walks. Exclusive restarant, private tennis court, games room, museum and play area. Enjoy golf and boat trips, cycling and hill walking locally. Self catering within the grounds. Email: glenvhse@iol.ie

VOUCHERS ACCEPTED

CARRICK-ON-SHANNON 5 km — Leitrim LM5

GORTMÓR HOUSE
Kevin & Imelda McMahon
Lismakeegan
Carrick-on-Shannon, Co. Leitrim

Tel: 078-20489   Fax: 078-21439
Open: 1st February – 30th November

No Rooms:	4	Triple:	-
Twin/Double:	3	Family:	1
Single:	-	En suite:	4

AM V

B&B:	£19	€ 24.13	HBW ES:	-	-	S.Supp: £10	€ 12.70	Dinner: £15	€ 19.04
B&B ES:	£19	€ 24.13	3 day HB:	-	-	CSP:	20%	High Tea:£11	€ 13.97
HBW:	-	-	3 day HB ES:	-	-				

Spacious house set in mature wooded gardens in quiet scenic location. Situated 2 miles off N4 (Dublin Road) on East side & 1 mile off R280 (Leitrim/Drumshanbo Road) on North side. Ideal base for touring North, West, North West & Midlands. 2 hrs from Dublin. 2½ hrs from Belfast. Ireland's finest fishing area. Homely atmosphere. Frommers recommended. Laundry facilities on request. Email: gortmorhouse@oceanfree.net

VOUCHERS ACCEPTED

CARRICK-ON-SHANNON 1 km — Leitrim LM4

Mrs Annie Guckian
MEADOW VALE
Dublin Road,
Carrick-on-Shannon, Co Leitrim

Tel: 078-20521   Fax: –
Open: 1st April – 1st November

No Rooms:	4	Triple:	–
Twin/Double:	3	Family:	1
Single:	-	En suite:	4

AM

B&B:			HBW ES:	-	-	S.Supp: £6.50	€ 8.25	Dinner: £14	€ 17.78
B&B ES:	£19	€ 24.13	3 day HB:	-	-	CSP:	20%	High Tea:-	
HBW:	-	-	3 day HB ES:	-	-				

A warm welcome awaits you at "Meadow Vale". Situated on main Dublin-Sligo road, 1 km from Carrick-on-Shannon. Established reputation for good food and a high standard of accommodation. Situated in one of Ireland's best fishing areas. All amenities within easy distance. Mixed farming.

VOUCHERS ACCEPTED

MOHILL 3 km — Farm Guesthouse — Leitrim LM6

Maloney Family
GLEBE HOUSE
Ballinamore Road
Mohill, Co Leitrim

Tel: 078-31086   Fax: 078-31886
Open: 1st January – 1st December

No Rooms:	8	Triple:	2
Twin/Double:	4	Family:	2
Single:	–	En suite:	6

OBA
AE AM V

B&B:	£26.50/32	€ 33.65/40.63	HBW ES:	£240	€ 304.73	S.Supp: £7	€ 8.89	Dinner: £16	€ 20.32
B&B ES:	£26.50/32	€ 33.65/40.63	3 day HB:	-	-	CSP:	Negotiable	High Tea:-	
HBW:	-	-	3 day HB ES:	£120	€ 152.37				

Dating back to 1823 this lovely Georgian rectory has been carefully restored by the Maloney Family, making it one of the most popular guesthouses in the region. Enjoy the lovely Leitrim countryside with many attractions on our doorstep. Ideal venue for family re-unions. Assistance given with genealogy. Recommended by many travel guides. Stately home & Gardens. Email: glebe@iol.ie Website: www.glebehouse.com

VOUCHERS ACCEPTED

The Euro

On January 1st 1999 the Euro came into effect. Since that time, all European national currencies have had their exchange rates permanently set against the Euro. You will be able to use the Euro for cashless transactions such as paying by cheque or credit card. Euro notes and coins come out in 2002, and from then on national currencies will begin to phase out and you will be able to travel throughout other single currency member states without having to change money at all.

Limerick

Limerick has a colourful and fascinating history, and Limerick City with its castles, ancient walls and museums is a testament to the glories of the past. The county of Limerick is dotted with picturesque towns and villages, including the beautiful thatched village of Adare. For visitors who wish to mix a city and country holiday Limerick provides the best of both worlds.

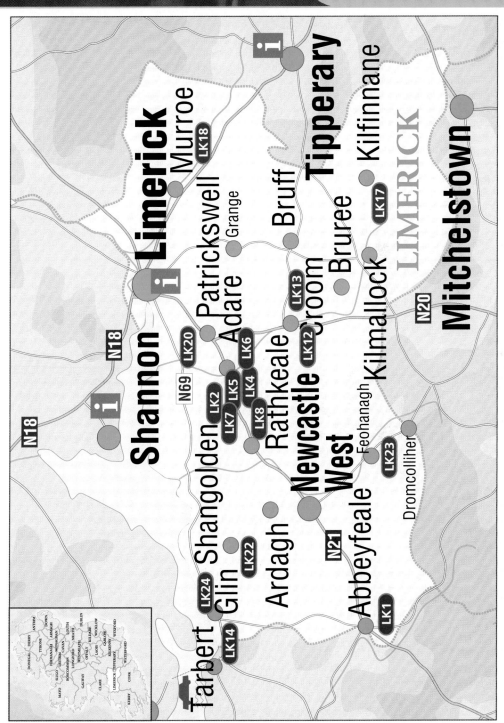

ABBEYFEALE 2 km | Limerick LK1

Kathleen & Tim Fitzgerald
FITZGERALD'S FARMHOUSE
& Equestrian Centre, Abbeyfeale Hill,
Abbeyfeale, Co Limerick

Tel: 068-31217   Fax: 068-31558
Open: 1st January – 31st December

No Rooms: 6	Triple: –
Twin/Double: 5	Family: 1
Single:	En suite: 6

AM V EC

B&B: -	-	HBW ES:	£235	€298.39	S.Supp: £6.50 €8.25	Dinner: £15 €19.05
B&B ES: £20	€25.39	3 day HB:			CSP: 25%	High Tea: £12 €15.24
HBW: -	-	3 day HB ES: £100	€127.00			

Luxury Farmhouse, Abbeyfeale (Hill Road) Via N21 Shannon, Limerick Kerry Route.
AIRE approved Horse Trekking/ Equestrian Centre, Summer Pony Camps, Petland on farm, Golf, Fishing, Beaches
and Drag Hunting within 30 mins drive. Ideal holiday base for families. Excellent stopover point for touring Kerry
and near to Tarbert Car ferry - Gateway to Clare. Email: fitzfarmhouse@eircom.net

VOUCHERS ACCEPTED

ADARE 4km | Limerick LK2

Anne & Melissa Burge
CASTLE HOUSE FARM
Smithfield, Croagh
Adare, Co Limerick

Tel: 061-395139   Fax: 061-395139
Open: 1st January – 31st December

No Rooms: 3	Triple: 1
Twin/Double: 1	Family:
Single: 1	En suite: 1

B&B: £18	€22.86	HBW ES:		S.Supp: £6.50 €8.25	Dinner: -
B&B ES: £22	€27.93	3 day HB:	-	-	CSP: 50%	High Tea: £8 €10.16
HBW: -	-	3 day HB ES: £110	€139.67			

Peaceful farmhouse, elegantly furnished, on grassland farm with horses.
Situated off N21 a few mins drive from heritage village of Adare and Clonshire equestrian centre.
Ideal touring base with wonderful local restaurants and many interesting and historical sights
to see.

VOUCHERS ACCEPTED

ADARE 3 km | Limerick LK4

Mrs Rita Curtin
ASHLAWN HOUSE
Beabus, Adare
Co Limerick

Tel: 061-396595   Fax: 061-395062
Open: April 1st – October 31st

No Rooms: 3	Triple: –
Twin/Double: 2	Family: 1
Single: –	En suite: 3

AM V EC

B&B: -	-	HBW ES:	-	S.Supp: -	-	Dinner: -
B&B ES: £19-20	€24.13-25.39	3 day HB:	-	CSP: 50%	High Tea: -
HBW: -	-	3 day HB ES: -	-		

Comfortable farmhouse dating from 1835. Tastefully restored with
modern conveniences. Situated 3km from Adare, taking the R519, off the N21. Shannon Airport
and Bunratty Castle within easy driving distance. Golf, fishing, horse riding available locally.
Regional winner AIB Agri Tourism Awards.

VOUCHERS ACCEPTED

ADARE 3 km | Limerick LK5

David & Hazel Fitzgerald
LACCABAWN FARMHOUSE
Drehidtrasna
Adare, Co Limerick

Tel: 061-396443   Fax: 061-396443
Open: 1st March – 30th October

No Rooms: 6	Triple: 1
Twin/Double: 4	Family: -
Single: 1	En suite: 4

AM V

B&B: £18	€22.86	HBW ES: -	-	S.Supp: £7 €8.89	Dinner: -
B&B ES: £20	€25.40	3 day HB: -	-	CSP:	High Tea: -
HBW: -	-	3 day HB ES: -			

Modern farmhouse in scenic location near Adare, just off the Limerick-
Killarney N21 road. Shannon Airport, Bunratty Castle & Folk Park within easy reach. Celtic Park
and forest walks nearby. Golf, fishing, horse riding locally. Visitors welcome to see animals on
working beef and cereal farm. Fluent French spoken. Hair dryers in all rooms.

VOUCHERS ACCEPTED

ADARE 2 km — Limerick LK6

Mrs Mary Fitzgerald
CLONUNION HOUSE
Limerick Road
Adare, Co Limerick

Tel: 061-396657 Fax: 061-396657
Open: 1st April – 31st October
OBA
AE AM V

			No Rooms:	4	Triple:	1
			Twin/Double:	2	Family:	–
			Single:	1	En suite:	3

B&B:	£20	€25.39	HBW ES:	-	S.Supp: £6.50 €8.25	Dinner:	-
B&B ES:	£20	€25.39	3 day HB:	-	CSP: -	High Tea:	-
HBW:	-	-	3 day HB ES:	-			

Delightful 200 year old farmhouse with spacious antique furnished rooms. Set in large tranquil gardens. Signposted at Crossroads 1 km on Limerick side of historical village of Adare (N21). You will be made very welcome in this family run working farm. Shannon Airport 33 km.

VOUCHERS ACCEPTED

ADARE 7 km — Limerick LK7

Mrs Mary Harnett
DUNEEVEN
Croagh
Rathkeale, Co Limerick

Tel: 069-63400 Fax: –
Open: 1st May – 30th September
OBA
AM V EC

			No Rooms:	4	Triple:	–
			Twin/Double:	3	Family:	–
			Single:	1	En suite:	–

B&B:	£17	€21.59	HBW ES:	-	S.Supp: £6.50 €8.25	Dinner:	-
B&B ES:	-	-	3 day HB:	-	CSP: 20%	High Tea: £10 €12.70
HBW:	-	-	3 day HB ES:	-			

Old gothic style farmhouse 0.5 km off N21, 7 km west of Adare. Car Parking. Ideal touring centre. Golf, fishing, tennis, equestrian centre, hill and forest walks. Historical and heritage centres. Traditional music locally. Convenient to Shannon Airport, Bunratty Castle. Pubs 300 metres. Small farm. Recommended in many travel guides. Email: duneeven@yahoo.com

VOUCHERS ACCEPTED

ADARE 5 km — Limerick LK8

Michael & Joan Piggott
MEADOWVIEW FARMHOUSE
Kiltannon, Croagh,
Rathkeale, Co Limerick

Tel: 069-64820/64374 Fax: –
Open: 1st March – 31st October
OBA

			No Rooms:	3	Triple:	–
			Twin/Double:	–	Family:	2
			Single:	–	En suite:	1

B&B:	£17	€21.58	HBW ES:	-	S.Supp: £6.50 €8.25	Dinner:	-
B&B ES:	£18.50	€24.13	3 day HB:	-	CSP: Negot.	High Tea: £8 €10.16
HBW:	-	-	3 day HB ES:	-			

Modern bungalow on a family run dairy farm, 6 minutes from Adare, off main Killarney N21 road. Shannon Airport 40 minutes. Equestrian Centre 2 km. Electric blankets, hairdryers, tea/coffee making facilities. Personal attention. "A Home from Home". Spacious garden, private car park. Families welcome.

VOUCHERS ACCEPTED

CROOM 3.5 km — Limerick LK12

Mrs. Mary B. Cronin
CRONIN'S FARMHOUSE
Ballymacamore
Croom, Co Limerick

Tel: 061-397497 Fax: 061-397117
Open: 1st January – 20th December
AM V EC

			No Rooms:	3	Triple:	1
			Twin/Double:	2	Family:	1
			Single:	–	En suite:	1

B&B:	£17	€21.59	HBW ES:	£200	€253.95	S.Supp: £6.50 €8.25	Dinner:	-
B&B ES:	£19	€24.13	3 day HB:	£75	€95.23	CSP: 50%	High Tea:	-
HBW:	£185	€234.90	3 day HB ES:	£81	€102.85			

Spacious modern farmhouse, large garden in scenic peaceful area on L118 Croom Ballingarry Rd., 3.5 km off Croom N20 at Croom Heritage Mills. Open farm 2k. Closes to Adare, Lough Gur, Shannon Airport and Limerick. Convenient for touring Kerry, Clare, Cork, Tipperary. Tea/scones on arrival. Mobile: 087 684 4902

VOUCHERS ACCEPTED

CROOM 3.5 km

Limerick LK13

Mrs Catherine Liston
KYLE FARMHOUSE
Glenbevan
Croom, Co Limerick

Tel: 061-397598 | Fax: 061-397598

Open: 1st January – 31st December

No Rooms:	5	Triple:	-
Twin/Double:	5	Family:	-
Single:		En suite:	3

V EC AM

B&B:	£17	€21.58	HBW ES:	-	-	S.Supp: -	Dinner: £14	€17.77
B&B ES:	£19	€24.13	3 day HB:	-	-	CSP: 25%	High Tea: £10	€12.69
HBW:			3 day HB ES: -					

Modern farmhouse situated on R516 Croom–Bruff road. 3.5 km off N20 at Croom. Central for Archaeological Lough Gur, golf at Adare and Charleville. Equestrian centre 5 km. Salmon and trout fishing on private stretch of River Maigue. Shannon Airport and Bunratty 30 km. Orthopaedic beds. Home cuisine. Email: kylefarmhouse@mail.com

---

GLIN 3 km

Limerick LK24

Getta & Maurice Fitzgerald
KILLACOLLA HOUSE
Glin, Co. Limerick

Tel: 068-34243 | Fax: -

Open: 1st April - 31st October

OBA

No Rooms:	3	Triple:	–
Twin/Double:	3	Family:	–
Single:		En suite:	3

V AM AE

B&B:	-	-	HBW ES:	-	-	S.Supp: £6.50 €8.25	Dinner: -	-
B&B ES:	£20	€25.39	3 day HB:	-	-	CSP: Negot.	High Tea: -	-
HBW:	-	-	3 day HB ES: -					

200 year old farmhouse in natural wooded setting, overlooking Shannon Estuary, 300m off N69 between Glin and Foynes. Limerick 45mins, Tralee 45mins. Convenient to Tarbert car-ferry. Ballybunion Championship Links Golf Course and beaches 25mins. Visitors welcome to see animals on working Dairy farm. Country & riverside walks. Family run, friendly atmosphere.

GLIN 2 km

Limerick LK14

John & Josephine O'Donovan
KNIGHTS HAVEN B&B
Tarbert / Glin,
Co Limerick

Tel: 068-34541 | Fax: 068-34541

Open: 1st January – 31st December

No Rooms:	3	Triple:	–
Twin/Double:	3	Family:	–
Single:	–	En suite:	3

AM V EC

B&B:	-	-	HBW ES:	£210	€266.64	S.Supp: £8 €10.16	Dinner: £15	€19.05
B&B ES:	£20	€25.39	3 day HB:	-	-	CSP: Negot.	High Tea: £10	€12.70
HBW:	-	-	3 day HB ES: £99	€125.70				

A luxurious Georgian residence in scenic landscaped gardens overlooking the Shannon Estuary. En route from Shannon to Ring of Kerry on N69. Ideal touring base for Tralee, Dingle, Killarney, Cliffs of Moher and Shannon Airport. All trips approx. 1hr drive . 7 minutes to Tarbert car ferry & 18 mins to Ballybunion beach/golf course. Well signposted off N69 half way between Tarbert and Glin. Email: knightshaven@esatclear.ie Website: www.knightshaven.com

---

KILMALLOCK 3 km

Limerick LK17

Mrs Imelda Sheedy-King
FLEMINGSTOWN HOUSE
Kilmallock
Co Limerick

Tel: 063-98093 | Fax: 063-98546

Open: 1st February – 1st December

OBA

No Rooms:	5	Triple:	-
Twin/Double:	4	Family:	1
Single:	–	En suite:	5

V M

B&B:	-	-	HBW ES:	-	-	S.Supp: £10 €12.97	Dinner: £20	€25.39
B&B ES:	£22.50-25	€28.57-31.74	3 day HB:	-	-	CSP: 50%	High Tea: £12	€15.24
HBW:	£120	€152.37	3 day HB ES: -					

250 year old house, situated at the intersection of three counties on R512 Kilmallock-Kilfinane Road, 4 km from R515 Tipperary-Killarney road. Recommended in "Good Hotel Guide", Karen Brown, Le Guide du Routard, AA ◆◆◆◆ Selected. National breakfast award. Colour TV in some rooms and King size beds. Website: http://www.ils.ie/flemingstown Email: flemingstown@keltec.ie

MURROE 3 km — Limerick LK18

Mrs Eilish Cooney
RIVERSDALE
Abington
Murroe, Co Limerick

Tel: 061-386225 Fax: –
Open: 1st March – 31st December

No Rooms:	4	Triple:	–
Twin/Double:	4	Family:	–
Single:	–	En suite:	3

B&B:	-	HBW ES:	-	S.Supp: £6.50 €8.25	Dinner:	£13	€16.50
B&B ES: £19	€24.13	3 day HB:	-	CSP: -	High Tea:-		
HBW:	-	3 day HB ES: £95	€120.63				

Spacious farmhouse set in peaceful surroundings with river flowing through this beef farm. Situated 5 km from Rosslare-Limerick road. 13 km from Limerick. Convenient to Shannon Airport. Glenstal Abbey, Clare Glens, Equestrian Centre, Pitch & Putt nearby. Excellent golf courses within 20 mins drive. Bunratty Castle locally.

NEWCASTLEWEST 10 km — Limerick LK23

Mrs Bridie Scanlan
ASHDALE FARM HOUSE
Feohanagh, Newcastlewest,
Co Limerick

Tel: 069-72282 Fax: -
Open: All year

V
AM

No Rooms:	3	Triple:	–
Twin/Double:	2	Family:	–
Single:	1	En suite:	2

B&B:	£18	€22.86	HBW ES: £224	€284.42	S.Supp: £20 €25.39	Dinner: £14	€17.78
B&B ES:	£20	€25.39	3 day HB: £90	€114.28	CSP: Negot.	High Tea:£7	€8.89
HBW:	£214	€271.72	3 day HB ES: £144	€182.84			

Delightful country house surrounded by ancient trees on 120 acres working farm. A warm welcome and relaxed atmosphere of quality accomodation. An ideal base for either activity filled or relaxing holiday. Historical trails, walks, golf and equestrian centre nearby. Ideal touring base for Tralee, Killarney, Cliffs of Moher and Shannon airport. All trips approx 1 hour drive. Email: ashdale.farm@oceanfree.net

PATRICKSWELL 1.5 km — Limerick LK20

Breda Mann
FORT ANN
Adare Road
Patrickswell, Co Limerick

Tel: 061-355162 Fax: 061-355162
Open: 1st January – 20th December

OBA
AM
V
EC

No Rooms:	4	Triple:	3
Twin/Double:	–	Family:	1
Single:	–	En suite:	4

B&B:	-	HBW ES:	-	S.Supp: £6.50 €8.25	Dinner: -
B&B ES: £19-20	€23.13-25.39	3 day HB:	-	CSP: 50%	High Tea:-
HBW:	-	3 day HB ES:	-		

Modern farmhouse set in peaceful surroundings amid lime & horse chestnut trees & landscaped gardens. Situated on N21 road, scenic route to Adare, 5 miles from Limerick City, 3 miles from Adare village. Working dairy & dry stock farm. Enjoy a warm welcome with good home cooking, log fires. Golf, fishing, horse riding locally. Visitors welcome to watch milking & animals on farm. Email: fortannfarmhouse@yahoo.co.uk

SHANAGOLDEN — Limerick LK22

Kathleen Prendergast
KNOCKOURA HOUSE
Shanagolden
Co. Limerick

Tel: 069-60187 Fax: -
Open: Jan 2001 - Dec 2001

AE
DC
AM
V
EC

No Rooms:	3	Triple:	-
Twin/Double:	2	Family:	1
Single:	-	En suite:	2

B&B:	£17	€21.58	HBW ES: £190	€247.60	S.Supp: Negot.	Dinner: £13	€17.14
B&B ES:	£19	€24.13	3 day HB: £85	€107.93	CSP: Negot.	High Tea:£8.50	€10.79
HBW:	£180	€228.25	3 day HB ES: -				

A luxurious georgian farmhouse set in peaceful surroundings on working environmentally friendly sheep farm. Situated 5km off the main N69 coastal route from Limerick to Tralee. Ideal base for touring - 70 mins Tralee/Killarney, 30 mins Limerick, 45 mins Ballybunion (Champion links golf course). Near Tarbert - Killimer Ferry crossing - Fishing, Golf, Cycling, Horse Riding, Clay Pigeon Shooting, Archery. Advice with planning itinerary. Families welcome. Tea/Scones on arrival. Laundry service. Mobile 087 6207364

Public Holidays 2001

January 1	New Year's Day
March 17	St. Patrick's Day
March 19	Bank Holiday
April 13	Good Friday
April 16	Easter Monday
May 7	Bank Holiday
June 4	Bank Holiday
August 6	Bank Holiday
October 29	Bank Holiday
December 25	Christmas Day
December 26	St. Stephen's Day

Longford

Longford's mixture of lush pastureland and wild bog contributes to the softly contrasting colours of the landscape. The excellent fishing facilities draw enthusiastic anglers from all over the world. The county has proud literary associations. Edgeworthstown, named after local author Maria Edgeworth, has played host to such luminaries as Sir Walter Scott and William Wordsworth.

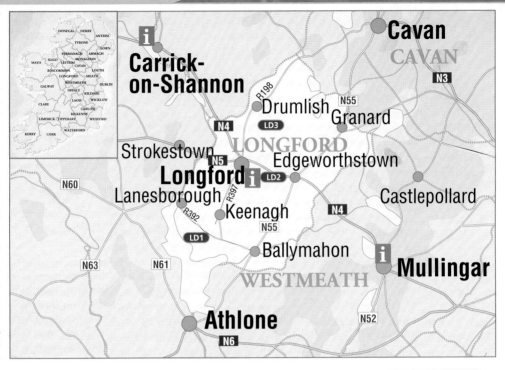

Cavan

CAVAN

N3

Carrick-on-Shannon

R198

Drumlish

N55

Granard

N4

LD3

Strokestown

LONGFORD

N5

Edgeworthstown

Longford

LD2

N60

Lanesborough

R397

Castlepollard

R392

Keenagh

N4

N55

LD1

Ballymahon

N63

N61

Mullingar

WESTMEATH

Athlone

N52

N6

BALLYMAHON 8 km — Longford LD1

Mary Gerety
DERRYLOUGH
Keenagh
Co Longford

Tel: 043-22126   Fax: 043 22126
Open: 1st April – 30th September   OBA
  AM V EC

	No Rooms:	3	Triple:	–
	Twin/Double:	3	Family:	–
	Single:		En suite:	2

B&B:	£17-20	€21.58-25.39	HBW ES:	-	S.Supp: -	Dinner: -
B&B ES:	£19-22	€24.13-27.93	3 day HB: -	CSP: -	High Tea: £10 €12.70
HBW: -	-		3 day HB ES: £90	€114.28		

Comfortable home in tranquil surroundings. Cattle, sheep and deer on farm. Home cooked food from farm and garden. 700 m off R392 between Ballymahon and Lanesborough, near Corlea Bog visitors centre. Good area for fishing, bird watching. Less than 2 hours drive Dublin, Galway, Sligo or Westport. Email: marytgerety@eircom.net

---

EDGEWORTHSTOWN 2.5 km — Longford LD2

Charlie & June Murphy
LACKAN LODGE
Edgeworthstown
Co Longford

Tel: 043-71299   Fax: 043-71299
Open: 1st April - 30th September   OBA
  AM V

	No Rooms:	4	Triple:	–
	Twin/Double:	4	Family:	–
	Single:		En suite:	2

B&B:	£18	€22.85	HBW ES:	-	S.Supp: £6.50 €8.25	Dinner: -
B&B ES:	£20	€25.39	3 day HB:	-	CSP: 40%	High Tea: -
HBW:	-	-	3 day HB ES:	-		

Modern farmhouse in peaceful surroundings 3 km the Longford side of Edgeworthstown on the N4 Dublin-Sligo/Mayo road. Family run farm with cattle, sheep and horses. Spacious car park. Television, open fire and tea/coffee making facilities in the lounge. Non-smoking throughout. Wheelchair access. Close to Ardagh Heritage Village.

LONGFORD 8 km

Longford LD3

Mrs Patricia Cumiskey
CUMISKEY'S FARMHOUSE
Ennybegs, Drumlish P.O.
Co Longford

Tel: 043-23320   Fax: 043-23516
Open: 1st March – 31st October
No Rooms: 6   Triple: 1
Twin/Double: 5   Family: -
Single: -   En suite: 5

OBA
AM
V

B&B:	£20	€25.39	HBW ES:	£310	€393.61	S.Supp: £6.50 €8.25	Dinner: £18 €22.85
B&B ES: £25/42.50 €31.74/53.96	3 day HB:	£108	€137.13	CSP: 25%	High Tea:- -
HBW: £266 €337.75	3 day HB ES: £125	€158.71

Award winning rambling Tudor style home with spacious gardens in peaceful country-side. Ideal location to relax & recharge in a beautiful atmosphere. Open Fires, exclusive sitting rooms, library loft. Family traditional musicians. Generous bedrooms & ensuite bathrooms. One suite with private lounge, king size bed, full bathroom, walk in closet. Home cooking available. Village pub 1km. Email: kc@iol.ie Website: www.iol.ie/~kc AA◆◆◆◆

To reach any of our farmhouses on the worldwide web,
why not look up the award winning
Irish Tourist Board Internet site at
http://www.ireland.travel.ie/farmhouses
or the **Irish Farmhouse Holidays Internet site**
http://www.irishfarmholidays.com
and view the full range of details available on each of our premises.
Email: farmhols@iol.ie

Louth

Louth's proud and colourful past is reflected in the many historical sites and museums in the area. The legacy of Celt and Viking, missionary and warrior, can be seen in the ancient walls of Drogheda, the splendid Mellifont Abbey, and numerous monuments and local museums. Pleasant coastal towns and villages like Carlingford are ideal places to get away from the stresses of modern living, and slip away to the restful atmosphere of the local pub.

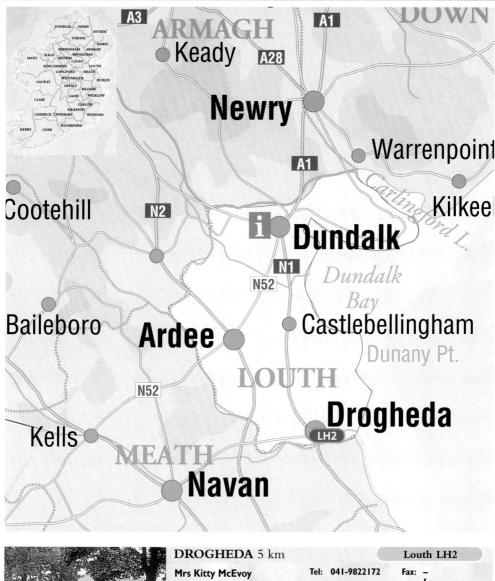

DROGHEDA 5 km					Louth LH2	
Mrs Kitty McEvoy **HIGHFIELD HOUSE** Termonfeckin Drogheda, Co Louth			Tel: 041-9822172 Fax: –			
			Open: 1st March – 31st October			
			No Rooms:	3	Triple:	–
			Twin/Double:	3	Family:	–
			Single:	–	En suite:	2
B&B:	-	HBW ES:	-	S.Supp: £25 €31.74	Dinner:	-
B&B ES: £20	€25.39	3 day HB:	-	CSP: U/12 50%	High Tea:	-
HBW:	-	3 day HB ES:	-			

1725 farmhouse beside the sea. Two 18 hole golf courses. Near Boyne Valley, Newgrange, , Newgrange, .Monaster Boice, Mellifont Abbey, Drogheda. Working farm. Beef, cattle, grain, turkeys and forestry.

Mayo

Mayo has a plethora of ancient and historical attractions including a 5,000 year old preserved field system (Ceide Fields) which is the most extensive stone-age monument in the world. There are several challenging golf courses in the region and there is ample opportunity to enjoy sporting and maritime activities to suit every taste. The county has many picturesque towns such as Westport which offer visitors the chance to experience a lively social scene in an attractive rustic setting.

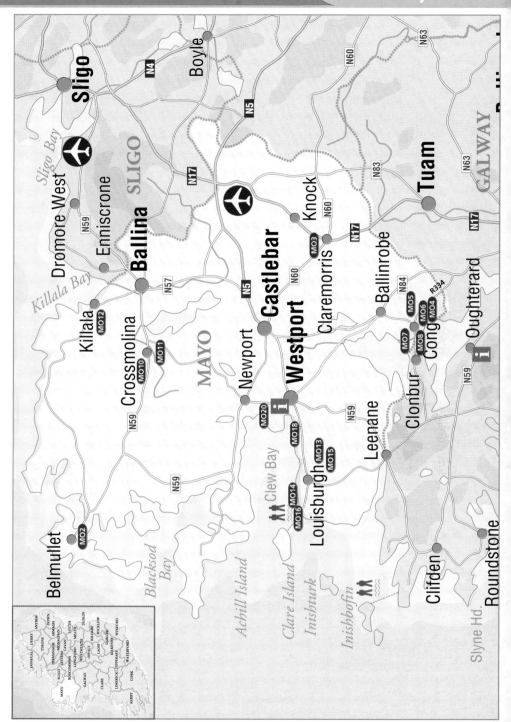

BELMULLET 1 km   Mayo MO2

Mrs Ann Healy
CHANNEL-DALE
Ballina Road
Belmullet, Co Mayo

Tel: 097-81377   Fax: 097-81377
Open: 1st April – 31st October

OBA

No Rooms:	3	Triple:	–
Twin/Double:	3	Family:	–
Single:	–	En suite:	3

B&B:	-	-	HBW ES:	-	-	S.Supp: -	-	Dinner: -	-
B&B ES: £19	€24.13		3 day HB:	-	-	CSP: -		High Tea: -	-
HBW:	-	-	3 day HB ES: -						

Spacious modern farmhouse set in peaceful surroundings with panoramic views of Broadhaven Bay, Mullet Peninsula. Situated on main Bangor-Erris-Belmullet Road. 5 minutes walk to Belmullet town. Convenient to Carn 18-hole Golf Course, blue flag beaches. Excellent restaurants in area. Email: ann.healy@oceanfree.net

---

CLAREMORRIS 10 km   Mayo MO3

Barrett Family
VALLEY LODGE
Facefield
Claremorris, Co Mayo

Tel: 094-65180   Fax: –
Open: 1st May – 1st October

OBA

No Rooms:	5	Triple:	1
Twin/Double:	4	Family:	–
Single:	–	En suite:	4

B&B: £17	€21.58	HBW ES:	-	-	S.Supp: £6.50 €8.25	Dinner: -	-
B&B ES: £19	€24.13	3 day HB:	-	-	CSP: 50%	High Tea: -	-
HBW: -	-	3 day HB ES: -				

Comfortable farmhouse on mixed farm in peaceful valley, signposted on N60 road 10km from Claremorris and 7km from Balla. Ideal touring centre for Westport, Achill Island, Connemara, Knock Shrine (10km). Goats, donkey and poultry on farm. Horse riding and golf (10km), night club entertainment (2km). Swimming pool nearby. Email: valleylodge@eircom.net

---

CONG 3 km   Mayo MO4

Mrs Mary Lydon
CORRIB VIEW VILLA
Gortacurra, Cross
Cong, Co Mayo

Tel: 092-46036 / 46815   Fax: 092-46036
Open: All Year

OBA
AM
V

No Rooms:	6	Triple:	4
Twin/Double:	2	Family:	–
Single:	–	En suite:	5

B&B: £17	€21.58	HBW ES:	-	-	S.Supp: £6.50 €8.25	Dinner: £13	€16.51
B&B ES: £19	€24.13	3 day HB:	-	-	CSP: 25%	High Tea: £10	€12.70
HBW: -	-	3 day HB ES: £95	€120.63			

Modern two storey farmhouse 1 km off R346 Cong-Galway road overlooking Lough Corrib and Connemara mountains. 3 km from Cong and Ashford Castle. Fishing on Lough Corrib and Lough Mask. Boats by arrangement. Horse riding and shooting in area. Ideal base for touring Connemara and Mayo.

CONG 4.5 km   Mayo MO5

Mrs Christina Moran
BREEZY HEIGHTS
Houndswood, Cross
Cong, Co Mayo

Tel: 092-46212   Fax: 092-46212
Open: 1st January – 20th December

OBA
AM
V
EC

No Rooms:	4	Triple:	1
Twin/Double:	3	Family:	–
Single:	-	En suite:	4

B&B: -	-	HBW ES: £190	€241.30	S.Supp: £6.50 €8.25	Dinner: £12	€15.24
B&B ES: £19	€24.13	3 day HB: -	-	CSP: 50%	High Tea: -	-
HBW: -	-	3 day HB ES: £81	€102.87		

Modern country home situated in scenic area overlooking Lough Corrib and Connemara Mountains. 0.3 km from Cross Village off R334 road, 4.5 km from Cong. Golf, fishing, cruises and horse riding locally. Ideal base for touring Connemara and Mayo. Ashford Castle and Cong Abbey nearby.

CONG 2 km

Mayo MO6

Fergal & Bernie O'Mahony
CONG GATEWAY
Lackafinna
Cong, Co Mayo

Tel: 092-46667   Fax: 092-46767
Open: April - October

No Rooms:	4	Triple:	–	V / EC
Twin/Double:	4	Family:	–	
Single:	–	En suite:	4	

B&B:	-	-	HBW ES:	£190/200 €241/255	S.Supp: £6.50 €8.25	Dinner: - -
B&B ES:	£19-20	€24.13-25.39	3 day HB:	- -	CSP: -	High Tea: -
HBW:	-		3 day HB ES:	£85/100 €108/127		

Luxury farmhouse on main Cong-Galway Road, with views of lake and
mountains. Connaught winner of Agri-Tourism Awards 1998, Fishing on Lough Corrib & Mask. Boats
available. Golf, cruises, horse riding and historic walks of Ashford Castle and Cong Abbey. Ideal base for
touring Connemara. Multi-channel TV & tea/coffee making facilities in rooms. Mobile: 087-2512857.

CONG 1.5 km

Mayo MO7

Mrs Bridie O'Toole
HILL VIEW FARM
Drumshiel
Cong, Co Mayo

Tel: 092-46500   Fax: 092-46500
Open: April - October   *OBA*

No Rooms:	3	Triple:	1	
Twin/Double:	2	Family:	–	
Single:	–	En suite:	3	

B&B:	£17	€21.59	HBW ES:	-	S.Supp: £6.50 €8.25	Dinner: - -
B&B ES:	£19	€24.13	3 day HB:	-	CSP: 33.3%	High Tea: -
HBW:	-		3 day HB ES:	-		

Warm hospitality in a modern farmhouse situated between Lough Corrib
and Lough Mask. Set in a peaceful, scenic location with magnificent view of Connemara mountains,
old castle and with view of lake from the farm. 1.5km from Cong and restaurants and signposted at
Cong village. Guest TV lounge. Home baking and tea/coffee facilities.

CONG 1.5 km

Mayo MO8

Mrs Kathleen Walsh
INISHFREE HOUSE
Ashford
Cong, Co Mayo

Tel: 092-46082/46622   Fax: –
Open: 1st January – 20th December   *OBA*

No Rooms:	4	Triple:	1	
Twin/Double:	3	Family:	–	
Single:	–	En suite:	4	

B&B:	-	-	HBW ES:	-	S.Supp: £6.50 €8.25	Dinner: - -
B&B ES:	£19	€24.13	3 day HB:	-	CSP: -	High Tea: -
HBW:	-		3 day HB ES:	-		

Situated between Lough Corrib and Mask on road R345 off N84, in the
heart of 'Quiet Man' country. Adjacent to Ashford Castle and Cong Abbey. Golf, horse riding,
fishing, walking. Lake cruising, 'Quiet Man' museum. Spacious farmhouse complying with full
Government safety standards.

CROSSMOLINA 1 km

Mayo MO10

Mrs Maureen Loftus
HILLVIEW
Cloonawillian, Belmullet Road
Crossmolina, Co Mayo

Tel: 096-31609   Fax: –
Open: 1st March – 1st November   *OBA* / EC

No Rooms:	4	Triple:	1	
Twin/Double:	3	Family:	1	
Single:	–	En suite:	3	

B&B:	£17	€21.58	HBW ES:	-	S.Supp: £6.50 €8.25	Dinner: - -
B&B ES:	£19	€24.13	3 day HB:	-	CSP: Negot.	High Tea: - -
HBW:	-	-	3 day HB ES:	£100 €126.97		

Modern luxury bungalow with peaceful view of the countryside on dairy
and livestock farm. Situated 1 km from Crossmolina on the main Crossmolina-Bellmullet Road.
Game angling on Lough Conn and River Moy. Golf at Ballina. Ideal centre for touring north Mayo.

CROSSMOLINA 5 km — Mayo MO 11

Joe & Madge Moffatt
KILMURRAY HOUSE
Castlehill, Crossmolina
Co Mayo

Tel: 096-31227		Fax: –	OBA
Open: 1st April – 1st October			EC
No Rooms: 6		Triple: 2	
Twin/Double: 2		Family: –	
Single: 2		En suite: 4	

B&B: £17	€21.58	HBW ES: -	-	S.Supp: £6.50 €8.25	Dinner: -	-
B&B ES: £19	€24.13	3 day HB: -	-	CSP: 50%	High Tea: -	-
HBW: -	-	3 day HB ES: -	-		

Large attractive farmhouse, mixed farming. 3 miles Crossmolina, 0.5 mile Rake Street pub/shop. Sea 12 miles. Game angling River Moy and Lough Conn, boats etc. arranged. Sea angling. Travel guides recommended. Excellent restaurants and pub food in area. Knock Shrine 50 km. Tea/coffee in bedrooms. Self catering house. Heritage centre nearby.

KILLALA 2 km — Mayo MO12

Mr Kevin Munnelly
GARDEN HILL FARMHOUSE
Killala,
Co Mayo

Tel: 096-32331		Fax: 096-32331	OBA
Open: 10th June – 30th August			EC
No Rooms: 4		Triple: 4	
Twin/Double: –		Family: –	
Single: –		En suite: 4	

B&B: -	-	HBW ES: -	-	S.Supp: £6.50 €8.25	Dinner: £14 €17.78
B&B ES: £19	€24.13	3 day HB: -	-	CSP: -	High Tea: -	-
HBW: -	-	3 day HB ES: £99	€125.73		

Modern farmhouse situated in scenic and tranquil surroundings. Landscaped gardens on a working farm. Observe the cattle and sheep graze on the green pastures. Seafood a speciality. Home grown produce. River Moy, Lough Conn and Ceide Fields nearby.

LOUISBURGH 0.4 km — Mayo MO13

Mrs Marian McNamara
PONDEROSA
Tooreen Road
Louisburgh, Co Mayo

Tel: 098-66440		Fax: –	
Open: 1st May – 30th September			V
No Rooms: 3		Triple: –	
Twin/Double: 3		Family: –	
Single: –		En suite: 1	

B&B: £17	€21.58	HBW ES: -	-	S.Supp: -	-	Dinner: -	-
B&B ES: £19	€24.13	3 day HB: -	-	CSP: -	-	High Tea: -	-
HBW: -	-	3 day HB ES: -	-		

Modern farmhouse in peaceful scenic location with view of mountains, 0.4 km from Louisburgh. Ideal touring base for Connemara and Achill Island. Close to safe, sandy beaches. River fishing, sea angling, surfing, mountain climbing, bicycle hire available locally. Nightly entertainment traditional music in family pub. Mixed farm.

LOUISBURGH 14 km — Mayo MO14

Mrs Martha Morrison
BAY SIDE
Thallabawn, Killadoon P.O.,
Louisburgh, Co Mayo

Tel: 098-68613		Fax: –	OBA
Open: 3rd January – 20th December			
No Rooms: 4		Triple: 1	
Twin/Double: 1		Family: 2	
Single: –		En suite: 3	

B&B: £17	€21.58	HBW ES: -	-	S.Supp: -	-	Dinner: £15 €19.04
B&B ES: £19	€24.13	3 day HB: -	-	CSP: -	-	High Tea: £7 €8.88
HBW: -	-	3 day HB ES: -	-		

Family run farmhouse on the seafront. Breathtaking scenic views. Relaxed atmosphere. Turf fires. Donkey on farm. Walks and mountain climbing. Ideal base for touring Connemara, Achill and Ceide Fields, House of Prayer and Knock Shrine.

LOUISBURGH 1 km — Mayo MO15

Mary O'Malley
RIVERVILLA
Shraugh
Louisburgh, Co Mayo

Tel: 098-66246   Fax: 098-66246   *OBA* `EC`
Open: 1st May - 31st October

No Rooms:	4	Triple:	–
Twin/Double:	1	Family:	2
Single:	1	En suite:	2

B&B £17	€21.58	HBW ES:	-	-	S.Supp: -	Dinner: -	-
B&B ES: £19	€24.13	3 day HB:	-	-	CSP: 50%	High Tea:-	
HBW:		3 day HB ES: £55	€69.84				

Peaceful location on banks of Bunowen River. Louisburgh 1 km. Signposted S ☎ ☑ ♪ B D 🛏🚲 ⊗ on Louisburgh/Westport R335 or via Chapel St., Louisburgh, past Spar to 'Rivervilla' signs. Touring base for Mayo/Galway. Beaches, mountains, riverside walks, salmon/sea trout fishing. Recommended by International Guides. Garden for visitors use. Excellent restaurants nearby.

VOUCHERS ACCEPTED

LOUISBURGH 1 km — Mayo MO16

Mrs Teresa Sammon
CUANEEN HOUSE
Carramore
Louisburgh, Co Mayo

Tel: 098-66460   Fax: 098-66460
Open: 1st April – 1st November

No Rooms:	5	Triple:	1
Twin/Double:	1	Family:	1
Single:	2	En suite:	2

B&B £17	€21.58	HBW ES:	£190	€241.25	S.Supp: -	Dinner: £13	€16.51
B&B ES: £19	€24.13	3 day HB:	-	-	CSP: 50%	High Tea:-	
HBW: -		3 day HB ES: -	-				

Seaside farmhouse overlooking Clew Bay 1km from Louisburgh. Views ✗ ♪ S 🛏 ☎ ⚙ from all windows of Croagh Patrick, Achill Island and Carramore Strand. 3 minutes walk to award winning beach (Blue Flag). Family run. Friendly and peaceful. Home cooking. Ideal for touring Mayo and Connemara. Sunday Telegraph & Cadogan recommended. Angling & river fishing close by.

VOUCHERS ACCEPTED

WESTPORT 10 km — Mayo MO18

Mrs Margaret Gill
BERTRA HOUSE
Thornhill Murrisk
Westport, Co Mayo

Tel: 098-64833   Fax: 098-64969   *OBA* `AM V`
Open: 1st March – 1st December

No Rooms:	5	Triple:	–
Twin/Double:	2/3	Family:	–
Single:	–	En suite:	4

B&B £18-19	€22.86+	HBW ES:	-	-	S.Supp: -	-	Dinner: -	-
B&B ES: £19-20	€24.13+	3 day HB:	-	-	CSP: -	High Tea: -	
HBW: -	-	3 day HB ES: -					

Seaside farmhouse, 3 minutes walk to long sandy beach at the foot of Croagh Patrick, 🛏 🖥 ∪ 🥾 ⊗ S `TV` Ireland's Holy Mountain. Ideal touring base for Achill Island and Connemara. All rooms with television, tea/coffee making facilities and hairdryers. Home made soda bread, breakfast menu. AA Listed ◆◆◆, 10km from Westport, 0.5 off main R335 Louisburgh road. Email: bertrahse@anu.ie Website: www.dirl.com/mayo/bertra-house.htm

VOUCHERS ACCEPTED

WESTPORT 9 km — Mayo MO20

The O'Malley Family
SEAPOINT HOUSE
Kilmeena
Westport, Co Mayo

Tel: 098-41254   Fax: 098-41903   *OBA* `AM V`
Open: 1st May – 1st October

No Rooms:	6	Triple:	2
Twin/Double:	3	Family:	1
Single:	–	En suite:	6

B&B -	-	HBW ES:	-	-	S.Supp: £8	€10.16	Dinner: -	-
B&B ES: £20	€25.39	3 day HB:	-	-	CSP: 20%	High Tea:-	
HBW: -	-	3 day HB ES: -					

Large modern country residence overlooking picturesque inlet of Clew S 🛏 🖥 ∪ 🥾 🥾 Bay with safe beach. Signposted on N59 Newport road 4 miles north of Westport. A.A. listed. Quiet location. Horse riding, golf, sailing nearby. Fishing in Clew Bay. Tea making facilities in bedrooms.

Vouchers Not Accepted

DISABLED VISITORS

Some farmhouses offer facilities for disabled/less able guests.

Please check individual requirements when booking.

Meath

It is here in County Meath that the great age of Celtic civilisation was nurtured. The large number of archaeological and historical sites, including the mighty Neolithic burial mounds of Newgrange and Knowth, bear witness to this fact. So also do the ancient monuments of Tara, seat of the Celtic kings. The region surrounding the river Boyne, one of the world's prettiest and most fertile valleys, was also the backdrop for many of the great battles and epics of Irish history.

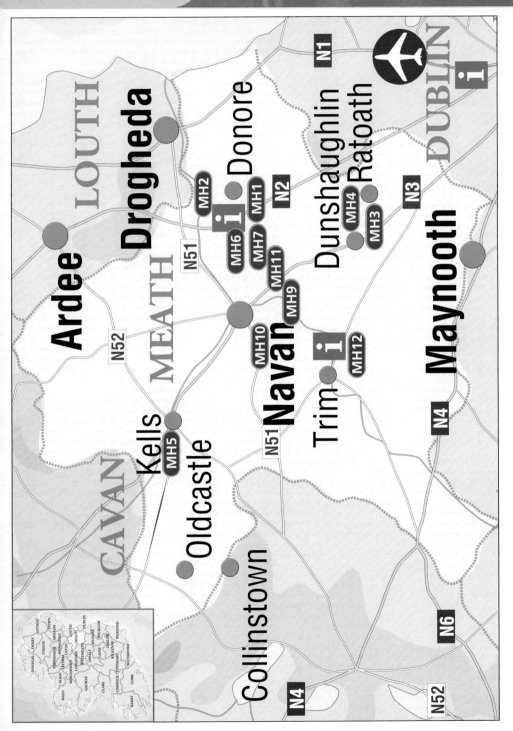

DONORE 2km

				Meath MH1

Mrs. Irene McDonnell
ROUGHGRANGE FARM
Donore
Co. Meath

Tel: 041-9823147 Fax: -
Open: 1st March - 31st October 2001 *OBA*

No Rooms:	3	Triple:	-
Twin/Double:	2	Family:	1
Single:	-	En suite:	3

B&B:	-	-	HBW ES:	-	S.Supp: £6.50 €8.25	Dinner:	-	-
B&B ES: £20	€25.39		3 day HB:	-	CSP: Negot.	High Tea:	-	
HBW:	-	-	3 day HB ES:	-				

17th Century Farmhouse. Situated in the Boyne Valley over looking Newgrange, Knowth and Dowth. 1/2km from Newgrange visitor centre - Brú-na-Bóinne. Working farm. Beef, suckling herd, sheep, free range hens and forestry. Private salmon trout and course fishing available to guests. Four 18 hole golf courses within 10 mile radius. Dublin airport 40 mins. T.V. in all bedrooms.

DONORE 2km

				Meath MH2

Mrs. Ursula Taaffe
WHITEROCK FARMHOUSE
Newtown, Donore,
Drogheda, Co. Meath

Tel: 041-9823135 Fax: -
Open: 1st March - 31st October *OBA*

No Rooms:	3	Triple:	-
Twin/Double:	3	Family:	-
Single:	-	En suite:	2

B&B:	£17	€21.58	HBW ES:	-	S.Supp: £6.50 €8.25	Dinner:	-	-
B&B ES: £19	€24.13		3 day HB:	-	CSP: 20%	High Tea:	-	
HBW:	-	-	3 day HB ES:	-				

Whiterock Farmhouse, a charming fourth generation family run B&B, situated 3km from Newgrange. Interpretive centre, an ideal base for touring the Boyne Valley. Working Dairy farm. Home baking a speciality with tea, coffee and homemade biscuits complimentary. Lovely bedrooms with luxurious ensuite facilities. Convenient to airport and ferry.

DUNSHAUGHLIN 2 km

				Meath MH3

Mrs Kathryn M. Delany
GAULSTOWN HOUSE
Dunshaughlin
Co Meath

Tel: 01-8259147 Fax: 01-8259147
Open: June, July, August

No Rooms:	3	Triple:	2
Twin/Double:	1	Family:	—
Single:	—	En suite:	3

B&B:	-	-	HBW ES:	-	S.Supp:	-	Dinner:	-	-
B&B ES: £20	€25.39		3 day HB:	-	CSP:	-	High Tea:	-	
HBW:	-	-	3 day HB ES:	-					

Elegant early 19th century farmhouse enjoying a rural setting on a drystock farm overlooking golf course, 2 km from Dunshaughlin (N3) off Airport Road (R125). Dublin City, Airport, Ferryport within 30 minutes. Dual Agri Tourism Award winner. Family Home of the Year Award. Recommended by Dillard/Causin Guide, Tipperary Water Guide and others. Parking & garden.

DUNSHAUGHLIN 3 km

				Meath MH4

Ms Kay McMahon Madden
FLEMINGTOWN HOUSE
Ratoath, Co Meath

Tel: 01-8256348 Fax: 01-8256988
Open: 1st January – 31st December

No Rooms:	3	Triple:	1
Twin/Double:	—	Family:	2
Single:	—	En suite:	3

B&B:	-	-	HBW ES:	-	S.Supp: £8 €10.15	Dinner: £18	€22.85
B&B ES: £20-22	€25.39-27.93	3 day HB:	-	CSP:	-	High Tea:	-
HBW:	-	-	3 day HB ES:	-				

Exclusive, spacious country residence surrounded by mature trees and garden. 3 km off N3. Dublin City, Airport, Ferryport within 30 minutes. Ideal for visiting Tara, Newgrange and Trim. Golf, fishing and horse riding nearby. Email: kay@flemingtownhouse.com Website: www.flemingtownhouse.com

KELLS 5 km

Meath MH5

Pauline Mullan
LENNOXBROOK
Carnaross
Kells, Co Meath

Tel: 046-45902 Fax: 046-45902
Open: All year

OBA

No Rooms:	4	Triple:	1	V
Twin/Double:	3	Family:	1	
Single:	–	En suite:	2	

B&B: £18	€22.85	HBW ES: -	-	S.Supp: £7	€8.88	Dinner: £15	€19.05
B&B ES: £20-25	€25.39-31.74	3 day HB: -	-	CSP: 20%		High Tea: -	
HBW: -	-	3 day HB ES: £150	€190.46				

Charming house, part of which is over 200 years old. Trees and a garden  stream complete an idyllic setting. Situated 5 km north of Kells on Kells-Cavan N3 road. Dublin Airport and Ferryport within 1.5 hours drive. Headford golf 4 km. Archaeological and historical area. Easy to find on N3 yet quiet and peaceful. Email: lennoxbrook@unison.ie

NAVAN

Meath MH6

Mrs. Anne Daly
PINEVIEW HOUSE
Harristown, Dean Hill Road
Navan, Co. Meath

Tel: 046-24147 Fax: -
Open: 2nd January - 18th December

AM
V
EC

No Rooms:	3	Triple:	-	
Twin/Double:	2	Family:	1	
Single:	-	En suite:	2	

B&B: £17	€21.58	HBW ES: -	-	S.Supp: -	Dinner: -
B&B ES: £19	€24.13	3 day HB: -	-	CSP: 25%	High Tea: -
HBW: -	-	3 day HB ES: -	-		

Spacious modern Farmhouse on drystock farm, near Navan Newgrange,  Tara, Bective Abbey, Trim Castle. Signposted on the N2 and R153. 40 minutes Dublin Airport, City and Ferryport. Golfing packages arranged, home baking, fishing and horse riding nearby. Friendly household. Email: pineviewhouse@ireland.com

NAVAN 2 km

Meath MH7

Mrs Pauline Daly
BLOOMFIELD FARMHOUSE
Daly's B&B, Duleek Rd., (R153)
Mooretown, Navan, Co Meath

Tel: 046-23219 Fax: –
Open: 2nd January – 20th December

AM
V
EC

No Rooms:	3	Triple:	-	
Twin/Double:	2	Family:	1	
Single:	-	En suite:	2	

B&B: £17	€21.58	HBW ES: -	-	S.Supp: £6.50	€8.50	Dinner: -
B&B ES: £19	€24.13	3 day HB: -	-	CSP: Negot.		High Tea: -
HBW: -	-	3 day HB ES: -	-			

On Dublin's doorstep. 30km N.W. Dublin Airport. 45km N.W. Dublin Ferryport. 10km off N2 at Balrath Cross. 12km Newgrange / Tara / Trim Castle. Tea making. Restaurants locally. From Navan coming from Dublin on N3, second set of traffic lights, turn right for R153/ Duleek / Kentstown / Ashbourne / Airport Road. Credit Cards accepted.

NAVAN 2 km

Meath MH9

Mrs Josephine McKeigue
BOTHAR ÁLAINN HOUSE
Balreask, Trim Road
Navan, Co Meath

Tel: 046-28580 Fax: –
Open: 1st January – 31st December

EC

No Rooms:	3	Triple:	1	
Twin/Double:	2	Family:	-	
Single:	–	En suite:	3	

B&B: -	-	HBW ES: -	-	S.Supp: £6.50	€8.35	Dinner: -
B&B ES: £19	€24.13	3 day HB: -	-	CSP: 10%		High Tea: -
HBW: -	-	3 day HB ES: -	-			

Spacious modern farmhouse situated 1.5km off N3 road from Dublin, 2km on Trim Road (R161) from Navan, opposite Balreask Arms Pub, 40km from Dublin, 30km from Dublin Airport. Ferryport 40 km. Mixed farming. Ideal base for touring Boyne Valley and visiting the archaeological sites. Fishing and golf nearby. Garden for visitors.

NAVAN 2 km — Meath MH10

Mrs Kathleen Reilly
HIGHFIELD HOUSE
Balreask Old
Navan, Co Meath

Tel: 046-27809   Fax: 046-27809
Open: January – December

No Rooms:	6	Triple: —
Twin/Double:	6	Family: —
Single:		En suite: 6

[V]

B&B:	-	-	HBW ES:	-	-
B&B ES: £19	€24.13	3 day HB:	-	-
HBW:	-	3 day HB ES:	-	-

S.Supp: £6.50 €8.25	Dinner:	-
CSP: Neg.	High Tea:	-

S 🛏 🖥 ♨ ⊠ 🖼 ♠ ♨ [TV]

Country home on farm. Luxury lounges, TV & tea making facilities. Rooms en suite. Many restaurants locally. Tour Boyne Valley, Newgrange, Trim, Castles etc. Horse riding lessons arranged. Many golf courses, fishing, driving ranges, Pitch & Putt etc. Dublin City and Airport 40 minutes. N3 1 minute. R161, 1 minute. Taxies. Families welcome. 3 Days B&B ES £50 - €63.49

NAVAN 2 km — Meath MH11

Mrs Mary Reilly
GAINSTOWN HOUSE
Trim Road, Navan
Co Meath

Tel: 046-21448   Fax: —
Open: 1st June – 1st September

No Rooms:	4	Triple: 2
Twin/Double:	1	Family: 1
Single:	-	En suite: 1

[V] [EC] [AM]

B&B: £20	€25.39	HBW ES:	-	-
B&B ES: £25	€31.74	3 day HB:	-	-
HBW:	-	-	3 day HB ES: £90	€114.28

S.Supp: £6.50 €8.25	Dinner:	-
CSP: -	High Tea: £10	€12.70

🛏 U ⊠ 🖼 ♨ ♠ ⊗ S

Exclusive, spacious period residence situated 2 km off Navan-Trim Road. Signposted on Navan/Dublin N3 Road at Old Bridge Inn. Central for touring archaeological sites in Boyne Valley. Elsie Dillard and Susan Causin, Country Inns and Alliance recommended. Dublin 32 km, Airport 30 km. Home baking and fresh produce. Mixed farming. Garden for visitors.

TRIM 8km — Meath MH12

Fergal Canning
COSY GIBBONS FARMHOUSE
Summerhill
Co. Meath

Tel: 0405-57232   Fax: -
Open: January - December

No Rooms:	4	Triple: -
Twin/Double:	3	Family: 1
Single:	-	En suite: 4

[AM] [V]

B&B:	-	-	HBW ES:	-	-
B&B ES: £22	€27.93	3 day HB:	-	-
HBW:	-	-	3 day HB ES:	-	-

S.Supp: £6.50 €8.25	Dinner:	-
CSP: -	High Tea:	-

🏠 🛏 ⊠ 🖼 U ♠ [TV]

Refurbished Pub/Farmhouse on small sheep/cattle farm in quiet rural area only 22 miles from central Dublin city, 15 miles M50, 20 miles airport. 8km Trim R158. 10km Kilcock N4/M4. 15km Dunboyne. Tara 8km. Safe parking. Garden. Underfloor heating. Historical sites. Golf. Ideal landscape painting. Pub next door. Dog kennel. Bike shed. Mobile: 087 2601392

GRATUITIES / TIPS

Gratuities/tips are not expected by the Farmhouses,
but are appreciated if the
guest wishes to do so.

Monaghan

Another of Ireland's famous fishing counties, Monaghan has a fascinating history. Immortalised in the poetry of Patrick Kavanagh, the county's famous sons also include James Connolly, hero of the 1916 Rising. Monaghan is world famous for its beautiful and intricate lace, and visitors can learn about lace-making at the craft centres of Clones and Carrickmacross.

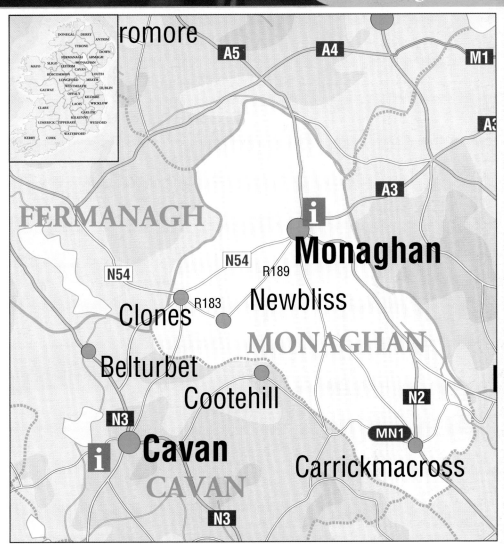

romore

A5 · A4 · M1 · A3

FERMANAGH

N54 · N54 · R189

Monaghan

N3 · R183

Clones

Newbliss

MONAGHAN

Belturbet

Cootehill

N2

MN1

Cavan

Carrickmacross

CAVAN

N3

CARRICKMACROSS 5 km			Monaghan MN1	
Mrs Christine McMahon **ARRADALE HOUSE** Kingscourt Road Carrickmacross, Co Monaghan		Tel: 042-9661941	Fax: 042-9661941	
		Open: All year except Christmas Day		
		No Rooms: 7	Triple: 1	
		Twin/Double: 5	Family: 1	
		Single: -	En suite: 2	

B&B:	£17	€21.58	HBW ES:	-	-	S.Supp:	-	-	Dinner:	-	-
B&B ES:	£19	€24.13	3 day HB:	-	-	CSP:	-	-	High Tea:	£8	€10.15
HBW:	-	-	3 day HB ES:	£90	€114.28						

Arradale House is situated on the Kingscourt Road. 5 km south of Carrickmacross just off N2. Places of interest in the area, lace, golf, fishing. TVs/tea making facilities in bedrooms. Lounge with video. Home cooking. Ideal location for touring Newgrange, Northern Ireland and Cooleys. Children under 5 years free. Lace making.

VOUCHERS ACCEPTED

Offaly

Offaly is in the heart of Ireland's central plain where the great Celtic warriors Cuchulainn and Fionn MacCumhaill hunted and fished. Evidence of a great monastic heritage can be seen at the extensive ruins and high crosses at Clonmacnoise. In this tranquil part of Ireland visitors can also enjoy the social pleasures of modern life while they explore the treasures of the past.

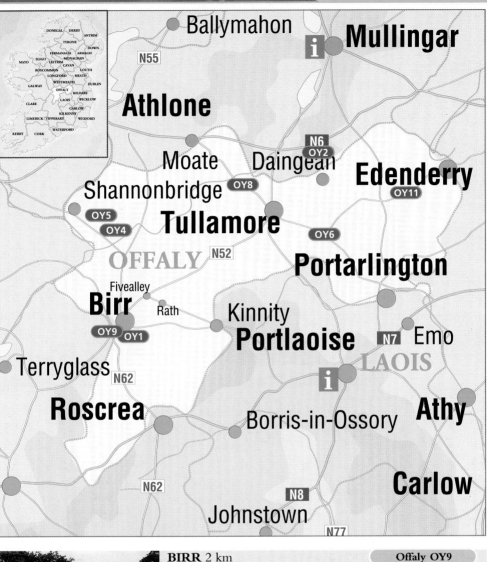

Ballymahon
Mullingar
N55
Athlone
Moate
Daingean
N6
OY2
Shannonbridge
OY8
Edenderry
OY11
OY5
Tullamore
OY4
OY6
OFFALY
N52
Portarlington
Fivealley
Birr
Rath
Kinnity
OY9 OY1
Portlaoise
N7
Emo
Terryglass
LAOIS
N62
Roscrea
Borris-in-Ossory
Athy
N62
Carlow
N8
Johnstown
N77

BIRR 2 km				Offaly OY9		
Carmel Carroll			**Tel:** 0509-20976	**Fax:** 0509-20976		
THE RING FARMHOUSE			**Open:** 3rd January – 22nd December			AM V
The Ring, Birr,			No Rooms:	3	Triple:	–
Co Offaly			Twin/Double:	2	Family:	1
			Single:	–	En suite:	2
B&B: £17	€21.58	**HBW ES:** -	-	**S.Supp:** £6.50 €8.25	**Dinner:** -	
B&B ES: £19	€24.13	**3 day HB:** -	-	**CSP:** under12: 50%	**High Tea:**	
HBW: -	-	**3 day HB ES:** -	-	under 2: free		

The Ring Farmhouse situated on the site of Loretto Castle is a homestead steeped in tradition and folklore with the present Carroll family tracing their roots back here for several generations. Today this family run dairy farm provides comfortable accommodation. Recommended by Lonely Planet Guide as an interesting alternative. Email: ringfarm@gofree.indigo.ie

BIRR 8 km

Padraig and Grace Grennan
PARKMORE HOUSE
Fivealley, Birr
Co. Offaly

Tel: 0509-33014 Fax: 0509-33054
Open: All year round

No Rooms:	3	Triple:	–
Twin/Double:	2	Family:	1
Single:	–	En suite:	3

B&B:	-	-	HBW ES:	£30	€ 38.09	S.Supp: £6.50	€ 8.25	Dinner:	£20	€ 25.39
B&B ES: £25		€ 31.74	3 day HB:	-	-	CSP:	20%	High Tea: £12	€ 15.24
HBW:	-	-	3 day HB ES:	-	-				

A Charming 18th Century Victorian Farmhouse situated in the navel of Ireland. Old world charm with modern comforts & antique furniture throughout. Parkhouse welcomes you with its homely atmosphere enhanced by a fine reputation for hospitality & excellent food for which it is renowned. Recommended in Karen Brown's and Frommer's Guide.

BIRR 3 km

Mrs Veronica Minnock
MINNOCKS FARMHOUSE
Roscrea Road
Birr, Co Offaly

Tel: 0509-20591/21684 Fax: 0509-21684
Open: January 1st - December 31st

No Rooms:	6	Triple:	1
Twin/Double:	3	Family:	2
Single:	–	En suite:	6

B&B:	-	-	HBW ES:	-	S.Supp: £6.50	€ 8.25	Dinner:	-	-
B&B ES: £19		€ 24.13	3 day HB:	-	CSP:	-	High Tea:	-
HBW:	-		3 day HB ES:	-				

Spacious, comfortable farmhouse set in mature gardens on N62 South. 3 km from Birr Heritage Town. Visit restored Castle Gardens, Historic Science Centre, Telescope. Recommended in '300 Best B&B's' 'Hidden places in Ireland'. Rooms en suite with TV and hairdryers. Tea/Coffee facilities. Direct dial telephones from bedrooms. Email: Minnocksfarmhouse@eircom.net Website: www.minnocksfarmhouse.cjb.net

DAINGEAN 5 km

Mrs Mary Margaret Smyth
BEECHLAWN FARMHOUSE
Clyduff, Daingean
Co Offaly

Tel: 0506-53099 Fax: –
Open: 25th March – 31st October   OBA

No Rooms:	5	Triple:	–
Twin/Double:	5	Family:	
Single:	–	En suite:	5

B&B:	-	-	HBW ES:	£200	€ 253.94	S.Supp: £6.50	€ 8.25	Dinner: £15	€ 19.05
B&B ES: £19		€ 24.13	3 day HB:	-	-	CSP:	20%	High Tea: £10	€ 12.70
HBW:	-	-	3 day HB ES:	£99	€ 125.70				

Luxury farmhouse on working dairy farm in the centre of Ireland. Ideal base for touring, golf, horse-riding, fishing, walking nearby. Recommended in Frommer's Guide. Evening dinner by candlelight. Home cooking our speciality. A warm welcome awaits our guests with complimentary tea/coffee. 5km Daingean, 11km Tullamore, 1 hour Dublin, 170km Rosslare.

EDENDERRY 8 km

Mrs Ann Mooney
ESKERMORE HOUSE
Mount Lucas,
Daingean, Co Offaly

Tel: 0506-53079 Fax: -
Open: 1st January - 20th December

No Rooms:	3	Triple:	–	**V**
Twin/Double:	2	Family:	1	**AM**
Single:	–	En suite:	3	

B&B:	-	-	HBW ES:	£250	€ 317.43	S.Supp: £6.50	€ 8.25	Dinner: £18	€ 22.86
B&B ES: £20		€ 25.39	3 day HB:	-	-	CSP:	25%	High Tea: £12	€ 15.24
HBW:	-	-	3 day HB ES:	£105	€ 133.32				

In the heart of Ireland, this early Georgian farmhouse is set in the curve of a stream in wooded grounds, surrounded by mature gardens. The house has been restored in sympathy with its period and makes an ideal location for a holiday away from town and city, where one can enjoy the tranquility of the surrounding area.

PORTARLINGTON 6 km | Offaly OY6

Mrs Ena Brennan
ASHMOUNT HOUSE
Cloweygowan
Tullamore, Co Offaly

Tel: 0506-43533	Fax: -	
Open: 1st May – 31st October		
No Rooms: 3	Triple: 1
Twin/Double: 1	Family: -
Single: 1	En suite: -

B&B: £17	€21.58	HBW ES:	-	S.Supp: £6.50 €8.25	Dinner: £14 €17.78
B&B ES: -		3 day HB:	-	CSP:	High Tea: -
HBW: -		3 day HB ES:	-		

Georgian house set in beautiful mature gardens. Situated on the outskirts ✕ S ∪ ⌐ of a small traditional village, 18 km west of Monasterevin-Tullamore N7 road. 1 hour drive from Dublin. Mixed farming. Fishing, swimming, canal cruises, mountain walks. Single letting. Approved riding stables and three 18 hole golf courses nearby. Swimming pool nearby.

SHANNONBRIDGE 2 km | Offaly OY4

Mrs Vera Carty
ASHBROOK
Shannonbridge
Co Offaly

Tel: 0905-74166	Fax: –	
Open: 17th March – 31st October		
No Rooms: 3	Triple: -
Twin/Double: 2	Family: 1
Single: -	En suite: 2

B&B: £17 €21.58	HBW ES: -	S.Supp: 6.50 €8.25	Dinner: £12 €15.25
B&B ES: £19 €24.13	3 day HB: -	CSP: 20%	High Tea: £10 €12.70
HBW: -	3 day HB ES: £90 €114.28		

Spacious farm residence set in beautiful landscaped gardens, 2 km from ✕ ✕ ⌐ ♘ ♪ ⌐ ∪ Shannonbridge. Fishing on River Shannon and Suck. 8 km from Clonmacnoise, one of Ireland's most historic sites. Bog Rail tour 1 km. Birr Castle, Slieve Bloom Mountains, golf, horse riding, river cruises. Close to official walking routes. Cycling nearby.

SHANNONBRIDGE 2 km | Offaly OY5

Mrs Marie McManus
LAUREL LODGE
Shannonbridge
Co Offaly

Tel: 0905-74189	Fax: 0905-74189	
Open: 1st March – 30th October		OBA
No Rooms: 6	Triple: 2	V
Twin/Double: 2	Family: 2
Single: –	En suite: 6

B&B: -	HBW ES: -	S.Supp: £6.50 €8.25	Dinner: £14 €17.77
B&B ES: £19.00 €24.13	3 day HB: -	CSP: 20%	High Tea: £10 €12.69
HBW: -	3 day HB ES: £95 €120.62		

Modern farmhouse situated in peaceful surroundings 2km from Shannonbridge ⌂ S ⌐ ☼ ⌐ ✓ ♪ well known for its fishing and cruising on the Shannon. Within 8km of famous historical site of Clonmacnoise. Bog Rail tours 1km. Fridge, tackle storage, golf and horse riding nearby. Home baking. Free transport to pub if required. Email: laurellodgefarm@eircom.net. Website: www.laurellodgefarm.ie

TULLAMORE 6 km | Offaly OY8

Agnes & Larry Mealiffe
BALLINAMONA FARM
Ballinamona
Tullamore, Co Offaly

Tel: 0506-51162	Fax: –	
Open: 1st Mar – 31st Oct		
No Rooms: 4	Triple: –
Twin/Double: 4	Family: –
Single: –	En suite: 4

B&B: £16.50 €20.95	HBW ES: -	S.Supp: £6.50 €8.25	Dinner: £15 €19.50
B&B ES: £19 €24.13	3 day HB: -	CSP:	High Tea: -
HBW: -	3 day HB ES: £90 €114.28		

Family run farmhouse and sheepfarm in the centre of Ireland. Set in ✕ ⌂ ➤ S ⌐ ✓ ⌐ peaceful and quiet countryside, 2 km off the N52 Tullamore & Kilbeggan Road. Have a cup of tea on arrival or a stroll in the garden. Relax and we will tell you about the local attractions.

Roscommon

Bordering the lovely river Shannon, Roscommon has much to offer the visitor. Sightseers can explore the ruins of the Cistercian Abbey in Boyle and go camping in Lough Key Forest Park. The natural beauty of the region is a fine setting in which to enjoy some wonderful trout and salmon fishing. Strokestown is well worth a visit for its lovely house and gardens, and also to see the Irish Famine Museum.

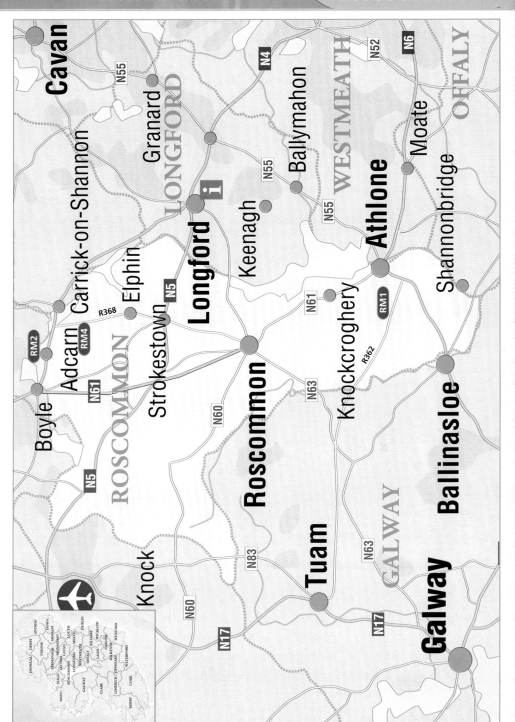

ATHLONE 8 km   Roscommon RM1

Miss Helen O'Brien
ST. RUTH'S FARMHOUSE
Milltown, Curraghboy,
Athlone, Co Roscommon

Tel: 0902-88090   Fax: –
Open: All Year

No Rooms:	5	Triple:	2
Twin/Double:	2	Family:	1
Single:	–	En suite:	5

 EC

B&B:	-	-	HBW ES:	-	-	S.Supp: £6.50 €8.25	Dinner: £17.50 €22.22
B&B ES: £19		€24.13	3 day HB:	-	-	CSP: 33.3%	High Tea:-	-
HBW:	-	-	3 day HB ES: £104		€132.05		

Experience rural tranquility at St. Ruth's - a restful Farmhouse, surrounded by natural gardens, river and lazy old millstream. 200 acres mixed farming. Convenient to Golf, Pitch & Putt, Folk Museum, country walks and historic Clonmacnoise. R362 off N6. 8km from Athlone - 2 hours Dublin. Classic combination of yesterday's charm with today's comforts.

✗ ⊠ S ⓑ ✓ ♪

BOYLE 12 km   Roscommon RM2

The Burke Family
RIVERSDALE HOUSE
Knockvicar
Boyle, Co Roscommon

Tel: 079-67012/67338   Fax: 079-67288
Open: 1st May – 1st October

No Rooms:	5	Triple:	3
Twin/Double:	2	Family:	–
Single:	-	En suite:	5

EC

B&B:	-	-	HBW ES:	-	-	S.Supp: £6.50 €8.25	Dinner:	-	-
B&B ES: £24		€30.47	3 day HB:	-	-	CSP: 33.3% reduction	High Tea:	-	-
HBW:	-	-	3 day HB ES:	-			

Georgian house 190 years old, former home of film star Maureen O'Sullivan. Fishing, shooting, ponies, boats on property. Golf (6 km). French spoken. Free boat with week reservations. Private access Boyle River, Lough Key. Panoramic view of lake and mountains. 4 km off N4 between Carrick and Boyle. Email: jpburke@indigo.ie

🍳 ⓑ 🖥 ♪ ⌨ ♜ 🐾 ⛹

CARRICK-ON-SHANNON 5 km   Roscommon RM4

Mrs Catherine McDermott
SCREGG HOUSE
Carrick-on-Shannon,
Co Roscommon

Tel: 078-20210   Fax: -
Open: 1st May-15th Sept

No Rooms:	4	Triple:	1
Twin/Double:	2	Family:	-
Single:	-	En suite:	2

B&B:	£17	€21.58	HBW ES:	-	-	S.Supp: £6.50 €8.25	Dinner:	-	-
B&B ES: £19		€24.13	3 day HB:	-	-	CSP: 10%	High Tea:	-	-
HBW:	-	-	3 day HB ES:	-			

Luxury farm residence in quiet area. Highly recommended for good food and hospitality. Galtee Breakfast award. Pike fishing in Lough Key Forest Park. Boats available. Golf and Equestrian Centre locally. 5 km from Carrick-on-Shannon. Signposted on Carrick-Elphin R368 road. Music in thatched pub nearby. Painting/artists room with lovely mountain scenery. Tea on arrival. Home baking.

✗ S ⓑ ⊗

Welcome to the homes of the

NORTHERN IRELAND FARM AND COUNTRY HOLIDAYS ASSOCIATION

WE HAVE HOMES IN EVERY COUNTY TO CATER FOR ALL TASTES

Enjoy a warm welcome, the best of Ulster's Farmhouse Breakfasts, traditional
Home Baked Bread, good wholesome Food.

Come and enjoy a few days relaxation with us, and experience a home from home.
For further information contact:

NIFCHA
47 Ballygroobany Road, Richhill,
Armagh, Northern Ireland. BT61 9NA
Telephone and Fax: 028 388 70081 Website: www.nifcha.com
Mobile: 0771 3085206 (from the Republic of Ireland: 00 44 771 3085206)

Sligo

Blessed with fine lakes and a coastline that has some of the best surf in the British Isles, Sligo is a paradise for water sports enthusiasts. The more culturally inclined can explore Yeats' country, and experience first hand the source of inspiration for some of Jack B. Yeats' paintings and his brother William Butler Yeats' passionate poetry.

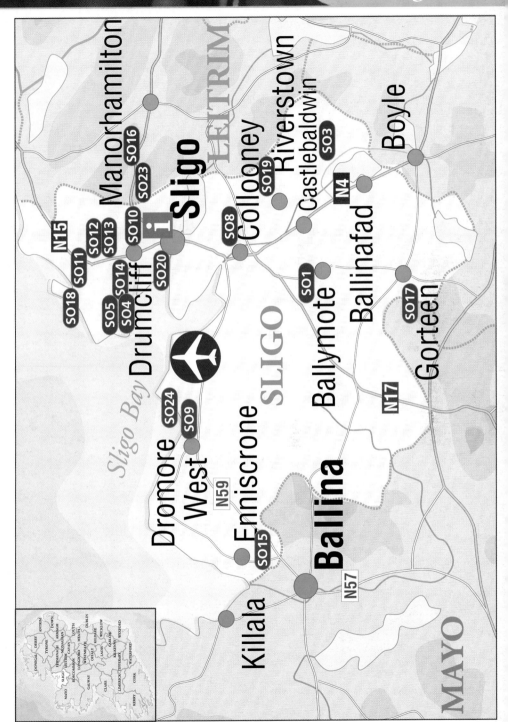

BALLYMOTE 8 km   Sligo SO1

Mrs D Perceval
TEMPLE HOUSE
Ballymote
Co Sligo

Tel: 071-83329		Fax: 071-83808	
Open: 1st April – 30th November			
No Rooms:	6	Triple:	–
Twin/Double:	5	Family:	–
Single:	1	En suite:	5

AE AM V EC

B&B:	£42	€53.3	HBW ES:	-	-	S.Supp: £10 €12.7	Dinner: £20	€25.39
B&B ES:	£45	€57.14	3 day HB:	-		CSP: Negot	High Tea: £3	€3.81
HBW:	-	-	3 day HB ES:	-				

Large Georgian mansion overlooking Temple House Lake on 1,000 acres cattle/sheep farm, woods and bog. Located 8 km from Ballymote and 20 km south of Sligo on N17 (Galway road). French spoken. Coarse angling (boat for hire). Recommended in Irish Food Guide. Bronze age graves in area. No perfumes please. Email: guests@templehouse.ie Website: www.templehouse.ie

Vouchers Not Accepted

BOYLE 12 km   Sligo SO3

Mrs Noeleen Henry
HILLCREST
Ballindoon, Castlebaldwin,
Via Boyle, Co Sligo

Tel: 071-65559		Fax: 071-65559	
Open: 1st March – 31st October			
No Rooms:	4	Triple:	-
Twin/Double:	4	Family:	-
Single:		En suite:	4

V

B&B:	-	-	HBW ES:	-	-	S.Supp: £6.50 €8.25	Dinner: £14	€17.78
B&B ES:	£19	€24.13	3 day HB:	-		CSP: 50%	High Tea: £9	€11.43
HBW:	-	-	3 day HB ES:	-				

Modern bungalow overlooking Sligo's renowned mayfly fishing lake. Lough Arrow. Views of Brickliene Mountains and Carrowkeel archaeological sites. Boating, fishing locally. Ideal for walking and cycling. Located off Boyle-Sligo Road N4. Signposted at Castlebaldwin 5 km. Car Parking available. Email: hillcrestfarm@eircom.net Website: http://homepage.eircomnet/hillcrestbandb/

VOUCHERS ACCEPTED

DRUMCLIFF 12 km   Sligo SO5

Mrs Mary Herity
SEAVIEW FARMHOUSE
Raghly, Ballinfull P.O.,
via Lissadell, Co Sligo

Tel: 071-63640		Fax: –	
Open: 1st April – 31st October			
No Rooms:	3	Triple:	–
Twin/Double:	3	Family:	–
Single:		En suite:	2

OBA
EC

B&B:	£17	€21.58	HBW ES:	-	-	S.Supp: £6.50 €8.25	Dinner: -
B&B ES:	£19	€24.13	3 day HB:	-		CSP: 25%	High Tea: -
HBW:	-	-	3 day HB ES:	-			

Welcome to Seaview Farmhouse situated on the Raghly Peninsula. Modern farmhouse on a dairy farm within 50 metres of Yellow Strand. Spectacular views of Sligo Bay and Yeates Country. We offer high standard accommodation with bright and spacious rooms. Tea/coffee making facilities. TV lounge. Excellent restaurants within 8 km. signposted to turn off N15 at Drumcliff for Carney Lissadell road.

VOUCHERS ACCEPTED

COLLOONEY 1.5 km   Sligo SO8

Mrs Lydia Murray
MARKREE HOUSE
Collooney,
Co Sligo

Tel: 071-67466		Fax: 071-67466	
Open: 1st April – 30th September			
No Rooms:	3	Triple:	–
Twin/Double:	3	Family:	–
Single:	–	En suite:	3

B&B:	-	-	HBW ES:	-	-	S.Supp: £10 €12.69	Dinner: -
B&B ES:	£25	€31.74	3 day HB:	-		CSP: -	High Tea: -
HBW:	-	-	3 day HB ES:	-			

This is a large country house set on 62 acres, bordered by the River Unshin and adjacent to Markree Castle. Seclusion and tranquility combined with luxury en suite accommodation assures you of a pleasant and memorable stay. Signposted off N4 from Collooney. Email: markree@eircom.net. Strictly no Smoking within the house.

Vouchers Not Accepted

DROMORE WEST In village   Sligo SO9

Pam & Ray Tully
DROMORE HOUSE
Dromore West
Co Sligo

| Tel: 096-47018 | Fax: 096-47018 |
| Open: 1st May – 31st October | OBA |

No Rooms:	4	Triple:	1
Twin/Double:	3	Family:	–
Single:		En suite:	4

B&B:	-	HBW ES:	-	S.Supp:	-	Dinner: -
B&B ES: £19	€24.13	3 day HB:	-	CSP:	-	High Tea:-
HBW:	-	3 day HB ES: -				

Situated in village convenient to pubs, walks, church within walking distance. Private car park. Georgian farmhouse over 200 years old, quiet and peaceful.

DRUMCLIFFE 1.5 km   Sligo SO10

Mrs Nancy Feeney
LISSADELL VIEW
Tullyhill, Rathcormac
Drumcliffe, Co Sligo

| Tel: 071-43892 | Fax: – |
| Open: 1st March - 20th November | OBA |

No Rooms:	4	Triple:	1	AM
Twin/Double:	3	Family:	–	V EC
Single:		En suite:	4	

B&B:	-	HBW ES:	-	S.Supp: £6.50 €8.25	Dinner: -
B&B ES: £19	€24.13	3 day HB:	-	CSP: 25%	High Tea:-
HBW:	-	3 day HB ES: -				

Spacious home in the heart of Yeats Country. Signposted on N15, 4 km from Sligo overlooking Benbulben Mountain and Drumcliffe Bay, scenic views from all windows. Bedrooms with TV, hairdryers and tea/coffee facilities. Guest TV, Lounge, Pub, restaurant and Yeats' grave nearby. Convenient to Lissadell House, Glencar Waterfall and Rosses Point Beach. Golf, hillwalking locally.

DRUMCLIFFE 3 km   Sligo SO11

Gemma Healy
URLAR HOUSE
Drumcliffe
Co Sligo

| Tel: 071-63110 | Fax: – |
| Open: 1st March - 14th October | OBA |

No Rooms:	5	Triple:	1
Twin/Double:	3	Family:	1
Single:	–	En suite:	5

B&B:	-	HBW ES:	-	S.Supp: £6.50 €8.25	Dinner: -
B&B ES: £20/£22	€25.39/27.93	3 day HB:	-	CSP:	-	High Tea:-
HBW:	-	3 day HB ES: -			

17th century residence set in the shadow of Benbulben 1 mile north of Drumcliffe, Yeats Tavern restaurant on N15 road. Recommended in Travel Guide for very high class accommodation. Good food highly commended, Galtee Breakfast Awards. Recommended in 300 Best B&Bs Guide Ireland. Convenient to Lissadell, Glencar Lake and Waterfall. Golf, horse riding, boat trips, sandy beaches, mountain climbing. Garden for visitors. Car parking. Email: urlarhouse@eircom.net

---

DRUMCLIFFE 2 km   Sligo SO12

Hennigan Family
BENBULBEN FARM
Barnaribbon
Drumcliffe, Co Sligo

| Tel: 071-63211 | Fax: 071-73009 |
| Open: 1st April – 1st October | |

No Rooms:	6	Triple:	2	AM
Twin/Double:	4	Family:	–	V EC
Single:	–	En suite:	5	AE

B&B:	£17	€21.58	HBW ES:	-	S.Supp: £6.50 €8.25	Dinner: -
B&B ES: £19	€24.13	3 day HB:	-	CSP: 50%	High Tea:£8 €10.16
HBW:	-	3 day HB ES:-			

Modern farmhouse in picturesque setting on slopes of Benbulben Mountain, overlooking miles of beautiful Yeats country. Signposted on N15 road north of Sligo. Recommended in "300 Best B&B Guide to Ireland" and Frommer. Close to Glencar Lake and Waterfall. Golf, horse riding, hillwalking, beaches. Self catering cottages on farm. Tea making facility in room. Email: hennigan@tinet.ie

DRUMCLIFF 11 km   Sligo SO4

Charles and Christa Henry
ARDTARMON HOUSE
Ardtarmon
Ballinfull, Co Sligo

Tel: 071-63156		**Fax:** 071-63156	
Open: 3rd January - 19th December			
No Rooms:	4	Triple:	–
Twin/Double:	4	Family:	–
Single:	–	En suite:	4

AM / V / EC

B&B:	-	-	**HBW ES:**	-	-	**S.Supp:** £6.50 €8.25	**Dinner:** £15 €19.05
B&B ES: £25/30	€31.74/38.09		**3 day HB:**	-	-	**CSP:**	**High Tea:** -
HBW:	-	-	**3 day HB ES:** -				

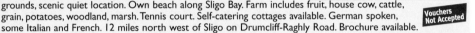

Family home since 1852. Spacious rooms and period ambience. Secluded grounds, scenic quiet location. Own beach along Sligo Bay. Farm includes fruit, house cow, cattle, grain, potatoes, woodland, marsh. Tennis court. Self-catering cottages available. German spoken, some Italian and French. 12 miles north west of Sligo on Drumcliff-Raghly Road. Brochure available.

Vouchers Not Accepted

DRUMCLIFFE 5 km   Sligo SO13

Mrs Anne McCaffrey
GLENVALE
Lislahelly, Drumcliffe
Co Sligo

Tel: 071-45937		**Fax:** –	
Open: 1st April – 31st November			
No Rooms:	3	Triple:	-
Twin/Double:	3	Family:	-
Single:	-	En suite:	3

OBA / EC

B&B: £17	€21.58	**HBW ES:** £215	€272.99	**S.Supp:** £6.50 €8.25	**Dinner:** -	-
B&B ES: £19	€24.13	**3 day HB:**	-	**CSP:** 25%	**High Tea:** -	
HBW:	-	**3 day HB ES:**	-			

Comfortable farm bungalow on mixed farm in the heart of Yeats country. Central location for touring North-West. Ideal locaton for hill-walking. Recommended in "Strolls and Walks in Sligo". Situated 10km north of Sligo. Signposted off N15 and N16 roads. Convenient to Glencar Lake and Waterfall, Yeats Grave and Lissadell House. Golf, fishing, beaches. Home Baking. TV lounge.

VOUCHERS ACCEPTED

DRUMCLIFFE 1 km   Sligo SO14

Mrs Martina Murphy
MOUNTAIN VIEW
Carney
Drumcliffe, Co Sligo

Tel: 071-63290		**Fax:** –	
Open: 1st March – 31st October			
No Rooms:	5	Triple:	–
Twin/Double:	4	Family:	1
Single:	–	En suite:	5

OBA / EC

B&B:	-	-	**HBW ES:**	-	**S.Supp:** £6.50 €8.25	**Dinner:** - -
B&B ES: £19	€24.13		**3 day HB:**	-	**CSP:** 25%	**High Tea:** -
HBW:	-	-	**3 day HB ES:** -			

A warm welcome awaits you at Mountain View Farm offering a high standard of accommodation with a view of Benbulben Mountain. Ideal base for touring the north west. Signposted on N15 road at Drumcliffe. Convenient to Lissadell House, Yeats' grave, Glencar Waterfall. Golf, fishing, horse riding, mountain climbing, beaches. Pubs, restaurants in walking distance. Galtee Breakfast Award. AA listed.

VOUCHERS ACCEPTED

ENNISCRONE 3 km   Sligo SO15

Mrs Catherine O'Hara
TARA
Ballina Road, Enniscrone
Co Sligo

Tel: 096-36398		**Fax:** 096-36398	
Open: 1st January – 20th December			
No Rooms:	5	Triple:	1
Twin/Double:	2	Family:	1
Single:	1	En suite:	3

OBA / V

B&B: £17	€21.58	**HBW ES:**	-	**S.Supp:** £6.50 €8.25	**Dinner:** £14	€17.78
B&B ES: £19	€24.13	**3 day HB:**	-	**CSP:** 50%	**High Tea:** -	
HBW:	-	**3 day HB ES:** £95	€120.63			

Welcoming farmhouse in peaceful scenic setting overlooking Killala Bay and championship golf course. Enniscrone 1.8 miles, famous for its seaweed baths and beach. Extensive Breakfast menu with special emphasis on home cooking. Complimentary refreshments on arrival. Guests TV lounge with peat fire. Pets welcome. Golf, fishing, horse riding locally.

VOUCHERS ACCEPTED

GLENCAR 4 km — Sligo SO16

Mrs Mary Coggins
GLEN VIEW
Drum East, Enniskillen Road
Sligo

Tel: 071-43770 Fax: –
Open: 1st April - 31st October

OBA

		No Rooms:	3	Triple:	–
		Twin/Double:	3	Family:	–
		Single:		En suite:	3

B&B:	-	-	HBW ES:	-	-	S.Supp: £6.50 €8.25	Dinner: £15	€19.04
B&B ES: £19	€24.13		3 day HB:	-	-	CSP: 50%	High Tea:£8.50	€10.79
HBW:	-	-	3 day HB ES: £95	€120.63				

Comfortable farm bungalow in beautiful scenic location along main Enniskillen (N16) road, 6 km from Sligo. Glencar Lake and Waterfall 4 km. Drumcliff 6 km. Home from home atmosphere. Mixed farming. Home cooking, breakfast menu, peat fires, convenient to beaches, mountain walks, fishing, pitch & putt, golf. TV lounge with tea making facilities, babysitting.

✕ ✕ 🛏 🛋 🎣 🐕 S

GURTEEN 1.5 km — Sligo SO17

Mrs Mary O'Grady
SAN GIOVANNI
Gurtygara
Gurteen, Co Sligo

Tel: 071-82038 Fax: -
Open: 2nd January – 20th December

AM
V

		No Rooms:	3	Triple:	–
		Twin/Double:	3	Family:	–
		Single:		En suite:	3

B&B:	-	-	HBW ES:	-	S.Supp: £6.50 €8.25	Dinner: -	-
B&B ES: £19	€24.13		3 day HB:	-	CSP: 25%	High Tea: -	-
HBW:	-	-	3 day HB ES: -				

Modern farmhouse situated in peaceful surroundings overlooking tranquil countryside and offering a high standard of accommodation and excellent food. 1.5 km from Gurteen on Boyle/Tubbercurry R294 road. Convenient to Coleman Heritage Centre. Traditional music in local pubs, home baking, complimentary tea on arrival. Email: sangiovanni@eircom.net

🐕 S 🎣 🏇 📷 ⊘ TV

LISSADELL 1.5 km — Sligo SO18

Mrs Ita Leyden
DUNFORE FARMHOUSE
Ballinfull
Co Sligo

Tel: 071-63137 Fax: 071-63574
Open: 1st March – 31st October

OBA

AM
V

		No Rooms:	4	Triple:	1
		Twin/Double:	3	Family:	–
		Single:	–	En suite:	4

B&B:	-	-	HBW ES:	-	S.Supp: £6.50 €8.25	Dinner: -
B&B ES: £20	€25.39		3 day HB:	-	CSP: -	High Tea: -
HBW:	-	-	3 day HB ES: -			

Turn off N15 at Drumcliffe or Grange. Peaceful location in the heart of the Yeats Country, near Lissadell beach. Featuring panoramic views of Benbulben and Sligo bay. Activities, tours and walks arranged. Putting green and lawn croquet. Traditional fish, vegetarian or pancake speciality breakfasts. Poetry, Arts and crafts.

🖥 🐕 S 🛏 🛋 📷 TV

RIVERSTOWN 1.5 km — Sligo SO19

Nicholas & Oriel Hill-Wilkinson
(Dom.Sc.Hons)
ROSS HOUSE
Riverstown, Co Sligo

Tel: 071-65140/ 65787 Fax: 071-65140
Open: 16th March – 1st November

OBA

AM
V
EC
AE

		No Rooms:	6	Triple:	1
		Twin/Double:	3	Family:	1
		Single:	1	En suite:	3

B&B:	£20	€25.39	HBW ES:	-	S.Supp: £6.50 €8.25	Dinner: £18	€22.86
B&B ES: £23	€29.20		3 day HB:	-	CSP: 20%	High Tea: -	
HBW:	-	-	3 day HB ES: £117	€148.56			

Family residence in a peaceful setting, 1.5 km from Riverstown, 15 km Sligo. Signposted on N4 road. Convenient to Lough Arrow and Lough Key Forest Park. Archaeological sites. Corrowkeel and Caramore boats for hire. Fishing, tennis, golf, swimming, horse riding. Open fires. Excellent home cooking.

✕ 🐕 ♿ ⛵ 🏇 🖥 🚲 S

SLIGO 5.6 km · Sligo SO20

Mrs Maisie Carter	Tel: 071-62005	Fax: –	
PRIMROSE GRANGE HOUSE	Open: 1st February – 1st December		OBA
Knocknarea	No Rooms: 6	Triple: –	EC
Sligo	Twin/Double: 4	Family: 2	
	Single: –	En suite: 2	

B&B: £20 €25.39	HBW ES: - -	S.Supp: £6.50 €8.25	Dinner: - -
B&B ES: £22.50 €28.57	3 day HB: - -	CSP: 20%	High Tea: - -
HBW: - -	3 day HB ES: - -		

Large farmhouse built in 1723. Operated as Sligo Grammar School until 1906. Situated 300 ft up the south slopes of Knocknarea Mountain. Along the coastal area which can be seen from the house are many sandy beaches, where Yeats found inspiration for his work. Surrounded by many historical sites. Dairy Shorthorn farm. Website: http://myhome.iolfree.ie/~primrosegrange

VOUCHERS ACCEPTED

SLIGO 5 km · Sligo SO23

Mrs Elma Stuart	Tel: 071-42808	Fax: 071-44461	
HILLSIDE FARM	Open: Easter – October		OBA
Hillside, Kilsellagh	No Rooms: 3	Triple: -	AM
Enniskillen Road, Sligo	Twin/Double: 2	Family: 1	V
	Single: -	En suite: 3	

B&B: - -	HBW ES: - -	S.Supp: £6.50 €8.25	Dinner: - -
B&B ES: £19 €23.13	3 day HB: - -	CSP: -	High Tea: - -
HBW: - -	3 day HB ES: - -		

Traditional 200 years old farmhouse in scenic area close to Glencar Lake and waterfall on N16 Enniskillen Road, working dairy and beef farm. Beautiful walks in area. Golf, pitch & putt, tennis, sailing, surfing, fishing, horse riding. Garden for visitors. Warm welcome. Fires.

VOUCHERS ACCEPTED

TEMPLEBOY 5 km · Sligo SO24

The Mulligan Family	Tel: 071-66674	Fax: 071-66674	
AVE MARIA	Open: 1st January - 31st December		V
Corkamore,	No Rooms: 4	Triple: 1	AE
Co. Sligo	Twin/Double: 3	Family: –	AM
	Single: -	En suite: 3	

B&B: £17 €21.58	HBW ES: £130 €165.07	S.Supp: - -	Dinner: £12 €15.24
B&B ES: £19 €24.13	3 day HB: £50 €63.49	CSP: - -	High Tea: £6 €7.62
HBW: £115 €146.02	3 day HB ES: £55 €69.84		

Modern Farmhouse on 300 acre dairy, beef and sheep farm. Home produced meats used. Breakfast menu. Beach 1km, Sligo Way 8km. House signposted off N59 (Sligo - Ballina) at Templeboy and Skreen. Email: ammulligan@eircom.net

VOUCHERS ACCEPTED

TELEPHONE RESERVATIONS
Telephone reservations may be guaranteed by
quoting a valid credit card number.
Check terms and conditions when booking.

Tipperary

In the heart of the 'Golden Vale' Tipperary is one of the most fertile and tranquil counties in Ireland. Its rolling hills and scenic mountain ranges are a delight for walkers, botanists, photographers and nature lovers. There are many castles and fortresses in the area including the majestic Rock of Cashel, which no visitor should miss.

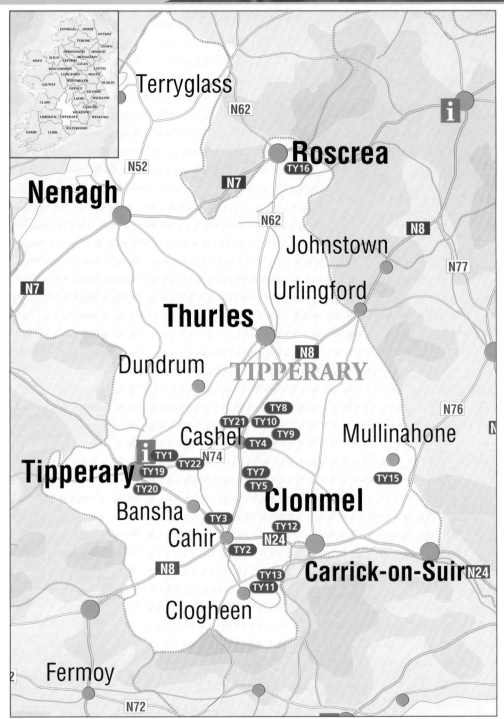

Terryglass

N62

N52

Nenagh

N7

Roscrea
TY16

N62

Johnstown

N8

Urlingford

N77

Thurles

Dundrum

TIPPERARY

N8

N76

Cashel
TY8
TY21 TY10
TY9
TY4

Mullinahone

TY1
Tipperary
TY19 TY22 N74
TY20
TY7
TY5
TY15

Clonmel

Bansha
TY3
Cahir
TY12
N24
TY2

Carrick-on-Suir N24

N8

TY13
TY11

Clogheen

Fermoy

N72

BANSHA 1 km | Tipperary TY1

John & Mary Marnane
BANSHA HOUSE
Bansha
Co Tipperary

Tel: 062-54194   Fax: 062-54215
Open: 28th December – 20th December

No Rooms:	8	Triple:	1
Twin/Double:	5	Family:	1
Single:		En suite:	5

V AM

B&B:	£24	€ 30.47	HBW ES:	£280	€ 355.53	S.Supp: £6.50 € 8.25	Dinner: £16.50 € 20.95
B&B ES:	£27	€ 34.28	3 day HB:	£115	€ 146.01	CSP: 25%	High Tea:- -
HBW:	£260	€ 330.13	3 day HB ES:	£120	€ 152.37		

Old Georgian country house set in its own spacious grounds. National award winning
farmhouse in 1994. Situated 0.25 miles from Bansha village off the Waterford-Limerick road [N24], 6 miles from
Tipperary town and 8 miles from Cashel. Ideally located for exploring the South-East. Local amenities include golf; fishing;
mountain walking and riding. AA QQQQ awarded. Website: www.tipp.ie/banshahs.htm Email: banshahouse@eircom.net

---

CAHIR 2 km | Tipperary TY2

The Hyland Family
CAHIR EQUESTRIAN CENTRE
Ardfinnan Road (R670)
Cahir, Co Tipperary

Tel: 052-41426   Fax: 052-41426
Open: All Year - except Christmas Period

No Rooms:	4	Triple:	1
Twin/Double:	2	Family:	1
Single:		En suite:	4

AE DC AM V EC

B&B:	-	-	HBW ES:	-	-	S.Supp: £6.50 € 8.25	Dinner: £12 € 15.25
B&B ES:	£19	€ 24.13	3 day HB:	-	-	CSP: 20%	High Tea: £8 € 10.16
HBW:	-	-	3 day HB ES:	£85	€ 108		

Beautiful country home set among spacious gardens, safe play area and toys for children.
Conservatory tea room. Nestled among Cahir park woodlands, surrounded by Knockmealdown and Galtee Mountains. Ideal base
for touring, golfing, fishing. Riding holidays our speciality. Novice and advanced cross country. Brochure on request. Leisure facilities.
Scenic walkways. Mobile: 087 676 2466 Email: devereaux@esatbiz.com Website: www.dirl.com/tipperary/cahir-equestrian.htm

---

CAHIR 3 km | Tipperary TY3

Mrs Phil O'Connor
BENMORE
Cloghabreedy
Cahir, Co Tipperary

Tel: 052-42900   Fax: 052-42900
Open: 1st April – 1st November

OBA

No Rooms:	3	Triple:	1
Twin/Double:	1	Family:	1
Single:	–	En suite:	3

B&B:	-	-	HBW ES:	-	-	S.Supp: £6.50 € 8.25	Dinner: £15 € 19.05
B&B ES:	£19	€ 24.13	3 day HB:	-	-	CSP: 20%	High Tea:-
HBW:	-	-	3 day HB ES:	£83	€ 105.4		

Spacious modern farmhouse with panoramic views of Galtee and Knockmealdown
Mountains near River Suir. 3 km north of Cahir, just off N8 bypass. 'Le Guide du Routard' recommended. Cahir
Castle, Rock of Cashel. The Vee within easy distance. 18 hole golf course at Cahir. Fishing, horse riding locally. Tillage
farm. Excellent touring or overnight stop. Mobile: 088-2790098. Website: http:www.dirl.com/tipperary/benmore.htm

---

CASHEL 0 km | Tipperary TY4

Mrs Moria Foley
RAHARD LODGE
Dualla Road, Cashel
Co Tipperary

Tel: 062-61052   Fax: –
Open: 1st April – 1st November

OBA V

No Rooms:	6	Triple:	2
Twin/Double:	2	Family:	2
Single:	–	En suite:	6

B&B:	£19	€ 24.12	HBW ES:	-	-	S.Supp: £6.50 € 8.25	Dinner: - -
B&B ES:	£22	€ 27.93	3 day HB:	-	-	CSP: 25%	High Tea:- -
HBW:	-	-	3 day HB ES:	-			

Modern farmhouse on outskirts of town (R691) overlooking historic
Rock of Cashel. Large mature award winning gardens. Ideal base for touring in south east region,
Glen of Aherlow, Vee Drive. Horseriding, fishing, tennis, pitch and driving range locally. Secure
parking area. Tea making facilities and hairdryers in all rooms.

CASHEL 4km — Tipperary TY5

Mrs Mary Hally
CARRON HOUSE
Carron, Cashel,
Co. Tipperary

Tel: 052-62142   Fax: 052-62168
Open: 1st May - 30th September

OBA

AM
V
EC

No Rooms:	4	Triple:	-
Twin/Double:	4	Family:	-
Single:	-	En suite:	4

B&B:	-	HBW ES:	-	S.Supp:	£7 € 8.89	Dinner:	-	-
B&B ES: £20	€ 25.39	3 day HB:	-	CSP:	-	High Tea:	-	-
HBW:	-	3 day HB ES:	-				

Carron house is situated on a working dairy farm, amidst a tree lined avenue in a very peaceful location, yet only 5 minutes from Cashel. Luxury accommodation, antique furnishing, rooms en suite with T.V, hairdryers, tea/coffee facilities. Ideal base for touring Limerick, Kilkenny. Take south bound N8 from Cashel for 2.5 miles and follow signpost at left of cross roads. Email: hallyfamily@eircom.net

---

CASHEL 7 km — Tipperary TY21

The McCan Family
BALLYOWEN HOUSE
Cashel
Co. Tipperary

Tel: 062-61265   Fax: –
Open: 1st February – 1st December

EC

No Rooms:	3	Triple:	1
Twin/Double:	3	Family:	1
Single:	1	En suite:	2

B&B:	£27	€ 34.29	HBW ES:	-	-	S.Supp:	£7 € 8.89	Dinner:	£22	€ 27.94
B&B ES: £27-40	€ 34.29-50.80	3 day HB:	-	CSP:	20-40%	High Tea: £15	€ 19.09
HBW:	-	3 day HB ES:	-				

Ballyowen House dates from 1750 and is listed for its historical and architectural importance. Home to the McCan family since 1864. Set in tranquil surroundings with specimen trees, woodland, lake and hillside walks. Candlelight dinners. 7km north of Cashel on N8 road, take junction signposted Dualla for 2km. Email: info@ballyowenhouse.com Website: www.ballyowenhouse.com

---

CASHEL 2 km — Tipperary TY7

Mrs Eileen O'Brien
KNOCK SAINT LOUR HOUSE
Cashel
Co Tipperary

Tel: 062-61172   Fax: –
Open: 1st May – 1st November

OBA

No Rooms:	7	Triple:	2
Twin/Double:	3	Family:	2
Single:	–	En suite:	7

B&B:	-	-	HBW ES:	-	-	S.Supp: £6.50	€ 8.25	Dinner:	-	-
B&B ES: £22	€ 27.93	3 day HB:	-	CSP:	20%	High Tea:	-	-
HBW:	-	3 day HB ES:	-				

Attractive homely farmhouse, tastefully furnished with antique furniture, spacious flower gardens and lawns. Panoramic views. Entrance on south bound N8 Cork road, 1.5 miles from Cashel, 7 miles Cahir. AA listed. All bedrooms En-suite with tea/coffee, hairdryer facilities.

CASHEL 8 km — Tipperary TY22

Mr Val O'Connor
KILFEACLE HOUSE
Kilfeacle, Cashel
Co Tipperary

Tel: 062-72487   Fax: -
Open: 1st May - 1st November

EC

No Rooms:	4	Triple:	–
Twin/Double:	3	Family:	-
Single:	1	En suite:	4

B&B:	-	HBW ES:	-	S.Supp:	-	Dinner:	-	-
B&B ES: £22-25	€ 27.94-31.74	3 day HB:	-	CSP:	-	High Tea:	-	-
HBW:	-	3 day HB ES:	-				

Elegant country house situated on N74 midway between Cashel and Tipperary minutes from scenic Glen of Atherlow. Lovely mature gardens. 1 hour from Shannon airport.

CASHEL 5 km — Tipperary TY8

Mrs Phyllis O'Halloran
THE CHESTNUTS FARMHOUSE
Dualla Road, Cashel
Co Tipperary

Tel: 062-61469   Fax: 062-61469
Open: 1st January – 30th November   *OBA*

No Rooms:	5	Triple:	1
Twin/Double:	2	Family:	1
Single:	1	En suite:	4

B&B:	£19	€24.13	HBW ES:	-	-	S.Supp: £7	€8.89	Dinner: £14	€17.78
B&B ES:	£21	€26.66	3 day HB:	-	-	CSP:	20%	High Tea:	-
HBW:	-	-	3 day HB ES:	-	-				

Award winning farm residence nestled amidst 170 acres, including ancient limestone buildings, landscaped scenic aromic gardens, guided walks by Hostess, home baking speciality. Worldwide acclaim. Luxury accommodation superbly appointed on the R691. Tranquil homely atmosphere with complimentary refreshments. Pub entertainment nearby. Historical monuments. Art classes. 0.5km from Cashel, 75 minutes Shannon Airport. Website: www.thechestnuts.com

---

CASHEL 10 km — Tipperary TY9

Mrs Sheila O'Sullivan
DERRYNAFLAN
Ballinure
Cashel, Co Tipperary

Tel: 052-56406   Fax: –
Open: 1st March – 1st December   *OBA*

No Rooms:	4	Triple:	1
Twin/Double:	2	Family:	
Single:	1	En suite:	3

B&B:	£20	€25.39	HBW ES:	-	-	S.Supp: £6.50	€8.25	Dinner: £14	€17.78
B&B ES:	£20	€25.39	3 day HB:	-	-	CSP:	-	High Tea: £10	€12.69
HBW:	-	-	3 day HB ES:	£60	€76.17				

18th century farmhouse in scenic location, 600 metre tree lined avenue, working farm on site of 15th century castle. Antique furniture throughout. Prizewinning farmhouse. Cheese made on farm. Situated on R691 Kilkenny Road. 8 km from Cashel, also off the N8. Pony trekking, golfing, fishing, pub entertainment nearby. "Guide de Routard" recommended. Email: dnaflan@iol.ie Website: tipp.ie/derrynaf.htm

---

CASHEL 4 km — Tipperary TY10

Mrs Mairead Power
DUALLA HOUSE
Dualla Road, Dualla
Cashel, Co Tipperary

Tel: 062-61487   Fax: 062-61487
Open: 1st March – 1st December   *OBA*

No Rooms:	4	Triple:	1
Twin/Double:	2	Family:	1
Single:		En suite:	4

B&B:	-	-	HBW ES:	-	-	S.Supp: £7.50	€9.52	Dinner:	-	-
B&B ES:	£20/25	€25/32	3 day HB:	-	-	CSP:	30-50%	High Tea:	-
HBW:	-	-	3 day HB ES:	-	-				

Elegant Georgian manor dating from 1790, situated in elevated scenic countryside amid 300 acres sheep/grain farm. Spacious rooms, orthopedic beds, antique furnishings, tea/coffee, hairdryers & TV. Recommended Special Places, AA QQQQ, Frommers etc. 4km from Cashel on R691. 5 Golf courses nearby. Horse racing, Fishing. Email: duallahse@eircom.net Website: www.tipp.ie/dualla-house.htm

Vouchers Not Accepted

CLONMEL 15 km — Tipperary TY11

John & Breeda Moran
BALLYBOY HOUSE
Ballyboy, Clogheen
Co Tipperary

Tel: 052-65297/65590 Fax: 052-65297
Open: All year

No Rooms:	4	Triple:	1
Twin/Double:	2	Family:	1
Single:	–	En suite:	4

B&B:	-	-	HBW ES:	-	-	S.Supp: £6.50	€8.25	Dinner: £15	€19.05
B&B ES:	£20/22	€25.39/27.93	3 day HB:	-	-	CSP:	-	High Tea: £10	€12.70
HBW:	-	-	3 day HB ES:	£85	€107.93				

Elegant Georgian farmhouse, tastefully furnished with antique furniture nestling under the Knockmealdown Mountains on the R665. Tranquil setting, log fires, home cuisine. Ideal touring base for touring the south east region. Highly recommended by travel guides. Complimentary refreshments on arrival. You are invited to bring your own wine. Email: ballyboy@eircom.net

CLONMEL 8 km   Tipperary TY12

Anna O'Donnell
WOODROOFFE HOUSE
Cahir Road, Clonmel
Co Tipperary

Tel: 052-35243		Fax: –	
Open: 1st April – 30th September			
No Rooms:	3	Triple:	.
Twin/Double:	2	Family:	1
Single:	.	En suite:	2

EC

B&B:	£18	€22.86	HBW ES:	-	-	S.Supp: £6.50 €8.25	Dinner: £16 €20.32
B&B ES:	£20	€25.39	3 day HB:	Negotiable		CSP:	High Tea:£10 €12.70
HBW:	-		3 day HB ES:	Negotiable			

 ✗ 🏠 ⌕ 🛏 ♪ ∪ ☀

Quite comfortable farmhouse on working farm situated 1km off N24 between Cahir and Clonmel on Limerick/Waterford/Rosslare route. Complimentary tea/coffee, homebaking on arrival. Afternoon tea provided for groups. One hours drive from coast and all major cities in south. Golf, horse riding/racing, angling locally. Email: odonnellanna@hotmail.com

VOUCHERS ACCEPTED

CLONMEL 19 km   Tipperary TY13

Kevin & Ber O'Donnell
KILMANEEN FARMHOUSE
Newcastle, Ardfinnan,
Clonmel, Co Tipperary

Tel: 052-36231		Fax: 052-36231	
Open: Easter - December			
No Rooms:	3	Triple:	1
Twin/Double:	2	Family:	–
Single:	–	En suite:	3

OBA

AM V

B&B:	-	-	HBW ES:	£262/280 €332/355.53	S.Supp: £7.50 €9.52	Dinner: £17.50 €22.22
B&B ES:	£20/22.50 €25/28.59	3 day HB:	-	CSP:	High Tea:£12.50 €15.87
HBW:	-	-	3 day HB ES:	£110/120 €140/152		

National Tourism Award winner 1999. 200 year-old farmhouse. Tea on arrival. ✗ ♪ 🛏 ☐ S ⊗ CD
Delicious, freshly prepared, home-cooked food. Large garden. Facility to visit private gardens. Working dairy farm. Private fishing on farm (free to guests) in rivers Suir and Tar. Three way-marked walking routes within 6km. Email: kilmaneen@eircom.net Website: www.dirl.com/tipperary/kilmaneen.htm

VOUCHERS ACCEPTED

MULLINAHONE 0.5 km   Tipperary TY15

Pat & Maria Collins
KILLAGHY CASTLE
Mullinahone
Co Tipperary

Tel: 052-53112		Fax: 052-53561	
Open: 14th February – 18th December			
No Rooms:	4	Triple:	1
Twin/Double:	2	Family:	1
Single:		En suite:	3

OBA

AM V

B&B:	£25/30 €31.75/38.1	HBW ES:	-	S.Supp: £10 €12	Dinner: £18/20 €22.86/25
B&B ES:	£30/35 €38.1/44.45	3 day HB:	-	CSP: -	High Tea:-
HBW:	-	3 day HB ES:	-		

✗ 🏠 🐎 ♣ ⌕ 👣 ♪ 🛏

Norman Castle sensitively restored with modern conveniences. Tranquil setting on 200 acre farm with ancient trees landscaped mature walled garden, nature walk with views of Slievenamon Mts. Comfortable, spacious rooms. Large central hallways. Antique furniture. Central heating, log fires, home cooking. Ideal base for touring Kilkenny, Waterford, Tipperary. Recommended in most travel guides. Email: killaghycastle@tinet.ie Website: www.dirl.com/tipperary/killaghy-castle.htm

VOUCHERS ACCEPTED

ROSCREA 3 km   Tipperary TY16

Mrs Carmel Moore
MONAINCHA HOUSE
Roscrea
Co Tipperary

Tel: 0505-23181		Fax: –	
Open: 1st April – 31st October			
No Rooms:	3	Triple:	1
Twin/Double:	1	Family:	1
Single:	–	En suite:	2

OBA

EC

B&B:	£25	€31.74	HBW ES:	-	S.Supp: £7 €8.89	Dinner: - -
B&B ES:	£25	€31.74	3 day HB:	-	CSP: 50%	High Tea:-
HBW:	-		3 day HB ES: £75	€95.22		

⌕ 👣 ♿ ✓ 📷 ♪

Beautifully appointed mid-18th century country house, set in delightful gardens and grounds with fully equipped gym, sauna, aerobics & massage with hard tennis courts and snooker room. Located 3 km from Roscrea on the N7. Beside 18 hole golf course. Shannon Airport 85 km, Dublin 120 km.

Vouchers Not Accepted

TIPPERARY 8 km | Tipperary TY19

Mrs Ursula Farrell
COOLEEN HOUSE
Ardane, Bansha
Co Tipperary

Tel: 062-54392		Fax: –	
Open: 1st January – 30th November			
No Rooms:	3	Triple:	1
Twin/Double:	1	Family:	–
Single:	1	En suite:	3

B&B:	-	-	HBW ES:	-	-	S.Supp: £6.50 €8.25	Dinner:	-	-
B&B ES: £19	€24.13		3 day HB:	-	-	CSP: 50%	High Tea:	-	
HBW:	-	-	3 day HB ES:	-					

Cooleen House is a modern farmhouse on fifty acres at the foot of the Galtee Mountains in the beautiful Glen of Aherlow. Five minutes drive from main Waterford-Limerick N24 road. Tipperary Town 5 miles. Cahir 5 miles, Cashel 10 miles. Mountain climbing, walking, fishing, golfing, horse riding all nearby. Leisure complex in Tipperary Town. Email: tipp@iol.ie

TIPPERARY TOWN 8 km | Tipperary TY20

Frewen Family
HOMELEIGH FARMHOUSE
Ballinacourty, Glen of Aherlow
Co Tipperary

Tel: 062-56228		Fax: –		AM
Open: 1st January – 31st December				V
No Rooms:	5	Triple:	1	EC
Twin/Double:	3	Family:	1	AE
Single:	–	En suite:	5	

B&B:	-	-	HBW ES: £220	€279.34	S.Supp: £6.50 €8.25	Dinner: £14	€17.78
B&B ES: £20	€25.39		3 day HB:	-	-	CSP: 50%	High Tea: £8	€10.16
HBW:	-	-	3 day HB ES: £100	€126.95			

Attractive farmhouse situated in the beautiful Glen of Aherlow, between the Galtee Mtns. and Sliabh na Much. 8 km from Tipperary Town off the N24, 8 km from Bansha Village off the N24 road. 7 km from Galbally on the R663 road. Cashel 16 km. Horse riding, pony trekking on farm and forest trails. Fishing, golf, mountain climbing, forest walks locally. Irish music. Ideal base for touring, pony trap rides. Email: homeleighfarmhouse@eircom.net

Waterford

There is a wonderful variety of landscape in
this busy maritime county. For the active
visitor there are plenty of pastimes including
golf, walking, cycling, angling and watersports.
If a relaxing break is more your cup of tea,
Waterford boasts many attractive fishing
villages and miles of unspoiled coastline. The
city is famous the world over for its beautiful
crystal, and visitors can tour the factory and see
its skilled craftspeople at work.

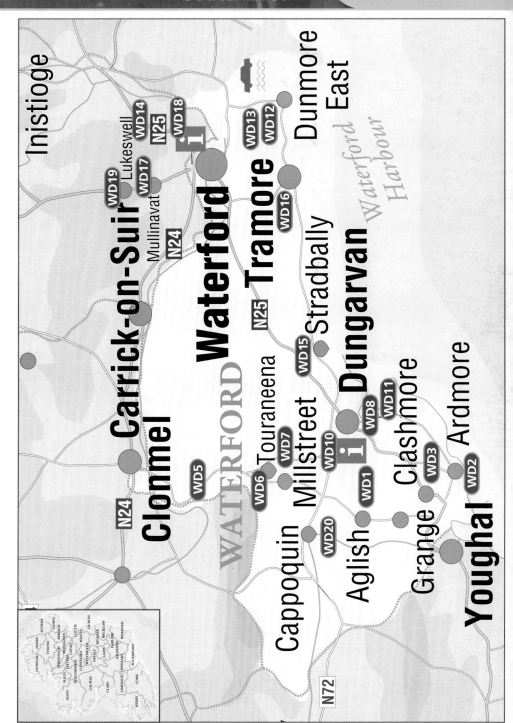

AGLISH 0.5 km
Waterford WD1

Tom & Teresa Moore
AGLISH HOUSE
Aglish
Co Waterford

Tel: 024-96191 Fax: 024-96482
Open: All Year *OBA*

No Rooms:	4	Triple:	–
Twin/Double:	2	Family:	2
Single:	–	En suite:	4

 AM V

B&B:	-		HBW ES:	From £300 €380.92	S.Supp: £10 €12.70	Dinner: £25 €31.74
B&B ES:	From £30	€38.10	3 day HB:	-	CSP: 50%	High Tea: £12.00 €15.24
HBW:	From £300	€380.92	3 day HB ES:	From £135 €171.41		

Tom and Teresa invite you to relax in our old world charm house lying between the Knockmealdown Mountains and the sea in the lush Blackwater Valley. The peaceful atmosphere is enhanced by a fine reputation for hospitality and excellent cuisine with own resident chef. Email: aglishhouse@eircom.net Website: www.aglishhouse.com

VOUCHERS ACCEPTED

ARDMORE 4 km
Waterford WD2

Mrs Sheila Budds
SUMMERHILL FARMHOUSE
Kinsalebeg
Ardmore, Co Waterford

Tel: 024-92682 Fax: 024-20916
Open: 1st March – December

No Rooms:	6	Triple:	1
Twin/Double:	4	Family:	1
Single:	–	En suite:	5

 AM V EC

B&B:	£18	€22.86	HBW ES:	-	S.Supp: £6.50 €8.25	Dinner: -
B&B ES:	£20-22	€25.39	3 day HB:	-	CSP: 50%	High Tea: -
HBW:	-	-	3 day HB ES:	-		

Modern farm bungalow with panoramic view of Atlantic Ocean situated between Dungarvan and Youghal on N25 road. Intensive dairy farm. Observe cows being milked. All rooms with TVs, hairdryers and tea making facilities. Games room, crazy golf, babysitting. Sandy beaches 2 km. Website: www.waterfordfarms.com/summerhill

VOUCHERS ACCEPTED

ARDMORE 6 km
Guesthouse ★★★
Waterford WD3

Mrs Teresa O'Connor
NEWTOWN FARM GUESTHOUSE
Grange, Ardmore (via Youghal)
Co Waterford

Tel: 024-94143 Fax: 024-94054
Open: All year

No Rooms:	7	Triple:	1
Twin/Double:	4	Family:	2
Single:	-	En suite:	7

 AM V

B&B:	-	-	HBW ES:	£235/245 €298/311	S.Supp: £7 €9	Dinner: £14 €17.8
B&B ES:	£22-27	€27.85-34.20	3 day HB:	-	CSP: 50%	High Tea: -
HBW:	-	-	3 day HB ES:	£110/115 €140/146		

Family-run farm guesthouse in scenic location, surrounded by its own farmland with dairying as main enterprise. With view of Atlantic Ocean, hills and cliff walks, comfortable spacious rooms all en-suite. With D.D. phone. Some with balcony. Signposted on N25 Rosslare Rd, halfway between Dungarvan/Youghal, turn left at Flemings Pub. 3 star approved. Email: newtownfarm@eircom.net Website: http://homepage.eircom.net/~newtownfarm/

VOUCHERS ACCEPTED

CAPPOQUIN 3 km
Waterford WD20

The Nugent Family
WOODLANDS
Dromana, Cappoquin
Co. Waterford

Tel: 024-96192 Fax: 024-96192
Open: 1st April - 31st October

No Rooms:	3	Triple:	–
Twin/Double:	3	Family:	–
Single:	–	En suite:	2

V

B&B:	£17	€21.58	HBW ES:	-	-	S.Supp: £22 €27.94	Dinner: -
B&B ES:	£19	€24.13	3 day HB:	-		CSP: -	High Tea: -
HBW:	-	-	3 day HB ES:	£110	€140		

Working farm set in a very senic and tranquil location on the Dromana Scenic Route. Warm home with room en-suite, tv/video lounge, tea/coffee and homebaking on arrival/request. Central to local amenities such as golfing, fishing, horse-riding, etc.

VOUCHERS ACCEPTED

CLONMEL 12 km — Waterford WD5

Paddy & Olive O'Gorman
GLASHA,
Ballymacarbry (via Clonmel)
Co Waterford

Tel: 052-36108 Fax: 052-36108
Open: 1st February - 1st November

No Rooms:	4	Triple:	.... —
Twin/Double:	2	Family:	1
Single:	1	En suite:	4

B&B:	-	-	HBW ES:	-	-	S.Supp: £6.50 €8.25	Dinner: -	-
B&B ES: £25/30	€31.74/39.28	3 day HB:	-	-	CSP: 50%	High Tea: -
HBW:	-	-	3 day HB ES: -	

AA Guest Accomodation of the Year Award 2000/2001. Luxury farmhouse situated off 671 between Clonmel and Dungarvan. All roooms ensuite including some jacuzzi baths. Arrangements made for golfing, walking, horse-riding. Private fishing on farm. AA 5◆◆◆◆◆ award. Twice nominated for the AA "Landlady of the year" award. Email: glasha@eircom.net Website: waterfordfarms.com/glashafarm/

Vouchers Not Accepted

DUNGARVAN 16 km — Waterford WD6

Jim & Breeda Cullinan
SLIABH gCUA FARMHOUSE
Touraneena, Ballinamult
Co Waterford

Tel: 058-47120 Fax: –
Open: 1st April – 1st November

OBA

No Rooms:	3	Triple:	—
Twin/Double:	2	Family:	1
Single:		En suite:	3

B&B:	-	-	HBW ES: £238	€302.19	S.Supp: £6.50 €8.25	Dinner: -	-
B&B ES: £20	€25.39	3 day HB:	-	-	CSP: 50%	High Tea: -	-
HBW:	-	-	3 day HB ES: -	

Country farmhouse with character, set in peaceful surroundings on a dairy farm, nestled between Comeragh & Knockmealdown Mountains. Located 16 km off the N25. Signposted on main Dungarvan-Clonmel (R672) road. Central for touring, walking, fishing, horse riding, golf. Warm family welcome, Irish music, complimentary refreshments. Children's playground. AA ◆◆◆◆ Website: www.sliabhgcua.com Email: breedacullinan@sliabhgcua.com

---

DUNGARVAN 5 km — Waterford WD7

Mrs Maireád Kennedy
ARD-NA-COILLE FARM
Colligan, Clonmel Road
Dungarvan, Co Waterford

Tel: 058-68145 Fax: –
Open: 15th March – 15th November

No Rooms:	3	Triple:	-
Twin/Double:	1	Family:	2
Single:	-	En suite:	3

B&B:	-	-	HBW ES: £220	€279.34	S.Supp: £6.50 €8.25	Dinner: £14.50 €18.41
B&B ES: £19-20	€24.13	3 day HB:	-	-	CSP: 50%	High Tea: £9.50 €12.06
HBW:	-	-	3 day HB ES: £99	€125.73

Charming, warm, farm residence on elevated setting on R672, 3 km off N72. Panoramic views of mountains, woods & sea. Surrounded by prize-winning gardens with patios & stream. Excellent cuisine, home baking. Many recommendations, Irish music, dancing by family. Pony rides, play area. Log fire, tea/coffee facilities, horse-riding, golf, fishing, windsurfing, swimming, "a walkers paradise". 3 days B&B ES £58 Email: kencol@iol.ie Website: www.waterfordfarms.com/ardnacoille

---

DUNGARVAN 4.5 km — Waterford WD8

Mrs Kathleen Kiely
BALLYGUIRY FARM
Dungarvan
Co Waterford

Tel: 058-41194 Fax: 058-41194
Open: 1st April – 31st October

No Rooms:	5	Triple:	1
Twin/Double:	1	Family:	2
Single:	1	En suite:	3

B&B: £20	€25.39	HBW ES: £220	€279.34	S.Supp: £6.50 €8.25	Dinner: £12.50 €15.87
B&B ES: £22.50	€28.59	3 day HB: £96	€121.89	CSP: 50%	High Tea: -	-
HBW: £210	€266.64	3 day HB ES: £105	€133.32

Georgian house, overlooking the beautiful Brickey Valley, and West Waterford Golf Course. Signposted on N25 road southwards of Dungarvan. Mixed farming, children's pony, play area, tennis court, sandpit, all on farm. Guided walking tours. Some bedrooms with TV and tea making facilities. Five to 15 mins drive to three 18 hole golf courses, heritage centres, scenic drives, beaches, bowling, heated swimming pool, trekking all locally. Website: www.waterfordfarms.com/ballyguiryfarm/

DUNGARVAN 15 km Waterford WD10

Joan Nugent
THE CASTLE FARM
Millstreet, Cappagh
Dungarvan, Co Waterford

Tel: 058-68049	Fax: 058-68099	
Open: 17th March - 1st November		
No Rooms: 5	Triple: 1	AE AM V EC
Twin/Double: 3	Family: 1	
Single: –	En suite: 5	

B&B:	-	-	BBW ES:	£170	€215.9	S.Supp: £7 €8.89	Dinner: - -
B&B: £25/30	€31.74/38.1	3 day HB:	-			CSP: 75 %	High Tea:£12 €15.24
HBW:	-	3 day HB ES: -					

This award winning country house on a 170-acre farm offers a warm welcome to all our guests, many returning again and again. A former 15th century castle, its spacious accommodation has been restored and offers every convenience, including an acre and a half of maturing gardens overlooking the river Finisk. Breakfast menu. RAC QQQQQ. AA QQQQ Awards. Located 15 km off N25. Signposted at N72 & R671. Email: Castlefm@iol.ie Website: www.waterfordfarms.com/castlefarm/

DUNGARVAN 12.5 km Waterford WD11

Mrs Margaret Power
THE HIDEAWAY
Rusheens, Old Parish
Dungarvan, Co Waterford

Tel: 058-46466	Fax: 058-46466	
Open: 1st April - 31st October		
No Rooms: 3	Triple: 1	AM V EC
Twin/Double: 2	Family: –	
Single: –	En suite: 3	

B&B:	-	HBW ES:	-	S.Supp: £6.50 €8.25	Dinner: - -
B&B ES: £21	€26.60	3 day HB:	-	CSP: 33%	High Tea: -
HBW:	-	3 day HB ES:	-		

Family run farmhouse in tranquil setting 2 km off N25, between the towns of Dungarvan and Youghal (7m west of Dungarvan 9m east of Youghal). Enjoy our extensive breakfast menu, especially local produce. Explore the woodlands and mountains to the north of the county, secluded coves and sandy beaches nearby. Vegetarians welcome. Email: hideaway@iol.ie Website: www.waterfordfarms.com/thehideaway

---

DUNMORE EAST 6 km Waterford WD12

Mrs Cally Carney
LAKEFIELD HOUSE
Dunmore East Road (off)
Co Waterford

Tel: 051-382582	Fax: 051-382582	
Open: Easter - 31st October		
No Rooms: 6	Triple: 1	AM V
Twin/Double: 5	Family: –	
Single: –	En suite: 6	

B&B:	-	HBW ES:	-	S.Supp: £10 €13	Dinner: - -
B&B ES: £20/22	€25/28	3 day HB:	-	CSP: -	High Tea: - -
HBW:	-	3 day HB ES: -			

Modern farmhouse with panoramic views of the lake. Recommended in many guides. Excellent breakfast menu. Signposted on the Dunmore East Road R684 about 5 miles from Waterford. 5 golf courses, 5-10 minutes drive. Ideal for touring the south east. Beaches, horseriding, tennis and Waterford Crystal within easy reach. Email: lakefieldhouse@oceanfree.net

---

DUNMORE EAST 1 km Waterford WD13

Marie Crotty
HILLFIELD HOUSE
Ballymabin, Dunmore East
Co Waterford

Tel: 051-383565	Fax: 051-383565	
Open: 1st May – 30th September		
No Rooms: 4	Triple: 1	V AM
Twin/Double: 3	Family: –	
Single: –	En suite: 4	

B&B:	-	HBW ES:	-	S.Supp: £7.00 €8.89	Dinner: - -
B&B ES: £25	€31.74	3 day HB:	-	CSP: 33%	High Tea: -
HBW:	-	3 day HB ES: -			

Located just a few minutes walk from Dunmore East. Luxury accommodation in peaceful setting on organic cattle & sheep farm. Views of bay & surrounding countryside. Tasty home baking, breakfast menu. Tea & coffee facilities with TV in all rooms. Choice of four major golf courses within 20 minutes drive. Recommended in many travel guides. AA QQQQ selected. Visit our Website: www.iol.ie/~crottym

MULLINAVAT 1 km — Waterford WD19

Mrs. Margaret Reade
"READES"
HILLVIEW FARMHOUSE
Lukeswell, Mullinavat, (N9 Road)
Co Waterford, (Via Kilkenny)

Tel: 051-898430 Fax: -
Open: All year

No Rooms:	4	Triple:	–
Twin/Double:	2	Family:	2
Single:	–	En suite:	3

V AM AE DC EC

B&B: £17.50	€22.22	HBW ES:	-	S.Supp: £6.50 €8.25	Dinner: £14	€17.78
B&B ES: £19	€24.13	3 day HB:	-	CSP: 20%	High Tea: £10	€12.70
HBW: -		3 day HB ES: -				

A warm welcome awaits you in this comfortable home with spectacular views of the countryside. Offering a high standard of accomodation, home cooking and fresh farm produce. Signposted on Waterford/Kilkenny road. Ideal touring base. On South Leinster Way Trail. Mount Juliet golf course, kart racing nearby. "Reades" pub next door. Mobile: 087 2911239

NEW ROSS 5 km — Waterford WD14

Mrs Kathleen Cody
GLENDALE
Weatherstown
Glenmore, Waterford

Tel: 051-880180 Fax: 051-880180
Open: 1st April – 30th November

OBA

No Rooms:	3	Triple:	1
Twin/Double:	–	Family:	1
Single:	1	En suite:	3

AM V EC

B&B: £17	€21.58	HBW ES:	-	S.Supp: £6.50 €8.25	Dinner: £15	€19.05
B&B ES: £19	€24.13	3 day HB:	-	CSP: 33.3%	High Tea: £8	€10.16
HBW: -		3 day HB ES: -				

Attractive farmhouse in quiet scenic area with spacious garden. Mixed farm, 3.5 km from N25 (Rosslare-Cork). Signposted at first turn right for Glenmore from New Ross and fourth turn left for Glenmore from Waterford. Convenient to Waterford city, New Ross, Mount Juliet golf course. Rosslare 0.5 hrs. Colour TV in bedrooms. Breakfast menu, facilities for children. Website: www.waterfordfarms.com/glendalefarm/

STRADBALLY 1 km — Waterford WD15

Mrs Peg Connors
PARK HOUSE
Stradbally
Co Waterford

Tel: 051-293185 Fax: 051-293185
Open: March - November

No Rooms:	5	Triple:	–
Twin/Double:	3	Family:	1
Single:	1	En suite:	2

B&B: £18.50	€23.49	HBW ES:	-	S.Supp: £6.50 €8.25	Dinner: -
B&B ES: £20	€25.39	3 day HB:	-	CSP: -	High Tea: -
HBW: -		3 day HB ES: -			

Superb 19th century farmhouse with mature gardens situated on 300 acres. A quiet haven on the Tay River, surrounded by beautiful oak forests, through which walking paths wind to our local fishing village & excellent swimming beaches. 15 mins drive to Dungarvan, Gold Coast & West Waterford golf clubs. Tennis & riding available close by. Dungarvin (6 miles) has several excellent restaurants. Website: www.waterfordfarms.com/parkhouse

TRAMORE 8 km — Waterford WD16

Mrs Myra Rockett
MOUNTAINVIEW
Fenor
Co Waterford

Tel: 051-396107 Fax: –
Open: 1st April – 31st October

No Rooms:	8	Triple:	2
Twin/Double:	2	Family:	4
Single:	1	En suite:	7

AM V

B&B: £17	€21.58	HBW ES:	-	S.Supp: £6.50 €8.25	Dinner: -
B&B ES: £19	€24.13	3 day HB:	-	CSP: -	High Tea: -
HBW: -		3 day HB ES: -			

Charming old style thatched farmhouse. Dates from the 1700's. 4 miles on Dungarvan coast road. From Tramore on R675 road. Splash World and sandy beaches closeby. Tea and coffee making facilities and central heating. Short drive to Waterford Glass. Tours arranged. Travel writers recommended. Menu.

WATERFORD 14 km | Waterford WD17

Mrs Bríd Fitzpatrick
GLENRAHA FARMHOUSE
Mullinavat, (N9 Road)
Waterford, (via Kilkenny)

Tel: 051-898423	Fax: –	
Open: 1st April – 1st December		OBA
No Rooms: 4	Triple: 1	
Twin/Double: 3	Family: 1	
Single: 1	En suite: 4	

B&B:	£18	€ 22.86	HBW ES:	-	-	S.Supp: £6.50 € 8.25	Dinner:	-	-
B&B ES:	£20	€ 25.39	3 day HB:	-	-	CSP: 50%	High Tea: £10 € 12.70
HBW:	-	-	3 day HB ES:	-	-		

Welcome to our spacious, luxurious home on our dairy farm. Situated 2 km off the Waterford-Kilkenny-Dublin N9 road at Mullinavat. Very well signposted. Peaceful holiday location. See the cows milking. Farm walks. Hairdryers, tea/coffee making facilities in bedrooms. TV lounge. Restaurant nearby. Gluten free food served along with home cooking and baking. Refreshments/Irish coffee on arrival. Warm hospitality awaits you.

WATERFORD 4 km | Waterford WD18

Mrs Agnes Forrest
ASHBOURNE HOUSE
Slieverue
Waterford

Tel: 051-832037	Fax: –	
Open: 1st April - 1st November		AM
No Rooms: 7	Triple: –	V
Twin/Double: 5	Family: 2	EC
Single: –	En suite: 7	

B&B:	£20	€ 25.39	HBW ES:	-	-	S.Supp: £6.50 € 8.25	Dinner:	-	-
B&B ES:	£20	€ 25.39	3 day HB:	-	-	CSP: 50%	High Tea:	-	-
HBW:	-	-	3 day HB ES:	-	-		

Old world house situated 2 miles north-east of Waterford. Short distance off N25 Waterford-Wexford Road. Ideal base for touring Nore/Suir valleys. Sea angling at Dunmore East. Horse riding locally. Tours of Waterford Crystal arranged. Traditional pub within walking distance.

'An Gaeltacht': the name given to parts of Ireland where Irish (or Gaelic) can still be heard as an everyday community language. Stretching from Cork to Donegal, the Gaeltacht boasts some of the most spectacular scenery along the west coast of Ireland.

Walkers on Beach, Donegal

Westmeath

The gentle rolling plains of Westmeath abound
with golf courses, equestrian centres and
walking trails. Visitors have a choice of castles to
visit and a number of tourist attractions such as
Locke's Distillery, Fore Abbey and the
Mullingar Bronze and Pewter Centre. Athlone
Castle is worth a visit, and tells the story of the
famous local tenor, Count John McCormack.

Longford
Edgeworthstown   WH2
Castlepollard
Fore
Keenagh   Collinstown
N4
Ballymahon   WH3
N61
Mullingar
N55   WH4
WESTMEATH
WH6
Athlone   N52
WH5
N6   Edenderry
Moate
Horseleap
OFFALY

ATHLONE/MULLINGAR 20 km   Westmeath WH6

Evelyn and Klaus Filsinger
CATSTONE LODGE
Mullenmeehan,
Ballymore, Co Westmeath

Tel: 044-56494   Fax: 044-56196
Open: 1st March - 15th January

No Rooms:	3	Triple:	–
Twin/Double:	3	Family:	–
Single:		En suite:	2

V
AM
AE

B&B:	£35	€44.44	HBW ES:	-	-	S.Supp: £15 €19.05	Dinner: £15 €19.05
B&B ES: £25		€31.74	3 day HB:	-	-	CSP: -	High Tea:- -
HBW:	-	-	3 day HB ES:-				

Old farmhouse, tastefully restored in the heart of Ireland. Spacious and charming decorated rooms (700sq ft) Sitting area with open fireplaces, luxury bathroom and kitchenette. Self catering possible. Close to all amenities, golf, angling, horse riding. Guided tours by arrangement. English language courses. Email: info@catstone.net Website: catstone.net

Vouchers Not Accepted

FORE 1 km   Westmeath WH2

Mrs Eithne Healy
HOUNSLOW HOUSE
Fore, Castlepollard
Co Westmeath

Tel: 044-61144   Fax: 044-61847
Open: 1st March – 30th November

No Rooms:	5	Triple:	–
Twin/Double:	3	Family:	1
Single:	1	En suite:	4

OBA
AM
V
EC

B&B:	£18	€22.86	HBW ES:	-	-	S.Supp: £6.50 €8.25	Dinner: £16 €20.32
B&B ES: £20		€25.39	3 day HB:	-	-	CSP: 33.3%	High Tea:£10 €12.70
HBW:	-	-	3 day HB ES:£100	€126.97			

Spacious 200 year old farmhouse set on wooded heights overlooking the lovely Fore Valley and its historic Abbey. Sweeping views and extensive grounds with swings and a games room. Tea on arrival. Convenient to Tullynally Castle, Lough Lene and Loughcrew Cairns. Recommended in the Rough Guide. Home baking, hairdryers, tea making facilities, babysitting. Email: Eithne_Healy_Hounslow@MailAndNews.com

MULLINGAR 4 km   Westmeath WH3

Martin & Aideen Ginnell
LOUGH OWEL LODGE
Cullion, Mullingar
Co Westmeath

Tel: 044-48714	Fax: 044-48771	OBA
Open: 17th March – 30th November		
No Rooms: 5	Triple: –	AM
Twin/Double: 4	Family: 1	V
Single: –	En suite: 5	EC

B&B:	-	-	HBW ES:	-	S.Supp: £6.50 €8.25	Dinner: - -
B&B ES: £20/22	€25.39/27.93	3 day HB: -	-	CSP: 33%	High Tea:- -
HBW: -	-	3 day HB ES: -	-		

Situated on pleasant grounds, overlooking Lough Owel. This interesting country lodge with its friendly family atmosphere is an ideal base for either an activity filled or relaxing holiday. 1 km from the N4 north of Mullingar. Tennis court, games room, lakeshore walks, cycling, historical trails, golf & equestrian centre nearby. Two bedrooms w/four poster beds. Recommended Karen Brown, 300 Best B&Bs. AA QQQQ. Email: aideen.ginnell@Ireland.com Website: www.angelfire.com/tx/aginnell

VOUCHERS ACCEPTED

MULLINGAR 12 km   Westmeath WH4

Mrs Eithne Pendred
MEARESCOURT HOUSE
Rathconrath, Mullingar
Co Westmeath

Tel: 044-55112	Fax: -	
Open: 3rd January – 19th December		
No Rooms: 4	Triple: -	V
Twin/Double: 3	Family: 1	AM
Single: -	En suite: 3	

B&B: £27.50	€34.91	HBW ES:	-	S.Supp: £10 €12.97	Dinner: £20 €25.39
B&B ES: £30	€38.09	3 day HB: -	-	CSP: 25%	High Tea: - -
HBW: -	-	3 day HB ES: £150	€190.46		

Gracious Georgian mansion. Ancient trees and sweeping parkland. Log fires. Seclusion, elegance and spaciousness combined with 20th century comfort. Situated 12 km from Mullingar off Ballymahon Road. Woodland walks. Central location for touring. Fishing, golf, riding nearby. The dining room offers country house cooking at its best.

VOUCHERS ACCEPTED

STREAMSTOWN 1 km   Westmeath WH5

Mrs Mary Maxwell
WOODLANDS FARM
Streamstown, Near Horseleap
Mullingar, Co Westmeath

Tel: 044-26414	Fax: -	
Open: 1st March – 1st October		
No Rooms: 6	Triple: -	V
Twin/Double: 4	Family: 1	AM
Single: 1	En suite: 4	

B&B: £18	€22.86	HBW ES: £240	€304.74	S.Supp: £6.50 €8.25	Dinner: £17 €21.59
B&B ES: £20	€25.39	3 day HB: £100	€126.97	CSP: 33%	High Tea:- -
HBW: £210	€266.64	3 day HB ES: £110	€140		

Charming old country house surrounded by ornamental trees on 120 acres working farm. Midway between Dublin and Galway. 4 km off N6 road at Horseleap. Frommer, AA, Best B&Bs recommended. Convenient to Clonmacnoise, golf and horseriding. Home cooking a speciality. Tea and coffee making facilities. Ponies and donkeys.

VOUCHERS ACCEPTED

LET THE TELEPHONE RING

Farmhouses are busy places!

Please let the telephone ring long

enough to let the host answer it.

Wexford

The warm sandy beaches of the 'Sunny South East' make Wexford an attraction for Irish people and visitors alike. Fishing villages along the coast provide a chance to enjoy the sea air as well as the local seafood. Inland, the county boasts several abbeys and national parks and also the 1798 National Visitors' Centre.

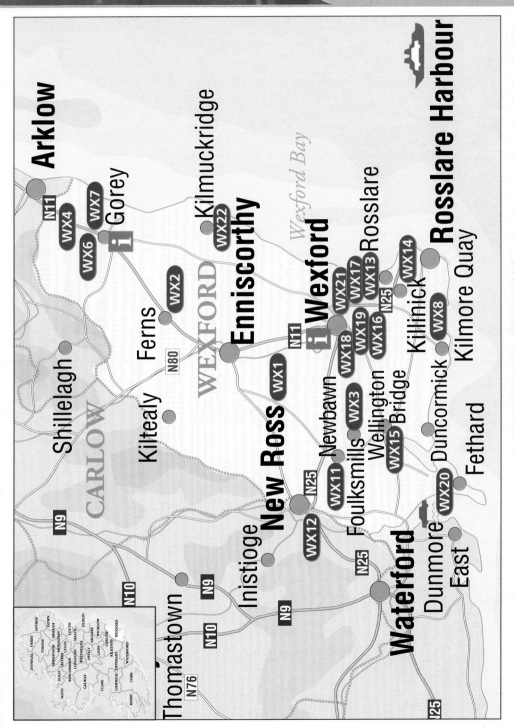

ENNISCORTHY 10 km — Wexford WX1

The Doyle Family
WOODVILLE
Ballyhogue, Enniscorthy
Co Wexford

Tel: 054-47810 Fax: 054-47810
Open: 17th March – 30th September *OBA*

No Rooms:	5	Triple:	1
Twin/Double:	3	Family:	1
Single:	–	En suite:	5

B&B:	-	HBW ES:	-	S.Supp:	-	Dinner:	-
B&B ES: £19	€24.13	3 day HB:	-	CSP:	-	High Tea:	-
HBW:	-	3 day HB ES:	-				

Award winning old style farm house set in mature oak woodlands on the west side of the River Slaney, 5 miles off N11. 6 miles south of Enniscorthy, Rosslare car ferry, 21 miles. Mixed farm in scenic location with open countryside, rivers, woods and mountains. Area of historical interest. Golf, fishing, pony trekking. Recommended in "300 Best B&B Guide to Ireland."

FERNS 3 km — Wexford WX2

Mrs Betty Breen
CLONE HOUSE
Ferns, Enniscorthy
Co Wexford

Tel: 054-66113 Fax: 054-66225
Open: 1st March – 31st October *OBA*

No Rooms:	5	Triple:	2
Twin/Double:	1	Family:	2
Single:	-	En suite:	4

B&B: £20	€25.39	HBW ES:	-	S.Supp: £6.50	€8.25	Dinner: £14	€17.78
B&B ES: £25	€31.74	3 day HB:	-	CSP: 25%		High Tea: £11.50	€14.60
HBW:	-	3 day HB ES:	-				

Award winning 17th century home, surrounded by 3 acres of magnificent gardens. An artists paradise or a lovers retreat. Angling, shooting on 300 acre working farm. Horse riding 5 mins drive. Highly recommended in many travel guides including RAC, AA, QQQQ Awards. Located 3 km south east of Ferns off N11. 1.5 hours drive from Dublin, 1/2 hour from Rosslare. TV in 4 rooms. Website: homepage.eircom.net/~clonehouse

FOULKSMILLS 3 km — Wexford WX3

The Young Family
HORETOWN HOUSE
Foulksmills
Co Wexford

Tel: 051-565771 Fax: 051-565633
Open: 1st March - 31st December closed 24/25/26
AM V EC

No Rooms:	12	Triple:	2
Twin/Double:	10	Family:	–
Single:	-	En suite:	10

B&B: £22.75	€28.89	HBW ES: £270	€342.83	S.Supp: £6.50	€8.25	Dinner: £17/22	€21/29
B&B ES: £26.75	€33.97	3 day HB: £117.75	€149.51	CSP: 20%		High Tea:	-
HBW: £253.50	€321.88	3 day HB ES: £129.75	€164.78				

The Young Family who run this 18th century country manor, 214 acre farm, Cellar Restaurant and residential Equestrian Centre, offer you the hospitality of their home, their highly commended country cuisine and a warm Irish welcome. Closed 24/25/26 December. Email: poloxirl@iol.ie.

GOREY 6 km — Wexford WX6

Mrs Philomena O'Sullivan
WOODLANDS COUNTRY HOUSE
Killinierin
Gorey, Co Wexford

Tel: 0402-37125 Fax: 0402-37133
Open: 1st April - 1st October *OBA*
AM V EC

No Rooms:	6	Triple:	1
Twin/Double:	2	Family:	3
Single:	-	En suite:	6

B&B:	-	HBW ES:	-	S.Supp: £10	€12.70	Dinner:	-
B&B ES: £25/30	€31.74/38.09	3 day HB:	-	CSP: 25%		High Tea:	-
HBW:	-	3 day HB ES:	-				

Built in 1836, award winning Woodlands Country House is set in 1.5 acres of mature gardens and court yard of old stone buildings. The O'Sullivan family offer you the hospitality of their home and its history. AA ★★★★ RAC ★★★★★ Karen Brown Frommer Guide recommended. TV and hairdryers in en-suite bedrooms, three with balconys. Tea and coffee facilities. Wine licence. Tennis court. 1.5km off Dublin, Rosslare N11 road. 4kms north of Gorey. Tea/coffee and scones on arrival. Email: woodlnds@iol.ie Website: www.woodlandscountryhouse.com

INCH

Wexford WX4

Gloria & Allen Anderson-Proby
RIVERFIELD FARMHOUSE
Inch, Gorey
Co Wexford

Tel: 0402-37232		Fax: 0402-37884			
Open: 2nd January - 20th December					
No Rooms: 6		Triple: 1			EC
Twin/Double: 4		Family: 1			
Single:		En suite: 6			

B&B:	-	-	HBW ES:	£210/225	€266.64+	S.Supp: £10	€12.70	Dinner: £15	€19.04
B&B ES: £20		€25.39	3 day HB:	-	-	CSP:	Negot.	High Tea:	-
HBW:	-		3 day HB ES: £100		€126.97				

Happy family home, 100 metres off N11 at Inch, 5 miles north of Gorey.
Spacious restful gardens, enclosed play garden. Children's adventure area, hard tennis court.
River fishing, small animal paddock, free pony rides. Nightly babysitting. Log fire, T.V.'s in bedrooms.
Coeliacs and vegetarians welcome. Local pub 1 minute. 30 acre farm. Brochure available.

INCH

Wexford WX7

Anne Donnelly
PERRYMOUNT HOUSE
Inch, Gorey
Co. Wexford

Tel: 0402-37387		Fax: -		OBA
Open: 1st April - 1st November				
No Rooms: 3		Triple: 2		AE / DC
Twin/Double: 1		Family: -		AM / V
Single: -		En suite: 3		EC

B&B:	-	-	HBW ES:	£224	€284.42	S.Supp: £6.50	€8.25	Dinner: £14	€17.78
B&B ES: £20		€25.39	3 day HB:	-	-	CSP:	50%	High Tea: £12	€15.23
HBW:	-		3 day HB ES: £96		€121.89				

Peter, our boys and I assure you of a warm welcome. Perrymount House was built
in 1795 in a beautiful scenic setting with 7 acres of gardens and riverside walks. Enjoy our varied breakfast menu
(vegetarians catered for), children's play area, farm petland, 5 minute drive to beach. We also have two award
winning cottages.

KILMORE QUAY 2 km

Wexford WX8

Greg and Philomena Stafford
MILL ROAD FARM
Kilmore Quay
Co Wexford

Tel: 053-29633		Fax: 053-29633		
Open: 2nd January – 20th December				
No Rooms: 4		Triple: -		AM / V
Twin/Double: 4		Family: -		
Single: -		En suite: 4		

B&B:	-	-	HBW ES:	-	-	S.Supp:	-	-	Dinner:	-
B&B ES: £19		€24.13	3 day HB:	-	-	CSP:	-	-	High Tea:	-
HBW:	-		3 day HB ES:	-					

Modern farmhouse on working dairy farm, overlooking sea. Close to new
marina, Saltee Islands and sandy beaches. Home baking, quiet, rural setting. Restaurants locally.
Early breakfast for guests travelling on Rosslare Ferries. All bedrooms are ensuite with
TV/hairdryer. Guest TV lounge. Visit us on the web: www.iol.ie/~millfarm Email: millfarm@iol.ie

---

KILMUCKRIDGE 3 km

Wexford WX22

The Kirwan Family
KIRWAN'S FARMHOUSE
Kilmuckridge, Gorey,
Co Wexford

Tel: 053-30168		Fax: 053-30168	
Open: 1st May - 31st October			
No Rooms: 3		Triple: 2	
Twin/Double: 1		Family: -	
Single: -		En suite: 3	

B&B:	-	-	HBW ES:	£203	€257.76	S.Supp: £8	€10.16	Dinner: £15	€19.05
B&B ES: £20		€25.39	3 day HB:	-	-	CSP:	50% -	High Tea:	-
HBW:	-		3 day HB ES: £99		€125.70				

Our home is located on the R742 (Coast Road) between Kilmuckridge and
Blackwater. 45 mins from Rosslare Ferryport and 2hrs from Dublin. It nestles in a peaceful countryside
landscape. Adjacent to miles of sandy beaches. We offer you a warm, friendly atmosphere. Good food and
facilities. Families welcome. Email: kirwansfarmhouse@eircom.net

NEWBAWN   Wexford WX11

Jim and Nancy Wall
CYPRESS HOUSE
Newbawn
Co Wexford

Tel: 051-428335   Fax: 051-428148
Open: 1st January – 30th November

No Rooms:	4	Triple:	
Twin/Double:	4	Family:	
Single:		En suite:	4

B&B:	-	-	HBW ES:	-	-	S.Supp: £6.50 €8.25	Dinner:	-
B&B ES: £19/20	€24.13/25.39		3 day HB:	-	-	CSP: 20%	High Tea:	-
HBW:	-	-	3 day HB ES:	-				

Family home in mature gardens. Hard tennis court. Pleasant, peaceful surroundings. Tillage farm. Hotel pub/restaurant 5 minutes. Village pub 2 mins. Good base for touring Wexford and adjoining counties. Early breakfast. Home baked brown bread. Open fire in lounge. Signposted on N25 near Cedar Lodge Hotel, Carrigbyrne. Take the R735 for Newbawn 3Km. 35 km Rosslare, 11 km New Ross, Foulksmills 3km. Parking. T.V. Hairdryers. Special weekend/3 day offers.

NEW ROSS 4 km   Wexford WX12

Mrs Brede Merrigan
MILLTOWN HOUSE
New Ross
Co Wexford

Tel: 051-880294   Fax: 051-880294
Open: 1st January – 31st December

No Rooms:	3	Triple:	–
Twin/Double:	3	Family:	–
Single:	–	En suite:	3

B&B:	-	-	HBW ES:	-	-	S.Supp: £6.50 €8.25	Dinner:	-
B&B ES: £19	€24.13		3 day HB:	-	-	CSP: 50%	High Tea:	-
HBW:	-	-	3 day HB ES:	-				

Relax and enjoy the scenery at Milltown House, a traditional 200yr old Farmhouse located just off N25. Five minutes New Ross, 20 minutes Waterford. Quiet & comfortable with bright airy rooms, traditional patchwork quilts and good food provided. T.V. & Hairdryer in bedrooms. Convenient to Rosslare Ferryport & Waterford City. Early breakfasts can be served. Email: milltownhouse@eircom.net

---

ROSSLARE HARBOUR 5 km   Wexford WX13

Doyle's B&B
ORCHARD PARK
Tagoat, Rosslare Harbour
Killinick, Co Wexford

Tel: 053-32182   Fax: 053-32759
Open: 1st January-31st December

No Rooms:	4	Triple:	1
Twin/Double:	3	Family:	–
Single:	–	En suite:	4

B&B:	-	-	HBW ES:	-	-	S.Supp: -	Dinner:	-
B&B ES: £23.50/27.50	€30/35		3 day HB:	-	-	CSP: -	High Tea:	-
HBW:	-	-	3 day HB ES:	-				

Country farmhouse with mature gardens and tennis court. All rooms en suite with TV. Tea/coffee room. Quiet location Seven minute drive from Ferry. Early breakfast served. Handmade crafts. Private carpark. No smoking. Email: doylesbandb.rosslare@ireland.com

Vouchers Not Accepted

ROSSLARE HARBOUR 5 km   Wexford WX14

Kathleen & Phil O'Leary
O'LEARY'S FARMHOUSE
Killilane, Kilrane
Rosslare Harbour, Co Wexford

Tel: 053-33134   Fax: –
Open: All year (except 24th/25th December)

No Rooms:	9	Triple:	–
Twin/Double:	5	Family:	2
Single:	2	En suite:	7

B&B: £17	€21.59	HBW ES:	-	-	S.Supp: £6.50 €8.25	Dinner:	-
B&B ES: £19	€24.13	3 day HB:	-	-	CSP: -	High Tea:	-
HBW:	-	-	3 day HB ES:	-				

Comfortable old farmhouse overlooking sea with mature garden. Beach 300 metres. Ideal for walks, swimming and bird watching. St. Helen's golf course nearby. Horse riding, fishing, pubs and restaurants closeby. Trains and ferries catered for. Vegetarian food available. Pets welcome, parking available.

SALTMILLS

Mrs Rita Power
GROVE FARM
St Kearns Saltmills
Fethard-on-Sea, Co Wexford

Tel: 051-562304	Fax: –	
Open: January – December		OBA
No Rooms: 3	Triple: –	
Twin/Double: 2	Family: –	
Single: 1	En suite: 3	

B&B:	£17	€21.58	HBW ES:	-	-	S.Supp: £6.50 €8.25	Dinner: -	-
B&B ES:	£19	€24.13	3 day HB:	£95	€120.63	CSP: -	High Tea: £8	€10.16
HBW:	-		3 day HB ES:	-				

Attractive farmhouse overlooking sea located 2.5 km off 733 Road. 5 km from Fethard-on-Sea and 10km Ring of Hook Peninsula. Garden for guests. Safe beaches, sea angling. Pony trekking nearby. Bird watching. Rosslare car ferry 26 km. Ideal for touring south east. Wexford town 20km. Baby sitting service. Tintern Abbey 10 minute walk.

WELLINGTONBRIDGE 2 km

Mrs Anne Breen-Murphy
RIVER VALLEY FARMHOUSE
Ballylannon, Wellingtonbridge
Co Wexford

Tel: 051-561354	Fax: 051-561354	
Open: All year		AM V
No Rooms: 4	Triple: –	
Twin/Double: 4	Family: –	
Single: –	En suite: 3	

B&B:	£17	€21.58	HBW ES:	£195	€247.60	S.Supp: £6.50 €8.25	Dinner: £13	€16.50
B&B ES:	£19	€24.13	3 day HB:	£88	€111.74	CSP: 30%	High Tea: £9	€11.42
HBW:	-		3 day HB ES:	£98	€124.43			

Modern farmhouse on 120 acres mixed farm, situated 1km off main Wexford to Fethard-on-Sea road - R733. Within 30mins driving distance of Rosslare ferries, 12km from Ballyhack, Passage East ferry, golf, horse riding within 5km. Sandy beaches 9km. Ideal base for touring. A private stretch of river which runs through our farm, is available to our guests for trout fishing. Email: Rivervalley@oceanfree.net

---

WEXFORD 5 km

Mrs Ella Cuddihy
RATHASPECK MANOR
Rathaspeck
Co Wexford

Tel: 053-42661	Fax: –	
Open: 1st June – 7th November		
No Rooms: 6	Triple: 3	
Twin/Double: 3	Family: –	
Single: –	En suite: 6	

B&B:	-		HBW ES:	-	-	S.Supp: £6.50 €8.25	Dinner: -	-
B&B ES:	£25	€31.75	3 day HB:	-	-	CSP: 25%	High Tea: -	
HBW:	-		3 day HB ES:	-				

Restored 17th century Georgian house in quiet location. All rooms en suite with colour TV and tea & coffee making facilities. Tennis court, 18 hole par 3 golf course. Green fees £6. Located off N25. Rosslare Ferryport 14 km. Early breakfast served. Car Parking. Central Heating. Garden for visitors use. AA recommended QQQ. Website: www.iol.ie/~ecuddihy

---

WEXFORD TOWN 3 km

John & Theresa Devereux
BROOM COTTAGE
Rosslare Road
Drinagh, Co Wexford

Tel: 053-44434	Fax: –	
Open: 1st May – 1st October		
No Rooms: 4	Triple: –	
Twin/Double: 4	Family: –	
Single: –	En suite: 4	

B&B:	-		HBW ES:	-	-	S.Supp: -	Dinner: -	-
B&B ES:	£20	€25.39	3 day HB:	-	-	CSP: -	High Tea: -	
HBW:	-		3 day HB ES:	£55	€69.84			

17th Century family farmhouse 3 km from Wexford Town, 10 minutes drive to Rosslare car ferry, near the first Rosslare roundabout towards Wexford town. Ideally suited for touring all of the historic sites of the southeast. Local pub & restaurant 100 metres stroll away. Tea & coffee making facilities. Early breakfast menu.

WEXFORD 3 km | Wexford WX18

John & Kathleen Hayes
CLONARD HOUSE
Clonard Great
Wexford, Co Wexford

Tel: 053-43141   Fax: 053-43141
Open: 18th March – 2nd November

No Rooms:	9	Triple:	3
Twin/Double:	4	Family:	1
Single:	1	En suite:	9

AM / V / EC

B&B:	-	-	HBW ES:	-	-	S.Supp: £6.50 €8.25	Dinner:	-	-
B&B ES: £22.50-25 €28.59-31.74	3 day HB:	-	-	CSP:	50%	High Tea:	-	-
HBW:	-	-	3 day HB ES: £65-75	€82.53+					

Built in 1783, award-winning Clonard House is an historic Georgian country home. Unwind over an Irish coffee in the elegant drawing room before retiring to one of the nine en-suite bedrooms, most with four-poster beds, all with TV & hairdryer. Early breakfast served, varied menu. Tea & coffee facilities. Wine license. Inclusive riding holidays available. Recommended Egon Ronay, Frommers, Guide du Routard, AA selected QQQQ house. Take the R733 south at N25/R733 roundabout. 1st left. http://indigo.ie/~khayes Email:clonardhouse@indigo.ie

WEXFORD 3 km | Wexford WX19

Jack & Kathleen Mernagh
KILLIANE CASTLE
Drinagh
Wexford, Co Wexford

Tel: 053-58885   Fax: 053-58885
Open: 17th March – 17th November

OBA

No Rooms:	8	Triple:	-
Twin/Double:	6	Family:	2
Single:	–	En suite:	8

AM / V / EC

B&B:	-	-	HBW ES:	-	-	S.Supp: £10 €12.70	Dinner:	-	-
B&B ES: £22.50-25 €28.57-31.74	3 day HB:	-	-	CSP:	20%	High Tea: £12 €15.24
HBW:	-	-	3 day HB ES: -			

To stay in Killiane Castle is to awake into an historical past with all the elegant accessories of the modern era. The 14th century castle with its adjoining 17th century house are on a modern dairy farm all run by the family. All bedrooms with TV & hairdryers. Early breakfast served for ferry. Tea room and varied breakfast menu. Signposted on N25 Rosslare-Wexford road. Recommended in most travel guides Email: castlej@gofree.indigo.ie or killianecastle@yahoo.com Website: http://gofree.indigo.ie/~castlej

WEXFORD 4 km | Wexford WX21

Mrs Jean Quirke
HAYESTOWN FARMHOUSE
Hayestown
Co Wexford

Tel: 053-42120   Fax: –
Open: 1st May – 10 November

No Rooms:	4	Triple:	1
Twin/Double:	3	Family:	–
Single:	–	En suite:	4

B&B:	-	-	HBW ES:	-	-	S.Supp: -	Dinner:	-	-
B&B ES: £19	€24.13	3 day HB:	-	-	CSP:	-	High Tea:	-	-
HBW:	-	-	3 day HB ES: -			

Lovely old farmhouse in quiet setting. Peaceful gardens. 1km from Johnstown Castle and Agricultural museum, 3km from heritage park and 1km from golf course. 1km from N25. Early breakfast for ferry.

GOOD FOOD

Why not book dinner at the Farmhouse and enjoy fresh wholesome food!

Those Farmhouses providing dinner are listed in the brochure

Wicklow

A short drive from Dublin, Wicklow's mountains and glens offer some of the most splendid scenery on the East coast. Walkers will not want to miss completing at least part of the 'Wicklow Way', a trail which covers glorious forests, old bog roads and mountainous terrain. The county abounds with pretty villages and country houses, including the impressive scenery and architecture of Powerscourt Desmesne.

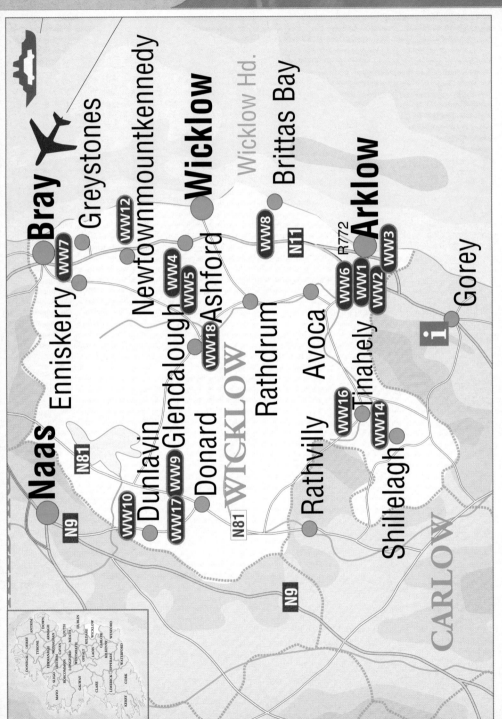

ARKLOW 2 km — Wicklow WW1

Michael & Lillie Byrne
MONEYLANDS FARM
Arklow
Co Wicklow

Tel: 0402-32259 Fax: 0402-32438
Open: 1st February – 30th November

No Rooms:	4	Triple:	1
Twin/Double:	3	Family:	
Single:	–	En suite:	3

AE
AM
V

B&B:	£22	€27.93	HBW ES:	-		S.Supp: £10 €12.70	Dinner:	-
B&B ES:	£25	€31.74	3 day HB:	-	-	CSP: 25%	High Tea:	-
HBW:	-		3 day HB ES:	-				

Georgian style farmhouse 1 km south of Arklow. From N11 take R772. Sign for "Moneylands Farm" is located on R772. Enjoy panoramic views of Arklow Bay, coast & mountains. Indoor heated swimming pool, gym & sauna. Tennis court, virtual golf and hovercrafting over land & water on farm. Dillard & Causin recommended. Rosslare & Dublin 1.5 hours. Email: mland@eircom.net

VOUCHERS ACCEPTED

ARKLOW 4 km — Wicklow WW2

Mrs Dympna Clune
ASHWOOD HOUSE
Arklow
Co Wicklow

Tel: 0402-31624 Fax: –
Open: 1st April – 1st November

OBA

No Rooms:	4	Triple:	
Twin/Double:	3	Family:	-
Single:	1	En suite:	2

B&B:	£18	€22.86	HBW ES:	-		S.Supp: £6.50 €8.25	Dinner:	-
B&B ES:	£20	€25.39	3 day HB:	-	-	CSP:	High Tea:	-
HBW:	-		3 day HB ES:	-				

Neo-Georgian residence on dry stock farm 4km south of Arklow. Signposted on main N11 road from Rosslare to Dublin. Commanding view of Wicklow, Wexford mountains. Close to all recreational amenities - golf, sailing, fishing, horse riding and pony trekking. Safe sandy beaches closeby.

VOUCHERS ACCEPTED

ARKLOW 7 km — Wicklow WW3

Mrs A. Nuzum
BALLYKILTY HOUSE
Coolgreany
Arklow, Co Wicklow

Tel: 0402-37111 Fax: 0402-37272
Open: 1st March – 31st October

OBA
AM
V
EC

No Rooms:	5	Triple:	1
Twin/Double:	4	Family:	-
Single:	-	En suite:	5

B&B:	-		HBW ES:	-		S.Supp: £10 €12.70	Dinner:	-
B&B ES:	£22-24	€27.93-30.47	3 day HB:	-	-	CSP:	High Tea:	-
HBW:	-		3 day HB ES:	-				

Enjoy the peace and tranquility of life on an Irish dairy & sheep farm. Olde-worlde farmhouse in spacious mature gardens on Wicklow-Wexford border. Arklow town 5 km, Coolgreany village 1 km. 1 hour drive Dun Laoghaire / Rosslare ferries. Fresh home cooking. 2 lounges with log fires. Hard tennis court on farm. Golf, horse riding and many sandy beaches nearby. Email: ballykiltyfarmhouse@eircom.net

VOUCHERS ACCEPTED

ASHFORD 4 km — Wicklow WW4

Catherine Byrne-Fulvio
BALLYKNOCKEN HOUSE
Glenealy, Ashford
Co Wicklow

Tel: 0404-44627/44614 Fax: 0404-44696
Open: 1st March – 30th November & Christmas and New Year.

No Rooms:	7	Triple:	2
Twin/Double:	5	Family:	-
Single:		En suite:	7

AM
V

B&B:	-	-	HBW ES:	-		S.Supp: £19 €24.13	Dinner: £18.75 €23.81
B&B ES:	£25-29.50 €31.74/37.46	3 day HB:	-	-	CSP: 25%	High Tea:	-
HBW:	-		3 day HB ES:	£120-138 €152-175				

Romantic 19th century Farmhouse, elegantly furnished with antiques. Charming bedrooms. Log fires. Splendid dinner using local produce, seafood, own vegetables & herbs. Wine list. Extensive breakfast menu. Ideal base near Wicklow Mountains, Glendalough, Powerscourt, golf & gardens. Walking Programme available. Dublin 46km, Airport 56km, Ferryport 26km. Frommer & Karen Brown recommended. Email:cfulvio@ballyknocken.com www.ballyknocken.com

Vouchers Not Accepted

ASHFORD 4 km

Mrs Geraldine Kelly
BALLYLUSK FARM
Ashford, Co Wicklow

Tel: 0404-40141	Fax: 0404-40141

Open: 1st March – 1st November

OBA

No Rooms:	4	Triple:	–
Twin/Double:	2	Family:	2
Single:	–	En suite:	4

B&B:	-	-	HBW ES:	-	-	S.Supp: £10 €12.70	Dinner: -	-
B&B ES: £20		€25.39	3 day HB:	-	-	CSP: 25	High Tea:-	-
HBW:	-	-	3 day HB ES:	-				

A working dairy farm on the side of Carrig Mountain. 4km from Ashford village. Ideal centre for touring Glendalough, Avoca, Ballykissangel, Powerscourt Garden, Mount Usher gardens, Devil Glens Wood. Dublin City 46km, Dun Laoghaire ferry 26km, Rosslare Ferry 96km. Tea and coffee on arrival. T.V. Lounge

VOUCHERS ACCEPTED

AVOCA 3 km

Joy & Charles Keppel
KEPPEL'S FARMHOUSE
Ballanagh
Avoca, Co Wicklow

Tel: 0402-35168	Fax: 0402-35168

Open: 1st April – 31st October

No Rooms:	5	Triple:	–
Twin/Double:	4	Family:	1
Single:	–	En suite:	5

B&B:	-	-	HBW ES:	-	-	S.Supp: £15 €19.05	Dinner: -	-
B&B ES: £22.50/25 €28.57+			3 day HB:	-	-	CSP: Negot. (over 10s)	High Tea:.	-
HBW:	-	-	3 day HB ES:	-				

Comfortable 19th century home offering luxury accomodation. Set in scenic countryside on dairy farm 3km from Avoca (location for BBC's "Ballykissangel"). Handweavers, Glendalough, Avondale, mountains, gardens, and much more all nearby. 75 minutes Dun Laoghaire/ Rosslare ports. Frommers and Dillard/Causin recommended. No smoking. hairdryers.

VOUCHERS ACCEPTED

BRITTAS BAY 3 km

Mrs Paschal Doyle
BALLINCLEA HOUSE
Jack White's Cross
Brittas Bay, Co Wicklow

Tel: 0404-47118	Fax: 0404-47118

Open: 1st April – 30th September

OBA

EC

No Rooms:	4	Triple:	-
Twin/Double:	4	Family:	
Single:	-	En suite:	2

B&B: £17	€21.58	HBW ES:	-	-	S.Supp: £7 €8.89	Dinner: -	-
B&B ES: £20	€24.13	3 day HB:	-	-	CSP: 25%	High Tea:-	-
HBW:	-	3 day HB ES:	-				

Georgian style farmhouse in scenic surroundings with log fires and good home cooking. Located 0.5 km off Dublin-Arklow-Wexford (N11) road at Jack White's Pub. Brittas Bay (south car park) 3 km. Road opposite car park will take you to Ballinclea. 40 minutes drive from Dun Laoghaire. Ideal touring base for Glendalough, Avoca, Ballykissangel.

VOUCHERS ACCEPTED

DONARD 2 km

Mrs Lilly O'Reilly
BRIDGE MEADOWS
Hollywood Glen road, Donard
Co Wicklow

Tel: 045-404603	Fax: –

Open: April – October

OBA

No Rooms:	3	Triple:	–
Twin/Double:	3	Family:	–
Single:	–	En suite:	2

B&B: £17	€21.58	HBW ES:	-	-	S.Supp: £8 €10.16	Dinner: £16 €20.32
B&B ES: £19/20	€24.13	3 day HB: £90	€114.28		CSP: -	High Tea:-£12 €15.24
HBW:	-	3 day HB ES: £95	€120.63			

Peaceful & tranquil location yet only 1 hour drive to Dublin Airport & ferries. Signposted from N81. 12km south of Blessington. Convenient to Glendalough, Russborough, Glen of Imaal, Japanese Gardens, National Stud, horse racing at Punchastown, Naas & Curragh. Locally golf, horsetreking & hillwalking. Plenty of homegrown food and home baking, breakfast menu. Open fire. Eceat Green Holiday Guide recommended. Email: bridgemeadows@esatclear.ie

VOUCHERS ACCEPTED

DUNLAVIN VILLAGE

Wicklow WW10

John & Caroline Lawler
TYNTE HOUSE
Dunlavin
Co Wicklow

Tel: 045-401561   Fax: 045-401586
Open: 2nd January – 23rd December

No Rooms: 6	Triple: 6
Twin/Double: –	Family: –
Single: –	En suite: 6

AM
V
AE

B&B: -	-	HBW ES: £230		S.Supp: £7 €8.88	Dinner: £14 €17.78
B&B ES: £20	€25	3 day HB: -	-	CSP: 40%	High Tea: -
HBW: -	-	3 day HB ES: £100	-		

Old world farmhouse in picturesque village of Dunlavin within 1 hour drive Dublin Airport and Ferry-ports. Ideal touring base for Glendalough, the Wicklow Gap and Kildare. Excellent golf courses nearby. Spacious rooms with antique furnishings. Tennis court, children's playground and games room on premises. Lounge with open fire. Frommer and Dillard & Causin recommended. AA ◆◆◆◆ selected. Top 20 landlady of the year UK & Ireland. French & Spanish spoken. Email: info@tyntehouse.com Web page: www.tyntehouse.com

VOUCHERS ACCEPTED

ENNISKERRY 3 km

Wicklow WW7

Mrs Yvonne Roe
COOLAKAY HOUSE
Enniskerry
Co Wicklow

Tel: 01-2862423   Fax: 01-2761001
Open: All year

No Rooms: 4	Triple: –
Twin/Double: 3	Family: 1
Single: –	En suite: 4

B&B: -	-	HBW ES: -	-	S.Supp: -	-	Dinner: -	-
B&B ES: £24-25	€30.47-33.01	3 day HB: -		CSP: -		High Tea: -	
HBW: -	-	3 day HB ES: -					

Large farmhouse tastefully furnished with spacious flower gardens and lawns. Panoramic view of the Wicklow Mountains. The premises has restaurant and heritage centre. T.V & hairdryers in bedrooms. Central heating. Wine licence with home cooking a speciality. Situated off N11 on Powerscourt waterfall road and 2km from Powerscourt Gardens & 20 min drive DunLaoghaire port.

Vouchers Not Accepted

HOLLYWOOD 2 km

Wicklow WW17

David & Eileen Allen
KNOCKRUE HOUSE
Donard, Dunlavin
Co. Wicklow

Tel: 045-401258   Fax: -
Open: All Year

No Rooms: 3	Triple: –
Twin/Double: 1	Family: 2
Single: –	En suite: 3

B&B: -	-	HBW ES: -	-	S.Supp: -	-	Dinner: -	-
B&B ES: £20	€25.39	3 day HB: -	-	CSP: -	-	High Tea: -	-
HBW: -	-	3 day HB ES: £100	€126.97				

Georgian House on Wicklow sheep farm. Walking facilities for guests on property. 9 and 18 hole golf course, pitch and putt, working farm, T.V. Non- Smoking house.

VOUCHERS ACCEPTED

LARAGH/GLENDALOUGH 5 km   **Wicklow WW18**

Mrs. Mary Byrne
DOIRE COILLE HOUSE
Glendalough, Cullentragh
Rathdrum, Co Wicklow

Tel: 0404-45131   Fax: 0404-45131
Open: January - November

No Rooms: 4	Triple: –
Twin/Double: 4	Family: –
Single: –	En suite: 4

V
AM
AE

B&B: -	-	HBW ES: -	-	S.Supp: -	-	Dinner: -	-
B&B ES: £19	€24.13	3 day HB: -	-	CSP: -	-	High Tea: -	-
HBW: -	-	3 day HB ES: -					

Comfortable farmhouse beside Wicklow's National Park. Surrounded by Oak Woods on the R755 in the Avonmore Valley. 5 minutes from Glendalough. 1 hr to Dublin and ferry ports. Ideal base for touring all the beautiful and historic places in Wicklow, Dublin and South Kildare. Email: marybyrne@esatclear.ie

Vouchers Not Accepted

NEWTOWNMOUNTKENNEDY 2.5km — Wicklow WW12

Mrs Myrtle Roberts
BUTTERFLY HILL FARM
Kilmullen
Newtownmountkennedy, Co Wicklow

Tel: 01-2819218 Fax: 01-2810145
Open: 10th March – 1st November

OBA
EC

No Rooms:	4	Triple:	1
Twin/Double:	3	Family:	–
Single:	–	En suite:	3

B&B: £19 €24.13	HBW ES: – –	S.Supp: £8 €10.15	Dinner: – –
B&B ES: £20/22 €25.39+	3 day HB: – –	CSP: –	High Tea: –
HBW: – –	3 day HB ES: – –		

Welcome to" The centre of the world". Enjoy Glendalough, Powerscourt, Avondale etc.
Relax in comfortable rooms. Tea & coffee in lounge. Golf, angling, archaeology guides/maps on request."Le Guide du
Routard" recommended. Convenient - well signed off N11 - 33km (22m) Dublin. 2.5km (1.6m) south of
Newtownmountkennedy. Webpage: http://www.wicklow.ie/farm/f-butter.html Email:butterflyhillfarm@tinet.ie

VOUCHERS ACCEPTED

SHILLELAGH 4 km — Wicklow WW14

Mrs Bridie Osborne
PARK LODGE
Clonegal, Shillelagh
Co Wicklow

Tel: 055-29140 Fax: 055-29140
Open: Easter – 31st October

OBA
V
AM

No Rooms:	4	Triple:	1
Twin/Double:	2	Family:	1
Single:	–	En suite:	4

B&B: £22 €30.47	HBW ES: – –	S.Supp: £6.50 €8.25	Dinner: £18 €22.86
B&B ES: £25 €31.74	3 day HB: – –	CSP: 20%	High Tea: £11 €13.97
HBW: – –	3 day HB ES: £110 €139.67		

Warm Irish hospitality, 17th century traditional style farmhouse in scenic
surroundings on a 200 acre working farm. Ideal walking country located on last two days of the
Wicklow Way. Horses on farm, riding available. 1.5 hours drive Dublin/Rosslare. Traditional Irish
music locally. Email: parklodgebb@hotmail.com

VOUCHERS ACCEPTED

TINAHELY 8 km — Wicklow WW16

Margaret & Hugh Coogan
KYLE FARMHOUSE,
Tinahely,
Co. Wicklow

Tel: 0508-71341 Fax: -
Open: 1st April – 1st October

V
AM

No Rooms:	3	Triple:	–
Twin/Double:	2	Family:	1
Single:	–	En suite:	1

B&B: £17 €21.59	HBW ES: £200 €279	S.Supp: £6.50 €8.25	Dinner: £15 €19.05
B&B ES: £19 €24.13	3 day HB: £85 €114	CSP: 50%	High Tea: £10 €12.70
HBW: – –	3 day HB ES: £90 €122		

4th generation farmhouse on working dairy and sheep farm in the Wicklow
Mountains. Enjoy Wicklow Mountains National Park, Glenmalure, Glendalough, or walk the famous "Wicklow
Way" which passes through the farm. Scenic hill walks, wildlife, childrens play area, farm pets on farm. Excellent
Food and accommodation. Signposted from R747 between Tinahely and Hacketstown. Rosslare/Dublin 1.5hrs.

VOUCHERS ACCEPTED

CONFIRMED RESERVATIONS

In order to avoid disappointments which can arise from misunderstandings

over the telephone when booking directly from your own country,

please confirm the reservation in writing

Self Catering

On the following pages are suggestions for those who like the freedom that a self catering holiday offers. If you like to relax and unwind without a set schedule to worry about, then this is the ideal holiday for you. Everything you need for a comfortable stay is provided, with the added bonus of fresh country air and a pleasant rural environment. Set in the heart of the Irish countryside, these houses provide the ultimate getaway for people who want to experience country life at its best.

Shannon	Clare

Theresa & Tim Donnellan
FIONNUAIRE
Mullagh, Quilty, Co Clare

Tel: 065-7087179   Fax: 065-7087179

Rates:		
Per Week:		
July/August:	£335	€440
April, May, June, Sept:	£180	€220
Per weekend: Negotiable. Per day: Negotiable.		

V
AM
EC

Beautiful holiday cottage on its own site on the farm. Beaches, village shops and pubs nearby. Quiet location. Ideal touring base for The Burren, Clare and West of Ireland. Experience life on a working dairy farm with cattle, farm pets and pony. Accommodation - three bedrooms. Cot available. Bed linen free. Electricity extra.
Email: fionnuaire@eircom.net

South West	Kerry

Richard and Anne Maybury
TARA FARM
Tubrid, Kenmare
Co. Kerry

Tel: 064-41272   Fax: 064-41377

Rates:		
May	£250	€317.43
June	£300	€380.92
July/August	£400	€507.90
September	£300	€380.92
October	£250	€317.43

River Lodge is a four star property overlooking Kenmare Bay with direct access to private shore. 3 bedrooms/2 ensuite. Luxury property. Quiet location on byroad off N70/N71. 1km from Kenmare town which has award winning restaurants. Cycle hire, boating, watersports, golf, horseriding. Just off Kerry Way walking route. Situated on Tara Farm - owner/prop supervised. Every comfort assured.
Email: tarafarm@tinet.ie

GLENVIEW SELFCATERING ENTERPRISE

Overlooking the Shannon-Erne Link, 500 metres from Lock 4. Europe's newest Waterway in the Heart of Leitrim Lakeland play area. Ideal base for touring West/North West.

Boating • Canoeing • Angling in a Fisherman's Paradise • Golf • Pony Trekking • Horse Riding • Hill Walking • Cycling

GLENVIEW TENNIS COURT, GAMES ROOM AND RESTAURANT

North West	Leitrim

Mrs. Teresa Kennedy
Glenview, Aughoo, Ballinamore,
Co. Leitrim

V AM

Tel: 078-44157   Fax: 078-44814   Email: glenvhse@iol.ie

1 Rates:			**2 Rates:**		
April - Oct.	£370	€469.9	April - Oct.	£310	€393.7
Rest of Year:	£240	€304.8	Rest of Year:	£190	€241.3
3 Rates:			**4 Rates:**		
April - Oct.	£280	€355.6	April - Oct.	£220	€279.4
Rest of Year:	£210	€266.7	Rest of Year:	£140	€177.8

1 2 Ultra Modern Bungalows - Full wheelchair facilities. H/C in each bedroom. Master room en suite and main bathroom. Kitchen cum dining room. Spacious TV lounge. Central Heating. NRB Blue Symbol.

2 Bridge House - Modern 2 storey house. Sleeps 6. Kitchen cum dining room. Lounge with open fire. Central heating. Upstairs bathroom. Shower downstairs.

3 Traditional Irish Cottage - 3 bedrooms H/C. Sleeps 6. Living room with open fire which provides central heating. Kitchen with modern conveniences.

4 Apartment - Single storey, 2 bedroom. Sleeps 4. Kitchen/dining room/living room combined. Shower room. Separate toilet. Central heating.

South East	Wexford

Peter & Anne Donnelly
PERRYMOUNT HOUSE
Inch, Gorey, Co. Wexford.

V AM

Tel: 0402-37387   Fax: -

Rates:		
Per Week:		
High season:	£410	€520.59
Mid Season:	£300	€482.50
Low season:	£260	€330.13
W.E. - £138	€168.70	B.H. W.E. - £260 €330.13

Farmhouse accommodation also available. Please phone for free brochure.

Rural Tourism Award winning (Four Star) Cottages. Built around a former courtyard in the select grounds of Perrymount House. With 7 acres of gardens and wooded riverside walks on 280 acre working dairy farm. Farm pet-land on farm, pony rides and children's play area. 1hrs drive from Dublin and Rosslare on N11 route. 5min drive to beach and only 3 min walk to village with traditional pub, shop and restaurant. "Country life at its best".

Irish Farmhouse Holidays Association is the promotional and marketing organisation for farmhouse accomodation in Ireland. Irish Farmhouse Holidays have been welcoming visitors for over three decades to experience the traditional, agricultural and social life of Ireland. Visitors can enjoy a restful stay at any of our farmhouse accommodations that are Irish Tourist Board approved and located countrywide. There they will have a unique opportunity to experience daily life in a rural setting with the very people who live and work there. All our guests can experience the magical nature of the countryside and enjoy appetising and healthy food in a clean and friendly environment. In addition to this, first time visitors can discover the traditions of Irish agriculture and music, the precious customs of rural living and also adjust to a slower pace of living. Some of our homes are located near towns, villages and cities while others are situated near our breathtaking world renowned coastlines. These homes offer a variety of reasonable prices and also a variety of activities that can be enjoyed by the whole family during the visit.

For further information contact

Irish Farmhouse Holidays
2 Michael Street, Limerick, Ireland.
Tel: 061 400 700/400 707
Int: +353 61 400 700/400 707

Fax: 061 400 771 Int: +353 61 400 771

Email: farmhols@iol.ie
Website: http://www.irishfarmholidays.com

Office Hours: Monday - Friday 9.00 am - 5.30 pm

Irish Farmhouse holidays wish to thank Bord Failte - Irish Tourist Board for their considerable
assistance with this publication.

Anything can happen.

We're here if it does.

From cattle prices to weather, nothing is predictable in farming. As the only insurance company set up by farmers, FBD understands your needs and provides policies to protect you, your family and your business.

For example, **FBD's B&B/Guesthouse Multiperil Policy** offers comprehensive cover, for a wide range of risks at competitive premiums. You choose the cover you need and if anything does go wrong, we're here to help you and your business to get back on track, as quickly as possible.

Find out more about **FBD's B&B/Guesthouse Multiperil Cover**, contact your local FBD office today.

For a better deal all round.

OFFICES NATIONWIDE